An Irish Flower Garden Replanted

to

Susan Elizabeth Nelson

An
Irish Flower Garden
Replanted

THE HISTORIES OF SOME OF OUR GARDEN PLANTS

E. Charles Nelson

with illustrations by

Wendy F. Walsh

CASTLEBOURKE *by* ÉAMONN DE BÚRCA
FOR EDMUND BURKE PUBLISHER
1997

second edition revised and enlarged

© Text E. Charles Nelson 1997
© Illustrations Wendy F. Walsh 1997
ISBN 0-946130-17-5
ISBN 0-946130-21-3

First edition: Kilkenny, 1984

Contents

Illustrations

COLOUR PLATES

Cover and frontispiece: An Irish garland

VIGNETTES IN PENCIL

FIGURES IN CHINESE INKS

Notes

This book is written primarily for the keen, amateur gardener. I have tried to avoid using too many Latin names, preferring common names throughout. However, species and cultivars (garden varieties) have only one correct, universally understood name, and that is the scientific one. The Latin name of each plant is given once in bold type and also appears at the head of the relevant chapter.

I ask my botanical friends to forgive the occasions when, for the sake of gardeners, I have used botanical terms in a less than precise manner; for example, I have preferred to use such words as petal instead of perianth segment

DIMENSIONS

Measurements are given in metric units; a conversion table is given below.

0.05 m	(5 cm)	2 ins
0.10 m	(10 cm)	4 ins
0.25 m	(25 cm)	10 ins
0.50 m	(50 cm)	20 ins
0.75 m	(75 cm)	30 ins, 2 ft 6 ins
1 m		3 ft 3 ins
2 m		6 ft 6 ins
5 m		16 ft 5 ins
10 m		32 ft 10 ins

Availability of Plants

The best way to discover whether the cultivars mentioned in this book are available commercially is to consult the current edition of *The RHS plant finder*, edited by A. Lord, and compiled by C. Philip, published for the Royal Horticultural Society by Dorling Kindersley; copies can be ordered from RHS Enterprise Ltd., RHS Garden, Wisley, Woking, Surrey GU23 6QB.

Unfortunately rather few Irish nurseries, both in Northern Ireland and the Republic, are included in this excellent directory, but recent changes in European plant import regulations mean that importing plants from European Union countries is not as complicated as hitherto. If in doubt, residents of the Republic should contact the Plant Health Section, Department of Agriculture and Food, Kildare Street, Dublin 2, and residents of Northern Ireland should contact the Plant Health Division, Department of Agriculture, Dundonald House, Upper Newtownards Road, Belfast BT4 3SB.

Preface

This book has been out of print for almost a decade, and in the intervening years many things have happened both in my own life and in the interwoven lives of my friends and colleagues, and gardens and their plants. I have also learnt more about the garden plants that we cultivate in Ireland. A new edition was required, and I have taken the opportunity to augment the original text. I have added a chapter on roses, based on my address to the ninth World Rose Convention held in Belfast during 1991, and I have drawn into this book, in edited form, a scattering of essays that were published elsewhere and the unpublished scripts for talks which I gave on Sunday Miscellany broadcast by Radio Telefís Éireann. I have also made corrections, and altered a few names to bring them up-to-date. In a few instances, the previously published history has been revised in the light of my more recent research.

Wendy Walsh has prepared ten new watercolours. We have also chosen to include several plates which have been published in other places; *Anemone nemorosa* 'Lucy's Wood' from *An Irish florilegium II* (London; Thames & Hudson. 1987), *Abelia triflora*, *Ulex europaeus* 'Strictus' and *Escallonia* 'C. F. Ball' from *The brightest jewel* (Kilkenny; Boethius Press. 1987), and *Garrya* x *issaquahensis* 'Glasnevin Wine' and 'Pat Ballard' from *Glasra*. Of the Chinese ink portraits, only one was not included in the original edition; the cone of *Pinus coulteri* was first published in *A man who can speak of plants* (Dublin; privately published by E. C. Nelson. 1994). The vignettes of places were originally published as tailpieces in *A prospect of Irish flowers* (Belfast; Blackstaff Press. 1990).

In the original book I wrote this dedication.

As a student of the art of gardening, I have had to learn my plants. There is still much I do not know, and I hope that I may continue to learn from my friends, the kindly senior gardeners of Ireland. As a token of thanks for the pleasures that their gardens have given, for their stories about great gardeners and gardens of which I can only dream, for the wisdom that they have shared so willingly, and for the plants that this novice now tries to grow, I would like to dedicate this book to Evelyn Booth (1897-1988), Molly Sanderson (1913-1995), and David Shackleton (1924-1988).

Evelyn, Molly and David have all, as we say, passed on, and we are the poorer for that. Their gardens, Lucy's Wood, Ishlan and Beech Park, have also vanished; others may own and cultivate those garden but they have changed utterly simply because Evelyn, Molly and David are not around to pamper their plants any more. However, the plants that they cherished and grew, and that their predecessors also admired and cultivated, are still available for us to enjoy and happily to share with our friends.

Other friends, who contributed to the original edition and subsequent research, have also died since this book was written: Elsie Miller, Sheila Pim, Eileen McCracken, Harry Bryce,

Billy Douglas, Brian Mulligan, Aidan Brady and Alan Grills are a few who I will always remember with gratitude.

Again I owe thanks to many people, and especially to my friends and former colleagues in the National Botanic Gardens, Glasnevin. I spent over 19 years working there as the horticultural taxonomist, and this book owes much more to the people who garden Glasnevin than I can possibly express in words. I must include a special tribute to Donal Synnott, since 1994 the Director of the National Botanic Gardens; he continually supported and aided my research, and now he carries the awesome responsibility of ensuring that the Gardens, its plant collections, glasshouses, scientific collections, library and archives - the legacy of his predecessors - continues to illuminate Irish horticulture.

The stories in this volume have been researched as carefully as possible. Some of the histories have been recorded in greater detail elsewhere, as acknowledged in the bibliography, which I have also taken the opportunity to bring up to date and to expand. Any errors that are found in the following pages are entirely my responsibility and I apologise for them; I would be pleased to receive corrections or further information about the plants and people mentioned.

Finally, I 'borrowed' the title for this essay from William Robinson's masterpiece *The English flower garden*, first published in 1883. Ireland's flower gardens derive much of their beauty from the ideas he articulated in that fine book. As I wrote before, *The English flower garden* is still well worth reading.

Some ther be that do defye
All that is newr, and euer do crye
The olde is better, awaye with the new
Because it is false, and the olde is true:
Let them this boke reade and beholde
For it preferreth the learnyng most olde.

William Turner: Comparison betwene the olde learnynge and the newe (1537)
by Urbanus Regius

Charles Nelson
Tippitiwitchet Cottage, Outwell, Norfolk
4 July 1996

I wish you friends whose wisdom makes them kind,
Well-leisured friends to share your evening's peace,
Friends who can season knowledge with a laugh;
A hedge of lavender, a patch of thyme,
With sage and marjoram and rosemary,
A damask rosebush and a hive of bees,
And cabbages that hold the morning dew,
A blackbird in the orchard boughs - all these,
And - God bless you.

Winifred M. Letts: 'Wishes for William'

Prologue

So all agreed through sweet diversitie
This Gardin to adorne with all varietie.

Edmund Spenser: 'The Faerie Queene'

The gardens of Ireland contain thousands of different plants, from every quarter of the globe. These trees, shrubs and herbs have a multitude of forms. Their flowers are of many colours, and their foliage exhibits an inexhaustible range of textures and shades of green. Each plant has its own beauty, its own charm, and its own individual history.

Our gardens are the consummation of more than five millennia of experience in cultivating plants. Some of our garden flowers are wild species that have been plucked from their native habitats and transplanted, without alteration, into our gardens. Others are garden varieties - cultivars - that are the products of human ingenuity, the beautiful results of manipulation by plant breeders. Yet other plants are cultivars that arose by chance, through mutation or crossbreeding, and were noticed, selected and perpetuated by discerning collectors and gardeners.

This book is a celebration of a small fraction of the plants that are cultivated in Ireland. The present-day gardener has tens of thousands of species and varieties from which to choose. Of these, I have selected over a hundred which have historic bonds with Ireland, through a garden, a nursery, an explorer, a botanist or a gardener. Some are indigenous in wild places in Ireland, but most of the plants had originals that came from far afield.

Despite the apparent profusion of lovely plants available in modern nurseries and garden-centres, numerous fine varieties are not stocked. Indeed some cultivars that were sold a few years ago are nearing extinction, and a long list of vanished varieties can be compiled. That list makes depressing reading. The plants included here are available although some might be elusive, lingering only in the gardens of a few enthusiastic plantsmen or in derelict gardens. I have attempted to intersperse rarities and common cultivars, so that the catalogue of plants is not composed of those which are difficult to grow or impossible to buy.

The selection is entirely a personal one, and at times it is arbitrary. There is a tale to tell about each of the chosen plants, and the narration of these histories is the main purpose of this book. Moreover, I have not attempted to write a garden manual, recounting how to cultivate the plants, for such information is contained in many other books that are readily available.

I hope that by providing keen gardeners with information about the origins of the trees, shrubs and herbs, they will be encouraged to grow and propagate Irish varieties and later share them with fellow gardeners so that these plants will be preserved for future gardeners. It is the responsibility of the present generation of Irish gardeners to perpetuate plants raised by the nurserymen and gardeners who were our predecessors, for no-one else has the same interest in this facet of Ireland's heritage. The surest way to achieve this goal is for us to stimulate interest in garden plants of Irish origin, so that more people will appreciate them and cultivate them, not necessarily in preference to other species or varieties, but at least alongside them. It would be parochial to exclude from our gardens any plant that lacked an Irish connection, and I am not advocating such a narrow attitude.

Be that as it may, a garden could be planted with nothing but Irish cultivars, native plants and exotic species discovered or collected by men and women who were born or who worked in Ireland. Such a garden would bloom every day of the year, and it would be as fragrant as any other, a garden adorned with wonderful variety. In writing this essay, that is the garden I have tried to imagine, an Irish flower garden, rich in memories of people and times past.

> Of al the herbys of Yrlonde,
> Here thu schalt knowe meny onde ...[1]

I
Gardens rich in memory

I walked entranced
Through a land of Morn;
The sun, with wondrous excess of light,
Shone down and glanced
Over seas of corn
And lustrous gardens aleft and right.

James Clarence Mangan: 'A vision of Connaught'

Ireland's first gardeners were the Stone Age people. About 5,500 years ago the earliest farmers started to ring-bark trees, and in the newly created glades of fertile soil within the wild woods they sowed grain. Einkorn, emmer and barley were the first plants cultivated, but as these are not native to Ireland the seed was imported from the European mainland. The ultimate origin of einkorn, an ancestor of modern wheats, and emmer, another wheat, was the Fertile Crescent of Asia Minor. Although they grew wheats and barley, the Stone Age gardeners supplemented their diet by fishing and trapping wild animals, and by collecting fruits and herbs from the woodlands and moors.

For about 3,000 years little changed. Later people grew flax, for its stem fibres that were woven into cloth, but few other crop plants were introduced. The implements used to cut down the trees and to till the soil slowly improved. Stone axes and crude digging sticks eventually gave way to metal implements, first of bronze and then of iron. By about 2,500 years ago, Irish farmers had learned to use a primitive plough so cultivating the land grew easier, and fields became a permanent feature in the landscape. The record of fossilized pollen grains shows that weeds increased in abundance about this time; many were alien plants brought here unintentionally as seeds mixed with the seeds of crop plants.

In the first centuries of the Christian era, more new plants arrived in Ireland, mainly as a result of the spread of the Roman Empire. While the Romans never invaded Ireland, their influence was far-reaching. They brought peas and beans to Britain as well as various herbs and these eventually were imported into Ireland. At the time, none of these species grew naturally in north-western Europe, but some escaped from cultivation and spread into our wild places, becoming naturalized. Flavoursome herbs such as onions and leeks were imported, and it is believed that a wild garlic found today in coastal habitats around Galway Bay is descended from such a prehistoric introduction.

The spread of Christianity to Ireland and the later activities of Irish missionary monks undoubtedly had marked influences on the diversity of plants grown in Early Christian Ireland. The hermit monks who lived in remote bee-hive huts probably had small gardens in which they grew vegetables to supplement the wild fruits and herbs. The importance of gardening to the Celtic church is signified by the fact that the patron saint of gardeners is Fiacra, a seventh-century Irish monk who founded an abbey in the valley of the River Barrow at Ullard, County Kilkenny, before going to France, where he joined a monastery near Meaux. Retreating further from the world, he was permitted to live in a solitary hut in the forest, and there he spent his days praying and gardening.

Missionary monks and students, returning to Ireland after studying in the great continental schools, may have brought seeds and plants with them. They would have learnt about the medicinal herbs of Italy and Greece, gleaning this valuable knowledge from the botanical manuscripts of ancient authors. Copies of the classical herbals were preserved in monastic libraries, and were laboriously transcribed by the monks. Many of the plants recorded in these handwritten volumes were unknown in Ireland, so the physician-monks had to import seeds and then cultivate the herbs before they availed of their healing properties. They could have imported dried herbs, but it was easier to grow plants in a monastery garden.

The Irish scribes who produced the exquisite manuscripts of the Holy Scriptures also needed plants. Some of the inks used to illuminate the vellum pages were made from vegetable dyes that came from plants not found in Irish fields and woods including one named *rud* (or *roid*) which was cultivated and required careful attention, and woad (*Isatis tinctoria*).[1] Again, it was easier to grow the herbs in gardens than to import dried leaves and flowers.

Thus the plants deliberately cultivated in Ireland in the first millennium after Christ's birth were all useful. They were eaten, they provided relief for the sick, or they yielded products that were needed. None of the earliest gardeners grew plants simply because they were beautiful.

THE LILY AND THE ROSE

We do not know when the first purely ornamental plants were cultivated in Ireland, but this probably happened after the arrival of the Normans in the late twelfth century. The coming of the well-organized religious orders, which established elaborate monastic communities, was undoubtedly significant. Witness the stark and ruined yet wonderful abbey dedicated to Our Lady of the Fertile Rocks at Corcomroe in The Burren, County Clare, which contains the earliest botanical carvings in western Europe - beautiful capitals crowning the limestone columns in the chancel depict poppy fruits and pendant bell-like blossoms, perhaps representing the flowers of lily-of-the-valley, henbane and foxglove.

Indirect evidence for the cultivation of roses is found in property deeds dating from the thirteenth century. A number of these documents stipulate the payment of roses, either in the form of chaplets or as single blossoms, as rent for land. The flowers were usually handed over on the feast of the Nativity of Saint John the Baptist, 24 June, the traditional Midsummer Day. The roses were 'paid' in the same way as ginger, cummin, cloves and peppercorns. While these spices were imported, the red roses were surely freshly picked.

Mediaeval roses were little different from the wild dog-roses of Irish hedgerows, quite unlike the cabbage-blossomed varieties of the present day, and were grown in the well-run gardens of the large monasteries. The Benedictine communities had gardens, especially kitchen gardens, attached to their monasteries. There were also physic gardens in which the herbs were cultivated for the use of the monk who served as physician. The plan for a great Benedictine monastery, preserved in the foundation situated on the shore of Lake Constance in Switzerland of the Irish missionary Saint Gall who came from Bangor in County Down, shows such a garden and lists the plants it included - iris, mint, sage, fennel, rosemary, lilies and roses.

Roses and lilies had medicinal uses, but they also had strong religious associations. As the cult of the Virgin grew, so Mary and the rose became inseparable. Lilies and roses were probably used to decorate churches during the great festivals, especially those of the Blessed Virgin. The rose and the lily became popular symbols of faith.

> Christ by His holy word and life sanctified
> The pleasant lily; dying
> He gave its colour to the rose.[2]

THE POETRY OF GARDENING

By the close of the fourteenth century in Ireland there was a substantial interest in horticulture, but possibly only in the areas settled by the Norman families. A scribe, working in eastern Ireland, perhaps in County Kildare, recorded some doggerel lines about gardening. This poem, attributed to a Master Jon Gardener, is the first written work on gardening in the English language. Remarkably, the earliest surviving manuscripts both have Irish connections, and include a reference to 'the herbs of Ireland'; this phrase is absent from the later manuscripts and was probably intended to please an Irish (or Norman-Irish) patron.

The verses of Jon Gardener give a fair indication of the garden plants of the late 1300s, and we may assume that most of those mentioned were available to gardeners in Ireland. Red and white roses are included, as are sweet-smelling herbs such as lavender, chamomile and rosemary. Lilies are noted along with some native plants. 'All these herbs must be sown in the month of April,' instructed the poet, 'before Saint Michael's Day'.

Jon Gardener, or Master Jon the Gardener, was not Irish. We can only guess who he was; perhaps he was a master gardener in the service of one of the English kings during the first half of the fourteenth century. His instructions are accurate, and were copied many times. The Irish scribe who recorded the poem did a scissors-and-paste job; his copy contains repetitions and extra material from various sources. For example, he incorporated instructions on the cultivation of rosemary and of a crocus from which saffron was made. These two plants did not reach Britain until the early 1300s and may not have been grown in Ireland until later in the century. The poet advised that the crocus should be planted about the Feast of the Nativity of the Blessed Virgin, 8 September, so this was a spring-flowering species and not the true autumnal saffron crocus. The details about the cultivation of rosemary, a tender plant that arrived in Britain about 1340, are taken from another manuscript, probably one written by Friar Henry Daniel.[3]

Master Jon's book contains instructions on more mundane plants - fruits and vegetables for the kitchen, and culinary herbs. He tells how to cultivate worts (cabbage). Parsley 'is to be sown in the month of March'. Directions are given about the grafting of apple and pear trees, on the 'setting of onions' and on the sowing of garlic and leeks - 'In the day of Saint Valentine, thou shalt sow these seeds in time'.

Thus six centuries ago, an Irish scribe recorded for his patron the first English gardening manual. In a sense his work is a landmark in Irish gardening, for it shows us that at the turn of the fourteenth century there was a burgeoning interest in gardens and a yearning for a set of written directions for future consultation.

Let me trace some of the succeeding milestones in our garden history.

JOYFULL NEWES OUT OF THE NEWE FOUNDE WORLDE

The next landmark falls two centuries later. The monasteries, with their sweet, herbed, fruitful gardens, had been dissolved but gardening as an art was well established. New plants were coming to Ireland in small numbers from other lands. Sir Walter Raleigh is credited with introducing the potato into Ireland at the end of the sixteenth century, but he may not have been responsible for this signal act. The potato had reached Europe from South America in the early 1500s and slowly was being circulated among gardeners - it was a botanical curiosity then, not a staple crop.

Until this time, little interest had been shown in our native plants. They were not studied for their own sake, as the science of botany was still only a minor adjunct to medicine, nor were native plants cultivated except for a few herbs. But, in the 1580s saplings of the strawberry tree (*Arbutus unedo*) were despatched to England so that this fascinating tree could be grown in the gardens of the Elizabethan aristocracy. Thus the traffic in plants became two-way. Ireland's indigenous species were prized as exotic delights in the gardens of other lands, just as plants from the recently explored regions of the New World could be enjoyed here.

Throughout the following decades the importation of plants quickened. In Ireland, botanical excursions were undertaken by learned gentlemen and the native flora was catalogued plant by plant. In the last quarter of the seventeenth century, new gardening techniques reached this country, and numerous exotic trees were planted in the great demesnes. Cedars of Lebanon, Spanish jasmine, laurustinus and the tender, sweet-scented tuberose (*Polianthes tuberosa*) from Mexico grew and flourished.

The next landmark occurs at the close of the 1600s. While the 'noise of battle' rumbled throughout Ireland, the first primitive greenhouses were built, so that keen gardeners could cultivate plants that were unable to stand out of doors during inclement Irish winters. The prototype had a slate roof and was heated by a furnace and flues incorporated into the brick walls - this was not ideal but it worked. Sir Arthur Rawdon of Moira, the 'Cock of the North', had such a conservatory in 1690, and two years later it was filled with an astonishing collection of plants. He had sent his gardener, James Harlow, to Jamaica to collect. Harlow's botanical booty was carefully packed in cases, loaded on to a ship and transported across the ocean to Carrickfergus and thence to Moira. Each case contained about 50 plants, and there were 20 cases - about 1,000 tropical plants were carefully transferred to Rawdon's conservatory. They flourished, and Sir Arthur was able to send young material to his friends in England, and to botanic gardens in Leipzig, Uppsala, Chelsea and Oxford.[4]

Arthur Rawdon was an extraordinary man, a great innovator. He was prepared to try growing plants that could not tolerate the Irish climate. He was an adventurous gardener, for before he sent Harlow to Jamaica he had written to his close friend, Dr Hans Sloane, who was a native of County Down but was living in Jamaica, asking him to send seeds of plants that grew on the tops of Jamaican mountains. Rawdon had read that frost occurred on the mountain peaks and he reasoned that plants growing there could survive at Moira. Such a venturesome spirit is the perennial driving force that has enriched our gardens, even beyond the fabulous cargo of James Harlow.

Rawdon was unique, but he was not the only active gardener in the 1680s and 1690s. Others tried to stimulate botany and horticulture. In 1687 a botanic (physic) garden was established on the campus of the University of Dublin. By the 1720s it contained plants from far-away places including African aloes that arrived in Dublin as gifts from the eminent Dutch botanist Hermann Boerhaave. Ireland was not an isolated backwater, but was benefiting from the work of the explorers and botanists of Europe.

A RAGE OF PLANTING

Moving forward to the close of the eighteenth century, the Irish House of Commons funded the establishment of a public botanic garden in Dublin. This was started on 25 March 1795 at Glasnevin, and opened to visitors in 1800, when it was the largest garden of its kind in the world.[5] One of the leading figures in its formation was John Foster, the last Speaker of the

Irish House of Commons, a great plantsman and gardener. He amassed a collection of trees and shrubs on his estate at Collon in County Louth, that excelled anything else in Ireland. Foster grew about 1,700 different species, and he eagerly sought new plants, sometimes using his political contacts to obtain rare seeds from overseas. He also purchased plants whenever he could. *Rhododendron ponticum*, the wild rhododendron that is now a pest in many parts of western Ireland, was among his prized possessions, as was the American snowberry (*Symphoricarpos albus*), which is so common in hedgerows today.

While John Foster was essentially a collector of things, his contemporary, John Templeton, was imbued with the same spirit of innovation that had characterized Arthur Rawdon. John Templeton was a pioneer in plant acclimatization. He grew *Camellia* and *Fuchsia* out-of-doors at Cranmore in the Malone district of Belfast, although these plants were, and indeed often still are, kept in glasshouses. *Fuchsia*, he noted, produced larger and brighter flowers when grown in the open air.

The eighteenth and nineteenth centuries were marked by a massive influx of exotic plants. Private gardeners like Foster and Templeton led the way, and the new botanic gardens in Belfast, Cork and Dublin soon overtook them. These institutions had an insatiable appetite for novelties and became the leading importers of new varieties.

From about 1830 onwards hundreds of seed packets and numerous wooden cases filled with plants arrived from the Argentine, California and Mexico, the Himalaya, China and Australasia. Species previously unknown to Europe's gardeners and botanists flowered for the first time in Glasnevin and its sister gardens. With pride, these plants were propagated and their offspring were shared with other keen gardeners, for, as stated by Glasnevin's greatest director, Sir Frederick Moore, the role of a botanic garden is 'to collect good plants and then distribute them'. Lilies, orchids, rhododendrons and cacti were among the spectacular plants introduced through Ireland to gardens throughout the world.

However, the style of gardening in the mid-nineteenth century was rigid and formal; it did not allow for much innovation in planting. A revolution in gardening fashion was required so that the countless new plants could be accommodated with equanimity. That revolution happened, and had its origins in Irish gardens.

THE WILD GARDEN

The next landmark comes in the latter decades of the 1800s, prompted by the Irish horticulturist, William Robinson, who is often called the 'Father of the English flower garden'! Vociferously, he challenged the convention of bedding-out tender annuals every year to provide a splash of colour for a few short summer weeks. Robinson argued that plants should be placed 'where they will flourish without further care or cost', that gardeners should cultivate the many fine plants from distant regions that were as hardy as native plants, and that these should be arranged in 'bold, natural groups with a free hand'.

William Robinson gained some of his inspiration from the wilder (probably somewhat derelict) gardens of his native Ireland - there were already informal gardens in the soon-to-be-fashionable 'Robinsonian' mode. He saw bamboos growing at Fota near Cork in a way that resembled the natural vegetation of China or upland Java. In the years that followed the publication of his book *The wild garden*, progress was made, and he was able to say that at Narrow Water House, outside Newry, a 'great cloud of daffodils covered a mound ... It was not only good as a picture but as a lesson in the planting of the wild garden'.

Released from the necessity of raising hundreds of thousands of annuals for planting out in patterned, carpet-like parterres, gardeners began to develop gardens that were less regimented. Great clumps of rhododendrons, overlooked by elegant conifers, surrounded by crowds of naturalized bulbs, took the place of 'the dreadful practice of tearing up the flower-beds and leaving them like new-dug graves twice a year'. The process accelerated as the inflow of plants increased again in the early years of the present century. A torrent of exciting, hardy species began to reach Europe from China and the remote mountains of Tibet and Burma. Exploration of these hills for botanical treasure yielded plants of outstanding beauty which soon became popular - one, the butterfly bush (*Buddleja davidii*), is now a prolific colonist of derelict city sites.

In Ireland, another revolution took place that helped to bring William Robinson's concepts to fruition. Nurseries were established to cater for adventurous gardeners. William Hartland of Cork supplied daffodils and began to breed new cultivars, thereby initiating an important industry. Throughout this century, Irish daffodil experts have led the world in raising fine varieties. In Newry, Rodgers, McClelland & Co. established a nursery in the 1870s, and its catalogue listed many rarities including tender Australasian species. This firm eventually gave way to Daisy Hill Nursery which acquired a reputation second to none. In the early 1900s, also in the north-east, the Slieve Donard Nursery was established by Thomas Ryan, and then taken over by the Slinger family.[6] In Dublin, Watson's Nursery was started. These three nurseries set standards in excellence that far out-strip many nurseries in Ireland today. The breeding and selection programmes carried out, particularly at the Donard Nursery, gave us plants of great beauty. Side by side with these nurseries were the great rose firms of Dickson at Newtownards and McGredy at Portadown.

All in all, the art of gardening was at its zenith in Ireland during the first half of this century. Then our greatest plant collections were established in gardens supplied by vibrant nurseries. The plants were of outstanding quality, and the keen gardeners were supported by horticulturists of international repute, people like Dr Augustine Henry and Sir Frederick Moore.

GARDENS RICH IN MEMORY

Will there be another milestone? Perhaps it is already set in time. The establishment in the early 1970s of a heritage gardens committee in the Republic of Ireland was promoted by the realization that great gardens are vulnerable - many had already vanished and others could follow unless resources were found to preserve and maintain this fragile and ephemeral heritage. In 1980 a similar committee was established in Northern Ireland, and in 1981 the Irish Garden Plant Society was formed to work for the conservation of Ireland's garden plants. In the mid-1990s, interest in historic gardens was further encouraged by the provision in the Republic of Ireland of funds for the restoration of important gardens.

Moira and Cranmore have disappeared, and nothing remains of the garden of John Foster. Many plants cultivated by our predecessors have vanished from gardens but gardeners are not despondent. There is still a spirit of adventure and good gardeners continue to experiment, to bring new plants into cultivation, to create interesting gardens, and to breed and select novel cultivars. Many fine gardens exist for our private pleasure and some are open for general enjoyment, and a great variety of plants remain in small and large gardens. Some of the best of Ireland's rich heritage of garden flowers are the subjects of the following pages.

II
A native garden

Arbutus unedo - Ulex europaeus 'Strictus' *- Taxus baccata* 'Lutea'
Taxus baccata 'Fastigiata' *- Sorbus hibernica - Salix hibernica*
Salix x *moorei - Juncus effusus* f. *spiralis*
Hieracium scullyi - Athyrium filix-femina 'Frizelliae'

I have a shieling in the wood,
None knows it but my Lord:
An ash tree on this side, a hazel on that,
A great tree by a rath encloses it.

Anonymous (c. 900 AD): 'The Hermit's Song'

For thousands of years after the art of cultivation had been brought to Ireland only exotic plants were cultivated. There was no need to grow the native species, as they were at hand in the woods, by the rivers and loughs, or in the clearings, to be gathered as pot-herbs, samples or sources of dyes.

The poem of Master Jon includes the names of a number of plants native to this island. As instructions are given about sowing their seed, we may assume that they were cultivated, perhaps from Irish stock. Cowslips, primroses, foxgloves and violets were grown by mediaeval gardeners, alongside daisies and groundsel. Nearby bloomed foreign herbs, rosemary, peonies, roses and lilies, all imports from the mainland of Europe. Yet there are plants in Ireland that are not found wild in Britain, and these began to attract the attention of gardeners in the late sixteenth century.

IMMORTAL STRAWBERRY TREE

In 1586, a bundle of saplings of the strawberry tree, ***Arbutus unedo***,[1] was sent to England from Munster. The Earl of Leicester and Sir Francis Walsingham, Queen Elizabeth I's Secretary of State, were keen to obtain the tree, for it was a curiosity that bore flowers and fruits at the same time. The gentlemen were advised to plant the young trees near a pond or in black 'moory' earth for that was the kind of soil they grew in near the lakes of Killarney.

The flowers of the strawberry tree are open in autumn. They are urn-shaped, in colour resembling translucent pearls, and they hang in clusters beside the fruits that, taking a whole year to mature, have developed from the previous year's blossoms. When ripe, the fruits are bright scarlet with a warty surface like strawberries. The berries are edible, but people differ in their opinions about the flavour and quality. Two and a half centuries ago, Dr Caleb Threlkeld noted the argument in his Irish flora:

> Some say the Fruit is eatable without Harm, but most say it hurts the Stomach, and causes Head-ach, being of hard Digestion: To some they are austere, and tart to others of no unpleasant Taste: *sed non est disputandum de Gustibus*; for in this Case every Man has a private Judgement, as in Religion ...[2]

Personally I think that the fruit is dry and insipid, but I have tasted less pleasing berries. In Corsica a liqueur is made from the strawberries, and I have tried making some myself with no great success - it was a flavourless, albeit alcoholic syrup.

The strawberry tree is an evergreen, tolerant of frost and a wide range of soil conditions, that slowly forms a sturdy, dome-topped tree. In its native haunts in counties Sligo, Cork and Kerry, this splendid tree thrives along the lough shores and in rocky woods. Some of the wild plants, now many-stemmed shrubby trees or clusters of trees that arose from a single rootstock, may be a thousand or more years old, and the late Professor David Webb suggested that individual plants are so long-lived 'as to be almost immortal'.

Arbutus unedo has been cultivated around Dublin for at least 300 years. In the 1650s, the English botanist, Dr William How, made a note in a copy of his own book *Phytologia Britannica* about a tree 'at Bellamount 3 miles from Dublin'. Irish gardeners often took plants from wild habitats; for example, Sir John Perceval's gardener collected 'a good many Arbutuses and good store of Ewe-trees ... out of ye County Kerry' in February 1711. There was a famous tree at Newtownmountkennedy that was recorded by Samuel Hayes in his book on tree planting published in 1794; it was considered to be very old then, but was blown down ten years later.

In 1687 a gardener, perhaps a member of the Lane family, wrote instructions about raising strawberry trees from seed. The ripe berries were gathered in autumn and placed in a box which was securely sealed to prevent mice enjoying a tasty meal. In the spring, the fruit was washed, dried in the sun and the strawberries were then crumbled into a powder and the small seeds removed. The seeds were sown 'in the fattest earth you can get', and the seed-tray was placed in a shady place. Soon the seedlings appeared. This is the easiest way to propagate *Arbutus*, but seeds can be sown in November and they will germinate in February. Seeds left inside the berries, which are planted whole, will germinate a few months later, about May. The various garden varieties must be raised by taking cuttings because they do not come true to type from seed.

There is a red-flowered strawberry tree, *Arbutus unedo* f. *rubra*, which has dusky-pink flowers, instead of translucent whitish-green bells. It blooms freely but does not set fruit abundantly. A double-flowered variety, *Arbutus unedo* 'Plena', is also in cultivation; instead of urn-shaped bells, the flowers are divided into many petals and the stamens look like petals too. It has been known to gardeners for many years. At one time a variegated form was cherished but appears to have become extinct, perhaps as long ago as the 1820s. John Foster grew a variegated strawberry tree at Collon about 1817, but his plant died. A few years later he tried to obtain a replacement from Edward Hodgins, an excellent nurseryman from Dunganstown near Wicklow, who had a well-stocked nursery - we will encounter Hodgins again, later.

GOLD UNDER THE FURZE

As a collector of plants, John Foster was insatiable. He was also generous and often gave plants from his garden to friends, including Maria Edgeworth, and to the Botanic Gardens, Glasnevin. As a powerful figure in the Irish establishment during the formative years of the Botanic Gardens - 'his botanical garden' Foster's influence extended to the appointment of staff. Both the head gardener, John Underwood, and the under-gardener, John White, were appointed on his recommendation. Underwood was a Scot, whereas John White was from County Louth.

One of the under-gardener's duties was to travel about Ireland, collecting native plants for cultivation in Glasnevin. By doing this, John White gained a fair knowledge of the native flora. In 1808 he published an accomplished book on grasses, nicely illustrated with coloured plates. Twenty-five years later, many of his records were included by Miss Katherine Baily in *The Irish flora*, which she published anonymously. One of White's earliest plant hunting expeditions was to the north-east. He visited Carlingford Lough in 1804 and travelled through County Down, along the shore of Strangford Lough and on to the Ards Peninsula. At Mount Stewart, the demesne of the Marquis of Londonderry, he discovered an unusual shrub from which he collected cuttings that he brought back to Glasnevin and rooted.

1. Ulex europaeus 'Strictus'

John White's find was a variety of gorse, ***Ulex europaeus* 'Strictus'**[3] (Plate 1), which has erect branches. The leaves of the ordinary gorse take the form of stout spines with long tapering points that are extremely sharp. However, the Mount Stewart gorse has a soft feel, for the spines are thin and not rigid. Alas, it is rather a shy shrub and does not flower well.

The new gorse was carefully tended at Glasnevin. Dr Walter Wade, the Dublin Society's Professor of Botany who was director of the Gardens, decided that it merited recognition as a distinct species, but he was slow to do something about it. In 1818 the authors of a history of Dublin noted that the new plant had not received a Latin name, but Dr Wade rectified that in 1823 and informally christened the gorse *Ulex downiensis*. Two years later, James Mackay, the curator of the botanic garden belonging to Trinity College, Dublin, named it *Ulex strictus*.

Today John White's gorse is regarded as a mere cultivar of the common furze, and Mackay's name is retained. But in those early days of the Glasnevin Botanic Gardens, the new plant was a source of much pride; it was the first novelty that Glasnevin could claim as its very own, and it was uniquely Irish. Wade sent a letter to John Foster when the plant flowered for the first time in 1821, telling Foster that specimens were being sent to London so that the gorse could be illustrated in a botanical magazine 'for the honour of poor old Ireland'.

About two centuries have elapsed since John White collected this strange, upright gorse. It still grows in Glasnevin, and has been returned by me to Mount Stewart where I hope it has a place of honour among the exotic flowers of that superb garden. At Glasnevin there are plants about a metre and a half tall that blossom every year but are never covered with solid gold like the wild whins. I have seen the Irish furze, as the variety is sometimes called, used as a hedge plant and its erect, disciplined form certainly lends it to this purpose. Last century the Irish furze attracted sporadic attention. It was supposed to have been used widely on Jersey for hedging, but my friends there think this is an error. The main interest was in using it as cattle fodder as the soft spines rendered it more palatable.

GOLD UPON THE YEW

Farm animals can eat gorse but the foliage of the yew is poisonous. Despite its fatal property, yew trees have been grown in gardens for centuries, and as Dr Threlkeld noted

> our Ancestors planted them in Church-yards, that the ever green Leaves might be a Symbol of immortality and eternal Life, which those who sleep in Jesus wait for, to their Bodies after the Resurrection.[4]

Yew is native in Ireland. Around Killarney, in The Burren and on the remoter hills of Ulster, a few lonely trees may still be seen in inaccessible places. The fruits have a scarlet, fleshy cup, enclosing the single seed. Birds eat the berries - I have watched mistle-thrushes gorge themselves on yew at Birr Castle in November. The seeds pass through the bird's gut undamaged and capable of germinating. Red squirrels adore the kernels and I have spied them at Glasnevin happily crunching open the seeds and devouring the contents, and they were so intent upon eating this delicacy that they ignored the person standing a metre away.

Although the yew berries are usually bright red, there is a variety with golden fruits. It was introduced into gardens through the Botanic Gardens at Glasnevin, but it caused less excitement than the gorse. Like the gorse it grows today in the National Botanic Gardens.

The story of the golden-berried yew, *Taxus baccata* **'Lutea'**,[5] is complicated. About 1810 a tree was noticed growing in the estate of the Bishop of Kildare on the north bank of the River Tolka adjacent to the Botanic Gardens in Glasnevin. Nothing is recorded about the fate of this yew with yellow fruits, but it seems to have vanished shortly afterwards. Remarkably, another golden-fruited yew was found at Clontarf, a short distance from Glasnevin, in 1833. Cuttings were taken and one of the saplings was donated to the Botanic Gardens in January 1837 by Lady Dufferin. This plant survives today, surrounded by many other varieties of yew. The original tree at Clontarf has disappeared.

It is strange that yews with yellow fruits have not been reported from any other country except India. Several golden-berried trees were recorded at Powerscourt by Henry Elwes and Dr Augustine Henry in their magnificent book *Trees of Great Britain and Ireland*. Those yews could also have been raised from the Clontarf tree.

The yellow-fruited yew is a fine sight when the fruits are ripe. Before the birds devour them, the bright yellow berries sparkle against the sombre dark leaves, often sparkling with rain or dew; the tree appears to be decorated with thousands of tiny golden ornaments.

THE OTHER IRISH YEW

The yew with golden fruit forms a lax tree with spreading and somewhat weeping branches. The other Irish variety of yew is starkly different, for its branches are upright and straight, and its habit is disciplined and compact. This is the true Irish yew, *Taxus baccata* **'Fastigiata'**, the Florencecourt yew.[6]

The Florencecourt yew was found almost one century before the yellow-berried tree. After more than 250 years this tree is a familiar ornament in large gardens and demesnes, as well as numerous cemeteries. It was a most fashionable plant in the middle of the last century because it was a columnar evergreen, hardier than the Italian cypress. The Irish yew does not need to be clipped, but it is often demeaned by being used in topiary - when subjected to this unnecessary treatment it is far too prim.

The home of the Irish yew is the foothills of Cuilcagh Mountain in County Fermanagh. Yews still cling to cliffs around the swallow-holes above the Marble Arch, but the original Irish yew came from a small rocky ridge overlooking Florencecourt. The traditional site is called Carraig-na-madadh, the rock of the dog. Today there are no trees there; it is a desolate patch of boulders surrounded by a sponge of *Sphagnum*, peat and ling. The plant was discovered between 1740 and 1760 by George Willis while he was on the moors coursing for hares. He spotted a sapling growing amongst the rocks. It looked different so he dug it up. The young yew had apparently produced two leading shoots and divided conveniently into two plants; one was kept by Willis and the other was given to his landlord, Lord Mountflorence (later created Earl of Enniskillen). Willis' tree died in the 1860s. The other tree was planted beside a little stream that was later overlooked by Lord Mountflorence's fine new mansion. It is still alive in the demesne at Florencecourt, a slightly dishevelled, lichen-covered yew, yet clearly recognizable as an Irish yew. This venerable tree, the mother of all Irish yews, was rescued in the early 1980s from encroaching laurels and when I last paid a visit it was continuing to thrive.

The Florencecourt yew was seen by George Cunningham, a wily Liverpool nurseryman, about 1780. He was impressed by its erect habit and persuaded Lord Enniskillen to part with some cuttings. Cunningham raised young plants and slowly released these onto the market. Even in 1830, five decades later, the Irish yew was a rarity, but other nurseries were propagating it and Cunningham began producing thousands of plants for export to Europe and America.

Like the Irish gorse, the Irish yew was believed to be a new species. However, botanists later realized that the difference between it and the predominant common yew (by inference now called the English yew) were of minor biological significance. The Florencecourt yew is now considered to be a cultivar, and is well worth growing even in a small garden. Careful pruning will keep it compact and spire-shaped.

IRISH WHITEBEAM

Plants of the two Irish yews and the Irish gorse that we grow today are all descended from unique individuals that were once found, by chance, in the wild. In contrast, there are numerous trees of Irish whitebeam in Ireland but it is not found growing wild anywhere else. It is one of Ireland's very few endemic species, although some botanists may quibble over its status.

Irish whitebeam, ***Sorbus hibernica***,[7] inhabits rocky places, limestone hills and eskers; it is sometimes seen in hedgerows but it is not a common wayside tree. Its silhouette is rounded and mature trees may be up to 15 metres tall. In late spring when the buds open, the new leaves, backed with silver-white felt, look like miniature *Magnolia* blossoms. The upper surface of each leaf soon loses its silvery hairs and becomes dark green, but the felt remains on the lower side, and in a stiff breeze the leaves flicker green and white. They are oval and not divided like those of the mountain ash or rowan (*Sorbus aucuparia*) which is related to the whitebeam. The creamy-white flowers appear in June. During autumn the trees bear trusses of red, speckled berries and the leaves turn yellow and brown before falling as winter sets in.

The English botanist, Edmund Warburg, made a detailed study of whitebeams and decided that there was a distinct species in Ireland to which he gave the scientific name *Sorbus hibernica*. Some botanists regard the Irish tree as a local race of a large, variable super-species; in the most recent flora of the whole of Europe, the Irish species has been grouped with several English and European whitebeams. The dispute arises because *Sorbus hibernica* and its near relatives are so similar that it is often very difficult, even for experts, to tell them apart. Another whitebeam, *Sorbus aria*, grows wild in Ireland but apparently only in the Galway area. This has elongated berries whereas the Irish whitebeam has globular fruits. In the Irish species the undersurface of the leaf is greenish-white, while in *Sorbus aria* the felt is pure white. However, in Connemara, where the two grow together, these features are insufficient to enable botanists to distinguish the species with certainty. Some years ago, Professor Webb offered dinner with Gaelic coffee as a prize to anyone who could point out the differences between the whitebeams and then put the right names on specimens collected when he was not looking. No such meal was ever consumed.

The Irish whitebeam is not cultivated outside a few botanical gardens. This is a pity, considering the number of whitebeams that are used in landscaping nowadays. One tree in Trinity College Botanic Garden, Palmerston Park, fruits heavily; the red berries are usually so abundant that the branches are weighed down. It is an attractive plant throughout the year, changing from silver in spring, through the green of summer, into autumnal red and gold.

BEN BULBEN'S WILLOW

Another controversial plant that is claimed as unique to Ireland is the Irish willow, **Salix hibernica** (Figure 1).[8] It only grows in counties Sligo and Leitrim, flattened against the cliffs of Ben Bulben and at The Glennans near Kinlough. This willow was discovered in June 1854 by David Moore, curator of the Botanic Gardens in Glasnevin, who gathered cuttings from male and female shrubs on Ben Bulben - willows have catkins of a single sex on each plant. The cuttings rooted and young plants were established in Glasnevin; these flowered in 1857. Moore diligently collected and dried samples of the cultivated plants, and these are preserved in the National Botanic Gardens today.

On Ben Bulben the Irish willow forms a dwarf shrub, but in cultivation it grows vigorously and eventually makes a robust bush several metres tall. Indeed, it is so rampant that severe pruning is necessary to keep it within bounds. Plants from The Glennans in County Leitrim which were grown in pots for many years at Glasnevin remained dwarf, so it is possible to grow the willow as a sort of bonsai. I have seen Irish willows growing at The Glennans; the plants are in almost inaccessible places and probably survive only where they are out of reach of goats, sheep and hares.

The Irish willow, especially the male, has much to commend it. The male catkins have long, silky hairs. In spring the young leaves are fresh apple-green, with a fringe of white hairs.

1. *Salix hibernica*

As they mature the leaves darken, although the lower surfaces remain paler and have a greenish-white bloom. I have found that cuttings taken in June will root very quickly (in about ten days) if they have some of last year's wood at the base. However, this is a protected species and cuttings cannot be removed from the wild plants, but it is in cultivation and is being propagated.

When dried specimens of the Irish willow were examined by the Austrian botanist, Karl Rechinger, in the early 1960s, he decided that they represented a new species. However, it is perhaps better to consider it as an isolated Irish race of the widespread and variable tea-leaved willow, *Salix phylicifolia*. Indeed David Moore, in one of his accounts of the Ben Bulben plants, noted that he had consulted a leading authority on *Salix*, the Reverend John Leefe, and commented that it was 'a dwarfed ... form of one of the states of *Salix phylicifolia*'.

MOORE'S MUCKISH WILLOW

David Moore was born in 1808 at Dundee on the east coast of Scotland. His father and grandfather had been gardeners and David was trained on the Earl of Camperdown's estate near the city. He received that thorough grounding in all aspects of horticulture for which Scotland is famous. In 1828 he migrated to Ireland and became an assistant gardener in the botanic garden of Trinity College, Dublin, under the supervision of James Mackay, who was also Scottish. Six years later, David applied unsuccessfully for the post of curator of the Glasnevin Botanic Gardens, but he was luckier elsewhere and was appointed botanist to the Ordnance Survey. For almost five years he worked in the north of Ireland, collecting and cataloguing the native flora, and gradually accumulating an excellent knowledge of indigenous plants. During this work he discovered a number of species new to the Irish list. He found several willows and took a special interest in plants which are botanical nightmares - willows, roses and brambles. In 1838, on the second attempt, he was appointed curator in Glasnevin following the resignation of another Scot, Ninian Niven. David Moore remained in this post until his death in 1879.

While in charge of the Glasnevin Botanic Gardens he continued to study native plants, and in 1866 published *Cybele Hibernica*, a flora of Ireland, with Alexander Goodman More. David Moore made numerous excursions to collect wild plants, including one to Donegal in September 1866. On Muckish Mountain, a great flat-topped monolith near Dunfanaghy, he discovered another willow which today bears his name.

Moore's willow, **Salix x grahamii** **nothovar.** **moorei**,[9] has not been collected since it was discovered. During June 1983, Donal Synnott and I spent an extremely windy morning on the top of Muckish trying to find it, but we left empty-handed. The vegetation on that mountain's table-top consists mainly of tiny, stunted bilberry and willow shrubs, interspersed with sea-pinks. None of the plants grows more than a few centimetres tall. According to David Moore his willow grew concealed - only the tips of the branches and two or three leaves poked above the stones and moss.

Fortunately Moore collected cuttings, and the little willow was established at Glasnevin. Unlike the Ben Bulben one it did not romp away; the branches remained short, none exceeding ten centimetres in length. The leaves grew a little larger, but they retained their oval shape and glossy, dark green colour. The plants all turned out to be female, with short grey catkins.

Some years later David Moore obtained cuttings of a Scottish willow, named *Salix* x *grahamii*, which, he thought, was similar to the Donegal plant. He suggested that these willows represented the same species, differing only in minor characteristics, in the way expected of plants that come from widely separate localities.

What is Moore's willow - or *Salix* x *moorei*, to employ its original name? Botanists suggest that it is a triple hybrid, the result of the interbreeding of dwarf willow (*Salix herbacea*), the only willow we saw on Muckish in 1983, creeping willow (*Salix repens*) and eared willow (*Salix aurita*). Such a complicated parentage is possible in the promiscuous willows, and could arise thus - suppose a female *Salix aurita* is pollinated by pollen from *Salix repens*, and then one of its male offspring, a hybrid, pollinated a female *Salix herbacea* - the resulting seedlings would be triple hybrids. *Salix* x *grahamii* is believed to have such a pedigree. The chance of such a plant arising is most unlikely, and that may explain the rarity of Moore's willow.

Leaving aside the conundrum of its parentage, Moore's little willow is still growing in gardens, and makes a useful plant for a rock garden, remaining dwarf and easily controlled.

THE CORKSCREW RUSH

David Moore was one of a group of Scottish horticulturists and botanists who lived and worked in Ireland in the last century. I have already mentioned that Moore's predecessors at Glasnevin, John Underwood and Ninian Niven, were also Scotsmen. James Mackay, of Trinity College Botanic Garden, was another. Indeed, in the late 1820s all the botanical gardens in this country were managed by Scottish gardeners. In Cork, James Drummond had completed 20 years as curator, but the garden was closed in 1829 and he emigrated to the Swan River Colony on the west coast of Australia. His younger brother, Thomas, was appointed curator of the newly established botanic garden in Belfast. Thomas Drummond was dismissed as curator after two and a half years and, having an urge to travel and collect plants, he returned to North America on another, final quest for plants.[10] His successor in Belfast was yet another Scot, David Bishop.

Bishop is not mentioned in early histories of the Belfast Botanic Gardens, yet his memorialist recorded that he took charge after Drummond's 'resignation'. He was born about 1789, and was the son of a gardener. David served his apprenticeship at Methven Castle under his brother, who had a special interest in alpine plants. Then he moved to various other gardens in Scotland, gaining useful experience, before going to London for a short period. David returned to Scotland and botanized in the Highlands, but he was a restless character, and eventually returned to London as amanuensis to John Claudius Loudon, the eminent landscape gardener and author of numerous gardening books.

David Bishop wrote a small book titled *Causal botany*, and according to his obituary, he carried this volume with him as he travelled through Britain and Ireland collecting mountain plants. It is said that he walked through every county in the kingdom in search of flowers. Strangely, if this is true, few discoveries are attributed to him, and I can find no mention of him in Irish floras. However, he made one remarkable find by which he should be remembered.

In the wilds of Connemara, David Bishop collected a peculiar form of the common rush which has spirally twisted stems and leaves. While it is known today as the screw or corkscrew rush, ***Juncus effusus* f. *spiralis***,[11] in the 1800s it was often called the Irish rush. James McNab, another Scottish gardener whose son, William, became Professor of Botany in the Royal College of Science in Dublin, remarked that Ireland was renowned for its upright, straight-stemmed plants - he gave the Irish yew and the Irish gorse as examples - yet the Irish rush was not erect and even contradicted the old Scottish proverb, 'as straight as a rush'.

Not many gardeners willingly plant rushes in their gardens. The common rush is an unpleasant weed, a nuisance in damp, wild gardens, but David Bishop's corkscrewing form is worthy of cultivation beside or in pools, in bog gardens and even in herbaceous borders. It is a curiosity, one of those plants that the great English gardener, E. A. Bowles, might have grown in his 'Lunatic Asylum' along with the wriggly hazel. It can be propagated easily by division, and apparently comes true from seed.

Robert Lloyd Praeger noted that the corkscrew rush can be found on Inishturk, Achill, Inishmurray and other islands off the west coast. He regarded it as an Atlantic form of the species. *Juncus effusus* f. *spiralis* is also reported from the western Scotland, the Orkney Islands and western Wales.

David Bishop did not remain as curator of the Belfast Botanic Gardens for long. He resigned and bought land in the Malone district, where he established a garden of rare, native plants. He was an accomplished musician, and was considered to be one of the 'most chaste violin amateur players in the kingdom'. He was mild-mannered, but was 'doomed to see many of the vicissitudes of life'. His horticultural expertise led him to produce two dwarf garden peas that were heavy-cropping varieties, and in the mid-1800s David Bishop's 'Early Long-podded Dwarf' was the best pea of its kind on the market.

SCULLY'S HAWKWEED

History is fickle. David Bishop's time as curator of the Botanic Garden in Belfast has not been adequately recorded, and now probably never can be accounted for. He is not even well remembered as an author, nor as a violinist. Bishop's 'Early Long-podded Pea' is probably extinct. As far as I know there is no plant named after him, no *Juncus bishopii*.

Other botanists have been immortalized more permanently. Dr Reginald Scully, for example, who wrote the splendid *Flora of County Kerry* after he had worked with Nathanial Colgan on a second edition of *Cybele Hibernica*, has at least two plants named after him. One is the natural hybrid between the two native Irish butterworts, *Pinguicula grandiflora* and *Pinguicula vulgaris*, namely *Pinguicula* x *scullyi*. The other is a hawkweed which is certainly worthy of a place in gardens.

Indeed I first encountered Scully's hawkweed in the late David Shackleton's garden, Beech Park. He was growing this erect, disciplined, yellow-blossomed daisy under a garbled, but immediately recognizable name. I was puzzled. David had bought the plant from a well-known English nurseryman who specialized in herbaceous perennials, yet it was strange that an almost unknown Irish hawkweed should find a place in an English nursery catalogue.

Spurred on by this, I determined to track down the plant in its natural habitats. Scully's hawkweed, ***Hieracium scullyi***,[12] only grows in a few places in County Kerry, and Scully had gathered it first in 1894 in the valley of the Roughty River which enters the sea at Kenmare. I studied the original publication in which the Reverend William Linton described and named *Hieracium scullyi*, and also Dr Scully's own notes in *Flora of County Kerry*, and set off for the valley. In June 1985, Judy Cassells and I found Scully's hawkweed growing on the stonework of one of the road bridges and on nearby rocks. Carefully we gathered a small plant and transferred this to the National Botanic Gardens, Glasnevin, where it flourished and proliferated. During the following year when a vigorous young plant came into bloom in my garden at Celbridge, Wendy Walsh was able to paint *Hieracium scullyi* for *An Irish florilegium II*.

Scully's hawkweed is a sturdy, compact perennial, with leafy stems rising about 60 cm tall. The foliage is bright green, and hairy. Being a member of the daisy (and dandelion!) family, the individual flowers are tiny with a single strap-shaped 'petal' - in fact this apparent petal is composed of five true petals fused together. These are clustered into bright yellow, dandelion-like heads. The erect stems are branched and produce at least three flower-heads each.

Although *Hieracium scullyi* is found only in the Roughty Valley in County Kerry, and nowhere else in the entire world, it is frost-tolerant and will thrive in good garden loam, even in heavy clay. There are fine clumps in the native plant collections at the National Botanic Gardens, Glasnevin, all progeny of the plant collected in 1985. Indeed, merely by dividing the proliferating rosettes, this handsome hawkweed can be propagated with great ease.

MRS FRIZELL'S FERN

Some native plants have proved much less amenable to propagation. Ferns are a good example, particularly those monstrosities that are loved by fern enthusiasts. Some ferns can be raised easily by germinating their minute spores. Some can be divided, but many increase too slowly for this to be a suitable method. Be that as it may, most of the extraordinary forms grown by the enthusiasts can only be propagated by division, as their sporelings do not 'come true', as gardeners say.

In the mid-nineteenth century ferns were among the most fashionable garden plants, and thus arose one of those Victorian gardening crazes, to the detriment of wild ferns. The delicate Killarney fern was almost exterminated by avaricious collectors and nurserymen, simply to satisfy acquisitive ladies and gentlemen who wished to decorate their conservatories and living rooms with the rarest species.

As the mania progressed, demand arose for unusual varieties - the common wild ferns were thought too plain. The search began for extraordinary variants, ferns with misshapen fronds, plants with crested instead of pointed fronds, anything that was out of the ordinary. Ireland produced its share of such monstrosities, which were given multitudes of varietal names. One unfortunate plant had the dubious privilege of being christened *Athyrium filix-femina medio-deficiens caudiculatum*. Of the 50-odd ferns of Irish origin listed in one Victorian fern book, only a few survive in cultivation.

The best-known of the Irish Victorian ferns was - I use the past tense deliberately - the Crawfordsburn fern, a form of the soft shield fern, *Polystichum setiferum*. It was found at Crawfordsburn, in north County Down, by one of Miss Crawford's workmen who dug up the fern and planted it in her garden. This variety was propagated and soon percolated to other gardens. The Crawfordsburn fern has beautifully divided and very broad fronds - pressed specimens of the fern have been preserved and these show that each little lobe overlaps its neighbours so the whole frond has a full, feathery appearance. Like so many of the once-collected mutants, the Crawfordsburn fern ceased to be popular when the fern craze petered out, and by the 1960s it was thought to have become extinct - perhaps it has survived, but I take a sceptical view of living examples of this fern. My reason is simple. The Crawfordsburn fern has many unlikely imposters, because people used to go to the Crawfordsburn area, dig up any old fern, and call it a Crawfordsburn fern.

A veritable survivor from the Victorian era and perhaps the most remarkable Irish fern is Mrs Frizell's lady fern, *Athyrium filix-femina* **'Frizelliae'** (Figure 2),[13] which is also called the tatting fern, because the fronds resemble the tatting work used of old to edge pieces of lace.

Mrs Frizell's fern is technically a monstrosity, but it is an elegant monstrosity. Instead of having elongated, almost triangular segments projecting from the central axis of each frond, it has small, congested, fan-shaped segments. The frond appears to have a series of beads strung

2. *Athyrium filix-femina* 'Frizelliae'

out along it. The fern can produce spores, and sporelings raised from the tatting fern retain the characteristic fronds, so this variety can be raised easily and in quantity.

The story of the fern was told by Mrs Frizell to Charles Druery who wrote one of the many books on garden ferns published during the craze. She recalled seeing the original plant in 1857, growing between two large boulders on a reach of the Avonmore River at Castle Kevin in County Wicklow. It was wedged firmly and appeared to be growing in very little soil. Mrs Frizell watched the plant for two years before she decided to lift it. Her husband, Dr Charles Frizell, who was a leading obstetrician in Dublin, helped her to dig it out. Mrs Frizell had looked for spores on the fern, hoping perhaps to raise young plants, but she could not see any. Eventually she presented the fern to John Bain, curator of the Trinity College Botanic Garden who put it in a greenhouse where the plant promptly produced spores. The tatting fern was soon distributed from Dublin to other gardens. A plant of the tatting fern grows today in the garden of Glendalough House, a short distance from Castle Kevin - this plant is a direct descendant of Mrs Frizell's original fern.

Twenty years later a strange event occurred. Henry Chichester Hart, son of the Vice-Provost of Trinity College and a knowledgable botanist, found the same mutant at Carrablagh in the north of Donegal. It is highly unusual for identical monstrosities to arise, especially in widely separate localities.

Ferns are enjoying a minor renaissance in popularity among discerning gardeners. They display as range of leaf textures that are not available in flowering plants, and for shaded places nothing could be easier to cultivate than a few humble ferns. Fortunately this rekindling of enthusiasm has not, and undoubtedly will not reach the passionate heights of the Victorian fern craze.

AFTER THOUGHTS

There are about 1200 flowering plants and ferns growing wild in Ireland. Each one could be cultivated but familiar plants are rarely treated as garden-worthy. The earliest gardeners had no desire to grow Irish plants as ornaments but the modern gardener may find delightful and amusing subjects in the fields and woods, and on the mountains and islands of Ireland. These can be the unblemished wild species, such as *Hieracium scullyi* or the lovely little marsh dandelion (*Taraxacum palustre*) which inhabits the turloughs of The Burren, both of which I admire, or a peculiar mutant like the corkscrew rush and the tatting fern.

Wild plants should not be dug up; they should be left alone, undamaged, for others to enjoy. A few cuttings carefully removed, or a few seeds gathered, will usually do no harm. However, there are some plants that are now fully protected by law and these cannot be touched; not even seed may be removed. These rare plants include the Irish willow and the Killarney fern, both protected in the Republic, and the cowslip in Northern Ireland. Let us hope that they will be allowed to remain in their natural habitats.

III

A winter garden

Ilex x *altaclerensis* 'Hendersonii' & 'Hodginsii'
Ilex x *altaclerensis* 'Lawsoniana' & 'Lady Valerie'
Garrya x *issaquahensis* 'Pat Ballard' & 'Glasnevin Wine'
Mahonia x *media* 'Charity' - *Hamamelis mollis*
Sarcococca humilis - *Prunus subhirtella* 'Autumnalis'
Galanthus 'Straffan' - *Galanthus* 'Hill Poë' - *Galanthus ikariae* 'Emerald Isle'
Helleborus orientalis 'Bowles' Yellow'

Winter has come with scarcity,
Lakes have flooded their sides,
Frost crumbles the leaves,
The merry wave begins to mutter.

Anonymous (c. 800 A.D.): 'Winter'

The poets who rejoiced in the loveliness of the Irish summer and who wrote exquisite hymns to the flower-filled seasons, could do little other than moan about the barrenness of winter. None of our native plants bloom during the short days of the coldest months. There were no snowdrops, early daffodils or hellebores in the fields and woods of ancient Ireland. The countryside was dreary, 'crude and black and dark and smoky'. But in winter, Ireland is not grim, nor is it a frozen wasteland. For that we may be thankful. The naked trees do form a natural lace against the thickly clouded skies, but in parts of the west and south the grass hardly ever stops growing, and throughout the island it is possible nowadays to create winter gardens that contain graceful evergreens, pretty flowers and delicate fragrances

Some of our native plants are more noticeable in winter; they stand out because they retain a clothing of leaves and seem to defy Nature, to be oblivious of the frosty, nose-nipping winter. Take a walk in winter through the woodlands about the Killarney loughs and you cannot fail to be impressed by the evergreen hollies and strawberry trees. When the mid-winter sun is low in the sky, sunlight glints off the rippled leaves of the hollies making the bushes sparkle. Nowhere is this play of light on leaves more dramatic than in The Burren where, again, the holly bushes stand out against grey rocks and the grey lace of hazel thickets.

HODGINS' HOLLIES

Chief among the native evergreens is the holly which in pre-Christian Ireland was a highly-regarded plant. The holly was sacred to the druids because they believed that the sun never deserted the evergreen. In Ireland's ancient law code, the Laws of Neighbourhood, holly was decreed as one of the four noble trees of the wood. Anyone who chopped down a bush without permission paid a fine of five cows, and anyone unlawfully removing a branch could be fined a year-old heifer.

Later, holly was adopted as a Christian symbol. Well-known carols include it in their imagery, sometimes alone, occasionally linked with that other potent evergreen, ivy. The prickles on the holly leaves have come to symbolize the crown of thorns, the bitter bark is likened to the gall offered to Christ on the cross, the simple white flowers are emblems of the Virgin birth, and the scarlet berries represent drops of blood.

As an ornamental garden shrub holly was probably first planted in Ireland during the sixteenth and seventeenth centuries in the formal knot-gardens of the period. As it is a native species, it is not mentioned in garden records until the early eighteenth century - in April 1702 a pair of holly bushes was supplied for the campus of Trinity College, Dublin. By that time several garden varieties were known, including the variegated and hedgehog hollies. After about 1800, the number of cultivars increased rapidly as exotic species were introduced and as hybrids were raised.

Two hybrids of outstanding merit, selections of *Ilex* x *altaclerensis*, were produced in Ireland during the early nineteenth century. Both were raised by Edward Hodgins of Dunganstown in County Wicklow. A third holly, a handsome variegated sport on one of these originals, also arose in Ireland and this has also been attributed to Edward Hodgins, but not long ago I discovered that the variegated one came from another nursery belonging to the Hodginses.

The older cultivars arose, probably by chance, as the result of cross-pollination of the common native holly (*Ilex aquifolium*) and the Madeira holly (*Ilex perado*). The Madeira species was cultivated here as early as 1800. James Mackay reported that a plant in the Trinity College Botanic Garden was one and a half metres tall by 1825.

Edward Hodgins started his nursery about 1780. It was situated near the coast, north-west of Wicklow town. He specialized in exotic trees and shrubs, and the nursery grounds contained a number of notable specimens including a magnificent cedar of Goa (*Cupressus lusitanica*) planted in 1787. Hodgins was an enthusiastic horticulturist and attempted to encourage other gardeners to grow the more unusual plants that he stocked. John Foster was one of his customers, and Hodgins supplied plants for the fledgling Botanic Gardens at Glasnevin. He introduced a number of garden plants, and propagated unusual varieties of native trees including forms of rowan and oak with erect branches. By 1835 when Ninian Niven of the

Glasnevin Botanic Gardens visited Dunganstown to measure its fine trees, Edward was an old, yet still active man. Remarkably, Niven does not mention any rare hollies among the treasures at Dunganstown, suggesting that these plants may not have been selected at that time, and consequently that Edward's successor, Robert, was the person who propagated and distributed them. Robert was in charge of the nursery in the 1840s.

The origin of Edward Hodgins' hybrid hollies is not documented in contemporary records, so we have to rely on later sources for the history. He probably raised a number of seedlings and then selected the ones that he thought were best. Fortunately, he chose a male and a female, for like the willow, holly bushes bear flowers of only one sex.

Hodgins' female holly, *Ilex* x *altaclerensis* '**Hendersonii**',[1] is a strong vigorous plant that may form a tree at least 15 metres tall. The small flowers appear in spring; in bud they are flushed with purple but when they open the four petals are pure white. The large, rounded leaves do not have the shining, waxy cuticle of wild native hollies, and are dull, dark green. They have few prickles on the margins. Large red berries are produced in abundance.

Cuttings of this plant were sent from Dunganstown to Lawson & Co. of Edinburgh, which distributed the plant as early as 1846 under the name *Ilex hodginsii*. Hodgins also sent propagation material to John Shepherd, curator of the Liverpool Botanic Garden, who in turn supplied the nursery of Fisher & Holmes of Handsworth. Fisher & Holmes distributed Hodgins' female holly as *Ilex hendersonii*, naming it after a Mr Henderson who was a friend of John Shepherd. Thus arose great confusion, but the correct name for the female variety is *Ilex* x *altaclerensis* 'Hendersonii'.

An ideal garden companion of 'Hendersonii' is its sibling, the male hybrid which Edward Hodgins also produced, *Ilex* x *altaclerensis* '**Hodginsii**'[2]; Fisher & Holmes distributed it as *Ilex shepherdii* at one time. 'Hodginsii' is, like its sister, a robust shrub that will eventually develop into a well-clothed tree. It has darkest green leaves, that are oval and almost spineless. The stems are tinged with purple. Being a male, this holly does not berry; its function is to produce pollen. However, very occasionally female flowers are produced by 'Hodginsii' so a few berries may form.

VARIEGATED HOLLIES

Plain green hollies sometimes produce shoots with variegated leaves; these peculiar branches are called sports. If propagated, the sports can provide new cultivars for gardens. Until recently 'Hodginsii' had produced only one variegated sport, but the world authority on hollies, Susyn Andrews (a native of Dublin who was trained at the National Botanic Gardens, Glasnevin and now works in the Royal Botanic Gardens, Kew), spotted a branch with gold-margined leaves in an English garden in 1978 and this has been propagated. In contrast, 'Hendersonii' had sported at least three times; two of the variegated forms arose in England, but the third was found in another of the Hodgins family's nurseries at Cloughjordan in County Tipperary. This nursery was run by John Hodgins, who was probably one of the sons of Edward Hodgins of Dunganstown and raiser of the parent holly. In the 1870s, William Hodgins was proprietor of the Cloughjordan nursery.

The Cloughjordan sport, named ***Ilex* x *altaclerensis* 'Lawsoniana'**,[3] was first distributed by Lawson & Co. of Edinburgh, which had received grafts from Hodgins sometime before 1869. 'Lawsoniana' is also a vigorous plant, with somewhat glossy leaves that have a central splash of creamy yellow and light green. At first the leaves are entirely green, but as they grow and mature, the central portion fades to emerald, then to cream. The stems are streaked with yellow. Like its parent, 'Lawsoniana' is female, but it does not produce berries as profusely. It has a tendency to revert to its original unmottled state, and branches with plain leaves should be removed.

The three Hodgins hollies can provide colour and variety for a winter garden - scarlet berries, golden leaves and dark evergreen foliage. By tradition, evergreens are brought into the house in winter, a custom perpetuated in the Christmas holly. Our pagan ancestors believed that green boughs brought indoors provided shelter for benign woodland spirits during the rigours of that season.

In recent years *Ilex* x *altaclerensis* 'Lawsoniana', the Cloughjordan holly, has also produced sports, one of which arose in the Gouldings' garden, Dargle Cottage, near Enniskerry in County Wicklow. The new cultivar, named **'Lady Valerie'**,[4] after Lady Valerie Goulding, has variegated leaves that are distinctly wavy and attractively twisted. Dr Neil Murray propagated this holly and named it after Lady Goulding. 'Lady Valerie' is very like 'Ripley Gold', another sport from 'Lawsoniana', with the same twisting of the leaves.

ISSAQUAH TASSEL BUSH

In holly, the female is the 'peacock', resplendent in scarlet and green. In other evergreens, the male is often the show-off, and this is the case with the tassel bushes.

During January and February, the male catkins slowly lengthen. Silver-haired, golden stamens emerge and, when ripe, shed their pollen into the wind. Waving in the breeze, the catkins look like tassels of silk plucked from the pelmets of a Victorian drawing-room.

The tassel bushes (*Garrya*) are natives of Western North America. The hardiest species grow in the north-western United States and in Canada, from California to Washington and into British Columbia. Until recent years the only one widely planted in Ireland was *Garrya elliptica*, but in the early 1960s plants were raised at Malahide Castle, north of Dublin, that turned out to represent a new hybrid. Seedlings were planted in the walled garden at Malahide, forming a hedge that eventually reached well over five metres tall. Lord Talbot de Malahide, an expert and perceptive plantsman, recognized that the hybrid was as elegant and as hardy as *Garrya elliptica*, and he also noted that the catkins were more brightly coloured. He selected some shoots from the hedge and sent them to London for exhibition in one of the shows of the Royal Horticultural Society. The new tassel bush gained a coveted award of merit for the display but Milo Talbot had broken the rules by sending material from more than one plant, and the award was withheld. In 1971 he sent more catkins from a single male and the award was confirmed.

Milo Talbot had great difficulty choosing the best male; they were so much alike. The one he chose was named 'Pat Ballard' after Mrs Ballard of Issaquah near Seattle in Washington State, from whose garden the original seed had come. The hybrid had no scientific name, but Lord Talbot suggested that it should be called *Garrya* x *issaquahensis*. I was privileged in 1980 to be able to prepare a full botanical description of the hybrid and this was published along with the name that Milo Talbot had proposed.

Garrya x *issaquahensis* **'Pat Ballard'** (Plate 2)[5] flourished at Malahide until 1983 when, for some unknown reason, the original plant died. By good fortune cuttings had been taken and plants were in cultivation at the National Botanic Gardens, Glasnevin, and in the Hillier Arboretum in Hampshire, England. 'Pat Ballard' is available from good nurseries in Britain and Ireland.

Lord Talbot's tassel bush is a resilient shrub. The leaves lack the grey, felty undersurface and wavy margins of *Garrya elliptica*, which was the mother plant; the pollen parent was a male *Garrya fremontii*. The most noticeable differences between *Garrya elliptica* and 'Pat Ballard' are in the colour and texture of the catkins. These are composed of overlapping bracts that conceal and protect the stamens. The bracts in 'Pat Ballard' lack the dense covering of silver hairs that characterises *Garrya elliptica*, so that the bright red base of each bract is displayed. When the golden stamens peep from the bracts, the catkins take on a bright orange hue - in reality they are banded with green, crimson and pale gold. But do not despise the female tassel bush. The catkins are stiff and dull, but when the flowers have been pollinated and the fruits are mature in summer, the shrubs seem to be covered with bunches of dark maroon baubles, like little bunches of grapes.

The tassel bushes contribute elegance to a winter garden, and a wider range of them seemed desirable. In the first edition of *An Irish flower garden*, I noted that 'perhaps work in progress at Glasnevin will add more colour, for plants with deeper red catkins have been raised'. One of the seedlings, produced by pollinating a female that lived a solitary, virginal life in my Celbridge garden, with pollen from 'Pat Ballard' then growing in Glasnevin, proved good and reliable. This was named **'Glasnevin Wine'** (Plate 2)[6] and it has been propagated and is now relatively easy to obtain from nurseries in Britain and Ireland. The foliage is like 'Pat Ballard' although the leaf margins are not so crinkled. In 'Glasnevin Wine' the catkin scales have a darker, more extensive patch of red and because this is not concealed by a silky felt of hairs the catkins are darker than those of 'Pat Ballard'.

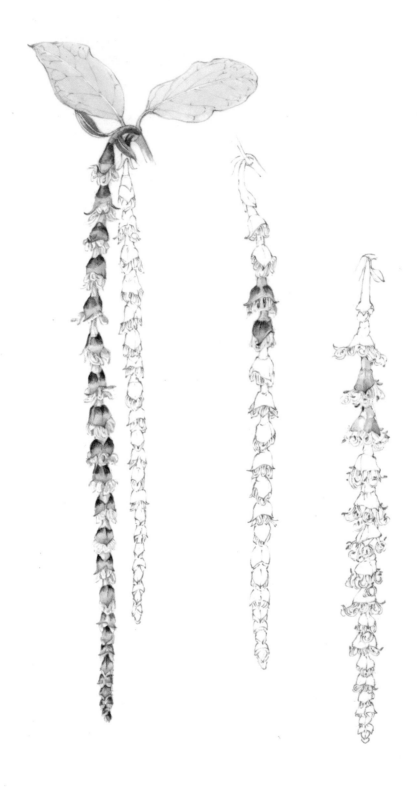

2. Garrya x *issaquahensis* 'Glasnevin Wine', 'Pat Ballard' & *G. elliptica*

Garrya elliptica was introduced to Europe by the Scottish plant hunter, David Douglas, in 1828. Its name commemorates Nicolas Garry, a director of the Hudson Bay Company, who helped Douglas during his arduous travels in North America.

CHARITY AND BERNARD McMAHON

It is quite usual for eminent botanists and gardeners and even for the occasional statesman or fictional character, to be immortalized in plant names One of the finest winter garden shrubs, *Mahonia*, is named after the American horticulturist, Bernard McMahon, who was born about 1776 'of good birth and fortune' somewhere in Ireland. He migrated to America in 1796, it is said for political reasons, and settled in Philadelphia. In 1802 McMahon opened a seed store, where he sold books on botany and gardening as well as gardening requisites. Four years later, he published *The American gardener's calendar*, the first manual for North American gardeners. His wife, Ann, often officiated behind the shop counter and together the couple built a business that was described as one of the greatest seed stores in the United States. 'Its bulk window [was] ornamented with tulip glasses, a large pumpkin, and a basket or two of bulbous roots'.

McMahon was befriended by botanists and gardeners who visited his store. Thomas Jefferson was among his more illustrious acquaintances, and it was Jefferson who allowed McMahon to have some of the seeds collected by Captains Meriwether Lewis and William Clark during their epic journey into the country beyond the Missouri River. Among the plants that the Irishman raised from Lewis and Clark's seeds were the pineapple weed, a snowberry and a sweetly perfumed shrub with spiny leaves called the Oregon grape. McMahon kept these in his greenhouse, and showed them to other botanists including the Liverpool-born Thomas Nuttall. In 1818 Nuttall described and named the Oregon grape, calling it *Mahonia* 'in memory of the late Mr. Bernard McMahon whose ardent attachment to Botany and successful introduction of useful and ornamental horticulture in the United States, lays claim to public esteem'.

Mahonia is a strange genus, one of a group of unrelated plants that are found in the wild in North America and the Far East. Indeed, there are more species of *Mahonia* in China than in America. *Mahonia* is closely related to the barberries, species of *Berberis*, but the only significant difference between them is in their leaves; *Mahonia* leaves are compound, with leaflets arranged along an central stalk, while all of the barberries have simple leaves. Two of the Oriental *Mahonia* species were the parents of ***Mahonia* x *media* 'Charity'**,[7] which has been described by Graham Stuart Thomas as one of the finest shrubs ever raised.

'Charity' is a seedling of *Mahonia lomariifolia* that had been pollinated by *Mahonia japonica*. It was raised in a batch of seedlings by the Slieve Donard Nursery in the 1940s. One hundred seedlings were sold to John Russell, owner of the Richmond Nursery (L. R. Russell Ltd) of Windlesham in Surrey. Sir Eric Savill saw them and selected three for his garden at Windsor. The shrubs flowered at Savill Gardens and the best was selected and named 'Charity' because, in the words of Leslie Slinger of the Slieve Donard Nursery,

> When my friend [John Russell], who had acquired the original seedling, first had proof of his foresight and ability to pick a winner, he began to investigate the origin of the seedlings and, of course, he traced them back to me. When he heard my story, his sympathy and compassion were expressed in his proposal of 'Charity' as the name of the plant.[8]

'Charity' has received two awards from the Royal Horticultural Society at its London shows; on 27 January 1959 it was recommended for an award of merit, and in November 1962 received a first class certificate.

This is an upright shrub with long leaves composed of about 19 leaflets. The leaves are crowded at the tips of the shoots, forming a ruff of prickly green. From the centre of this arise the erect spikes of lemon-yellow flowers. The long trusses form a slightly fragrant coronet of yellow blossom from November until March. This is slowly transformed into a coronet of purple-blue berries in early summer.

'Charity' will make a shrub up to five or six metres tall, and the original plant is still growing in the Savill Gardens at Windsor. A second seedling, also planted out at Savill Gardens, was selected and named 'Charity's Sister'. The Donard Nursery, having retained many other seedlings, later selected one of the remaining plants and named it 'Winter Sun' - this less well-known plant has perfumed flower spikes that are not as long nor as erect as those of 'Charity'. Leslie Slinger wondered whether 'Winter Sun' was not better than 'Charity', and we must allow him the privilege of believing his own plant was the best.[9] Confirmation of his opinion has come recently from Chris Brickell, former director-general of the Royal Horticultural Society and a horticulturist of considerable experience, who has listed 'Winter Sun' in his selection of the choicest garden plants.

WYCH HAZEL

The wych (or witch) hazels are also beautiful shrubs for a winter garden. Like *Mahonia*, they come from America and the Orient. The Chinese wych hazel, **Hamamelis mollis**,[10] tends to be more showy than the American species, but there are now numerous fine garden varieties that excel the wild species. Unlike the hollies, tassel bushes and *Mahonia*, the wych hazels are deciduous, and their autumn colour is most attractive.

The flowers of the wych hazel appear in January, before the leaves unfold. The individual flowers are small but several are grouped together in a tight knot. At the base of each flower are five, deep maroon sepals which glow richly in the winter sun. From this calyx emerge five strap-like, spiralling, yellow petals, looking like slivers of lemon peel. The clusters of flowers have a curly, fluffy appearance, and at flowering time the bushes seem to be covered in a mist of yellow. In summer the green leaves which are like those of the native hazel - hence the plant's name - conceal the strange horned fruits that resemble furry hazel nuts.

The wych hazel is not related to the hazel nut, but belongs to another family of plants that includes shrubs famous for their autumn tints, for example *Parrotia, Corylopsis* and *Fothergilla*. Like these shrubs, the foliage of wych hazel changes through yellows, reds and browns as winter approaches.

Charles Maries discovered the Chinese wych hazel in 1870 when he was working in central China for the famous English nursery of Veitch & Sons Ltd. Seeds were collected and at least one young plant was raised at the Exeter nursery but this seedling was put aside and no notice was taken of it until many years later.

Meanwhile, Augustine Henry arrived in Yichang to take up a post as a medical doctor in the Chinese Imperial Maritime Customs Service. He became involved in work on cataloguing the ingredients of indigenous Chinese medicines, and found it difficult to name the extraordinary plant materials used. Thus his interest in botany was stimulated and in 1884 he began to collect plants in areas around Yichang. Dr Henry sought the assistance of botanists in the Royal Botanic Gardens, Kew, and they soon began to receive parcels of specimens from him. Rapidly it became obvious that many of the plants were new, so Augustine Henry was encouraged to expand his collecting activities.

Henry was unable to give up his duties in the Customs Service so he employed native collectors, who were paid for the plant specimens that they dried and pressed. These specimens were sent to Kew with material that Henry collected himself. Among specimens in a parcel of plants from Dr Henry's native collector in the village of Patung was a sample of the Chinese wych hazel, then an unnamed shrub, unknown to western botanists. The species was described and named using the specimens supplied through Augustine Henry.

Hamamelis mollis was published in 1888, but not until 1898 did the Veitches notice that they already had it in cultivation. They promptly rectified their tardiness and introduced this fine plant into commerce.

Augustine Henry lived in China from 1881 until 31 December 1900, 'the last day of the last year of the nineteenth century'. He was influential in promoting further exploration of central China and the exploitation of its superb plants for horticulture. Indirectly, Henry prompted Harry Veitch to send another collector to China in 1899. Ernest Wilson was much more successful than his predecessor Charles Maries. Wilson met Dr Henry in southern China, received advice and encouragement and went on to explore and collect. Among the seeds from his first expedition was more material of the wych hazel. In a short time the shrub was widely planted and it flowered in Ireland for the first time at Hamwood near Dunboyne, County Meath, in 1903.

DWARF SWEET-BOX

Augustine Henry was born in Dundee on 2 July 1857. His father, Bernard Henry, was a native of County Londonderry, but his mother, Mary MacNamee, was Scottish. The Henrys and their baby son came to Ireland shortly after his birth and Augustine was brought up at Tyanee, a townland to the north of Portglenone on the County Londonderry side of the River Bann. He went to Cookstown Academy, and later to Queen's College, Galway, where he graduated with a first class honours degree in natural sciences. Augustine then moved to Queen's College, Belfast, where he took his master's degree, and embarked on a career in medicine. He went to London to study in one of the major teaching hospitals, but during a visit to Ireland he met Sir Robert Hart who persuaded him to join the Chinese Customs Service. Henry rapidly obtained his medical qualifications and a working knowledge of Chinese, and departed for China.

He began to collect plants three years after he arrived in that vast country. His base was Yichang, a port about 1200 kilometres inland on the banks of the Yangtze River. It was a botanist's paradise, 'a Klondyke of plant gold', and Henry revelled in its gems. The parcels of dried, pressed plants that reached Kew contained many novelties, new species, new genera and even a representative of a hitherto unknown plant family.

While resident in Yichang, Augustine Henry made two extensive trips into the surrounding countryside to collect plants. In March 1888, he set out from Yichang with Antwerp Pratt, and spent six months in the wild country west and north of Yichang. At Wushan in eastern Sichuan province and at Changyang, west of Yichang, he collected a small, unimpressive shrub. He sent specimens to Kew. Several years later Dr Henry found the same plant at Mengsi in southern China. Ernest Wilson collected seeds of this shrub too, in 1900, and consequently introduced it into European gardens. However, the plant was not distinguished as a separate species until 1911. Using Henry's dried specimens, and plants raised from Wilson's seed, Dr Otto Stapf, a Kew botanist, described and named the dwarf sweet-box, *Sarcococca humilis*.[11]

This is a twiggy shrub that rarely grows over 25 centimetres tall. It has long, pointed, evergreen leaves. The small flowers are hidden by the foliage, but they make up for their insignificant size by their wonderful perfume. The male flowers are the most conspicuous; they have pink stamens that fade to a delicate creamy-white. In autumn the shrub has shining black berries. It is not an enthralling plant to look at, but the pervasive fragrance gains it a place in my winter garden. Dwarf sweet-box is suitable for the front of borders and for rock gardens, although it does spread by underground stems.

TOM SMITH'S WINTER CHERRY

So far the winter garden has been planted with hollies and shrubs that flower during the cold months. There is colour and perfume. My chosen tree is a flowering cherry that bridges the gap between autumn and spring. It comes from Japan where it was known long before it was brought to Europe; its Japanese name is Jagatsu-zakura, the October cherry. The scientific name is **Prunus subhirtella 'Autumnalis'**,[12] but it was called *Prunus miquelliana* and later received the name *Prunus microlepis* var. *smithii*. In the last instance this cherry was christened after Thomas Smith, founder of the famous Daisy Hill Nursery at Newry in County Down.

Tom Smith was born on 31 August 1840. His father was a gardener in Birmingham and young Tom received a good horticultural training, which included several years as an apprentice in Veitch's Nursery at Chelsea. He came to Newry as manager of a nursery belonging to Andrew Daly, which later became Rodger, McClelland & Co., and was one of the best in these islands in the 1880s. However, Thomas Smith decided to start his own business. In 1886 he found a superb site at Daisy Hill, just outside the town; there, in years to come, the nursery prospered until it covered almost 70 acres and contained a collection of plants unexcelled by other nurseries. The praise heaped on Daisy Hill had no bounds. Eminent botanists and gardeners from Europe and America travelled to Newry just to visit Tom Smith. In 1906 he advertised his nursery in Irish gardening with this slogan - 'Daisy Hill Nursery, Newry, is the only Nursery in Ireland worth a button, and is the most interesting nursery probably in the World'.

Smith imported plants from all parts of the globe. He raised plants from seed, and despatched material to botanic gardens and plant collections in several continents. In 1911 he included a beautiful winter cherry in his catalogue, having obtained stock plants from Japan. The new tree was one of Daisy Hill's best varieties and even in 1923 its price could only be obtained 'on application'.

This cherry begins to flower in November. The first blossoms usually appear on bare twigs after the leaves have fallen and last until Christmas. The flower stalks are short and bear fragrant, semi-double blooms that are white, blushing pink. Each flower has ten to fifteen notched petals, each about one centimetre long. A second flush of blossom comes with the young leaves in April. These spring flowers have longer stalks, but the blooms are the same delicate, palest pink.

It is not known for certain when Tom Smith acquired *Prunus subhirtella* 'Autumnalis'. His son, writing in 1932, stated that the tree was received in the spring of 1901. Shortly after it arrived in Newry a few plants were released. Apparently Colonel Stephenson Clarke of Borde Hill in Sussex also imported this cherry in the early 1900s for one was planted in his garden about 1906, although it could have been obtained from Newry.

The October cherry has many virtues. It forms a small spreading tree, that can be accommodated within a suburban garden. Given that *Prunus subhirtella* 'Autumnalis' blossoms in winter, it is best planted against a background of dark evergreens so that the flowers are highlighted. The sprays can be cut and brought indoors; they will last in water for several weeks. Lady Moore rightly remarked that Tom Smith deserved 'the gratitude of all plant-lovers for having been the first to draw attention' to this marvellous cherry.

THE STRAFFAN SNOWDROP

Tom Smith was one of the great characters who gardened during the golden years of Ireland's gardens. In those halcyon days there was great excitement as new plants poured in from the Far East. Yet the old established gardens also contributed much to the vitality of the first decades of this century.

One of the best-known gardens was at Straffan House in County Kildare, situated on the banks of the River Liffey. This fine demesne once was a place of pilgrimage for botanists and gardeners; today it is an expensive, exclusive golf course. Frederick Burbidge, curator of the Trinity College Botanic Garden, often bicycled to Straffan, riding through the Phoenix Park, past the Strawberry Beds and on to Lucan and Celbridge.

> The rabbits are nibbling the short grass beside the drive, [he recalled], and scarcely trouble to get out of your way as the silent wheels glide past them; and in swerving suddenly into the narrow side-path leading to the garden-cottage, the wheels nearly went over a splendid cock-pheasant's tail, which chortled quite indignantly as it disappeared among the bushes.[13]

Burbidge extolled the setting of the garden. Winter was his favourite season when the twigs of the lime trees were red, the dogwoods and willows were crimson and gold, and beneath in the lawns floated clouds of snowdrops.

> No words could give anything like an adequate idea of the soft and varied shades of colour, not alone of the planted banks themselves but of their still more soft and delicate reflections in the water below.[14]

Snowdrops were only one of Frederick Burbidge's interests, and it is appropriate that he was the first to describe the Straffan snowdrop, *Galanthus* **'Straffan'**.[15]

Straffan House was the home of the Barton family. They were keen gardeners, and Mrs Hugh Barton is said to have introduced a little bicolour daffodil from the Pyrenees. Her brother, Major Eyre Massey, knew about her love for plants. He fought in the Crimean War, and while in the battle area managed to collect bulbs of a snowdrop. These came to Straffan and were planted in the lawn. Little notice was taken of them until the head-gardener, Frederick Bedford, saw a snowdrop flowering after the others had faded. He carefully tended this one, and increased it gradually.

This late-flowering snowdrop produces two flowering stalks, instead of a single one like most other varieties. The second flower appears after the first one, so that the flowering season is extended. The Straffan snowdrop begins to bloom in February and may continue well into March, depending on the weather. It also naturalizes easily, increasing by means of bulblets.

Galanthus 'Straffan' has large, well-formed flowers. The outer petals are pure white and the inner ones have bright green markings. The bulbs are robust and the leaves pleasant greyish-green.

The Straffan snowdrop is believed to be a chance hybrid that arose when Major Massey's Crimean snowdrop (possibly *Galanthus plicatus*) interbred with the common species (*Galanthus nivalis*). Frederick Bedford noticed this lovely winter flower sometime after he arrived at Straffan House in 1875. By 1900 the Straffan snowdrop was well-known to gardeners. Edward Augustus (E. A.) Bowles, an expert on bulbs, praised the Straffan variety as the most beautiful of all. It is still one of the very best, and is now a reminder of a garden that has vanished, or is at best a travesty of its former state, when the snowdrops drifted under the red-twigged lime trees, and daffodils danced by the waters of Anna Livia.

POË'S DOUBLE SNOWDROP

Another Irish snowdrop can be ranked as the best double-flowered variety, and can remind us of a garden that is an even more faint memory than Straffan House. This one is Captain James Hill Poë's double snowdrop, *Galanthus* **'Hill Poë'** (Figure 3).[16]

Double-flowered snowdrops are misnamed, for they usually have a single flower that is composed of more than six petals. Each normal blossom has three large outer petals and three smaller inner ones. In the so-called double-flowered varieties, there are many more than three inner petals and occasionally more than three outer ones too. The stamens are replaced by petal-like segments, and the ovary is abortive, so that these snowdrops cannot produce seeds. Captain Poë's snowdrop follows this scheme, but unlike some double snowdrops the flowers are neat, not untidy and malformed. The flowers vary in their composition, but they often have five outer petals that are spoon-shaped and have rounded tips. There are over 15 inner segments, all of which are heart-shaped like those of the single snowdrop. The leaves are pale grey-green and at flowering time tend to be splayed along the ground.

Galanthus 'Hill Poë' is probably another hybrid. Its parents may have been the Crimean species *Galanthus plicatus* and a fertile double-flowered variety of the common snowdrop, *Galanthus nivalis*. This marriage took place in the garden of the Poë home, Riverston, at Nenagh, in County Tipperary. James Poë was an enthusiastic gardener, although his younger brother, John Thomas Bennett-Poë was more prominent in horticultural circles. James Poë spotted the double-flowered snowdrop early this century. The original bulb grew under the walnut tree near the dining-room window in front of Riverston. His daughter, Blanche Poë, kept the snowdrop in her garden and gave bulbs to Miss Christine Shackleton. In the early 1950s, her nephew, David Shackleton, sent bulbs to Brigadier and Mrs Mathias who ran the Giant Snowdrop Company at Chalford in Gloucestershire, and it was through this delightfully named nursery that 'Hill Poë' was introduced into other gardens.

3. *Galanthus* 'Hill Poë'

Both of these snowdrops have received the commendation of the Royal Horticultural Society. 'Straffan' gained an award of merit when shown by R. D. Nutt on 15 March 1968. The Reverend R. J. Blakeways-Phillips exhibited 'Hill Poë' on 19 February 1974 and received a certificate of preliminary commendation.

AEGEAN EMERALDS

There were several other snowdrops with Irish connections in circulation among snowdrop enthusiasts; others have become extinct and yet others are not now regarded as distinct varieties. The one-time Provost of Trinity College, Dublin, Dr John Pentland Mahaffy collected snowdrops in Greece in the 1880s. These were planted in the College Botanic Garden and flowered in the autumn. Two different forms were named after his daughters, *Galanthus* 'Elsae' and 'Rachelae' - Rachel's snowdrop is still in cultivation although very rare. They were treasured by Frederick Burbidge, who, tongue-in-cheek, penned these lines, 'One of the minor miseries of my life is having to live in a garden containing thirty distinct kinds of snowdrops'. To him, these flowers of Candlemas were the 'pearls of the opening year', and Straffan House was 'a very paradise ... one of the most hospitable gardens, all things beautiful are welcomed there'.

Recently, I was the conduit for another snowdrop which, as I write, is perhaps the most sought-after in Britain. I did not raise this one, but was given it by a friend, Megan Morris, and keeping faith with the adage that the best way to keep a plant is to give it away, I passed it on to a very few of my gardening friends. Wendy Walsh was one, and last winter I was able to get the snowdrop back from her.

This 'new' snowdrop has a pale blush of yellow-green on each of the long, white, outer petals, and the notched inner petals are almost entirely deep green with only a narrow white rim. The leaves are rich, glossy green without the greyness of the ordinary snowdrop, so the whole plant has a fresher appearance. When the snowdrop was studied, its identity was certain. The characteristics displayed that it belonged to an Aegean species named *Galanthus ikariae* which inhabits moist places including stream banks.

Megan found this snowdrop naturalized in quantity in the derelict garden of Drews Court, a County Limerick house, about 1986. She transferred some bulbs to her own cottage garden, and sent me a watercolour sketch of a flower when they bloomed. Later she shared some with me, as I have said, and in turn I shared the bulbs with several other gardeners. After I had checked the literature, and found no reference to any form of Galanthus ikariae with such distinctive green inner petals and green-flushed outer petal, and after it had become obvious that this snowdrop was about to be named contrary to Megan's wishes, I chose **'Emerald Isle'** as its name - various other names have been suggested, but none is correct.[17]

A GOLDEN CHRISTMAS ROSE

Gardens, great and small, can easily become derelict when the owners depart. They may be left to become a wilderness and then vanish under golf greens and concrete. On the other hand, plants can survive for generations, as long as gardeners pass seeds or slips on to their friends. So I complete my winter garden with a much travelled Christmas rose, which has vanished from Ireland but is perhaps alive in England.

In 1921 two collections of hellebores (Christmas and Lenten roses) were packed in Glasnevin and sent to England; one lot went to Sander's Nursery in St Albans and the other went to E. A. Bowles who lived at Myddelton House in Enfield. The forms were carefully selected by Sir Frederick Moore from various seedlings that had been raised in the Glasnevin Botanic Gardens over at least five decades. Among the hellebores was one called 'Dr Moore' after David Moore; this beautiful speckled form is now extinct. Two other varieties are of interest; they were named *Helleborus luteus grandiflorus* and *Helleborus* 'Yellow Seedling'. The yellow seedling is also extinct, but *Helleborus luteus grandiflorus* throve at Myddelton House. In 1957, E. B. Anderson noted that it had formed a large plant, which 'when in flower stood out strikingly against a dark background' of evergreen shrubs. E. A. Bowles was delighted with this Christmas rose, and more than 20 years after he received it wrote to Lady Moore saying:

> Hellebores are better than usual. The set of green forms from Glasnevin are among my favourites and I am always blessing the kind friend who collected so many and gave me of the best so generously. The butter yellow one is the one visitors prevent becoming a circular specimen. It has sown itself and one is almost as good as mamma, real butter, not marge ...[18]

From Myddelton House, the butter-yellow hellebore was given to Graham Stuart Thomas who has grown it for over 40 years. It is now known as *Helleborus* **'Bowles' Yellow'**,[19] after the kind-hearted man who allowed people to leave his garden with 'big basketfuls of treasures'.

'Bowles' Yellow' is an early hellebore, sometimes opening its flowers in December and lasting until March. It has very large leaves, a bit like those of a horse-chestnut, but dark green and stiff, with serrated margins. The flowers rise on stalks above the leaves and are delicately coloured. Bowles' own description can stand unaltered.

There are other hellebores ranging in colour from deep velvety purple to pure white, and all can be planted in a winter garden. Alas, the most famous Irish Christmas Rose, 'Saint Brigid', is lost, or perhaps - just perhaps - grows unrecognised and unrecognizable in some garden. *Helleborus niger* 'Saint Brigid' came from Kildare, and was named by Frederick Burbidge. I shall tell some of its story later.

E. A. Bowles was a great friend of the Moores and exchanged plants with them for many years, while Sir Frederick was Keeper of the Glasnevin Botanic Gardens and after his retirement. About 1900 Bowles established a small club for like-minded gardeners which was called the Plant Exchange Society. Edward Walpole of Mount Usher was a member, as was Sir Frederick Moore. Sir John Ross-of-Bladensburg and William Gumbleton, both of whom I shall mention again, were included and so was Augustine Henry. The club's motto was 'It is more blessed to give than to receive', but for some unknown reason it was not a success, and withered away about 1907. However the principle embodied in that motto remains vital; for example in 1983 Graham Thomas wrote about his long experience in gardening:

> As the years go by one's enthusiasms for different classes of plants come and go, and with the zeal of a fresh subject one comes into contact with a fresh group of people, enriching one's circle of friends and acquaintances. Plants as a rule increase likewise and the giving away of manavilins is a blessed form of friendship in which we all take pleasure![20]

IV
An arboretum

Acer henryi - Davidia involucrata - Tilia henryana
Juniperus recurva 'Castlewellan' - *Cupressus macrocarpa* 'Keown'
Picea abies 'Clanbrassiliana' - *Chamaecyparis lawsoniana* 'Kilmacurragh'
Embothrium coccineum 'Longifolium' - *Eucryphia* x *intermedia* 'Rostrevor'
Eucryphia x *nymansensis* 'Mount Usher' - *Laburnum alpinum* 'Newryensis'
Betula utilis 'Trinity College' - *Pinus coulteri*

At the entrance to the enclosure is a tree
From whose branches there comes beautiful music.
It is a tree of silver, which the sun illumines;
It glistens like gold.

Anonymous: 'The Sick-bed of Cu Chulainn'

In July 1899, Dr Augustine Henry was stationed in an isolated customs post at Simao, in the extreme south of China, near the frontier with Indo-China (Vietnam). As it had been raining for several days, the rough road to Simao was impassable and there were no visitors and no mail. Henry had time to contemplate the future, and to write to his life-long friend, Miss Evelyn Gleeson, who lived in Dublin. He told her that he was planning to leave China, but that he would continue to collect plants until his departure. 'This is my last great collection', he wrote, 'it keeps me busy and prevents me from eating my heart out'. On the previous day, he had been in the local forest and had thought about the wood and its trees, the forest birds and animals.

The calm way in which man extirpates animals and ruins forests annoys me. Man is an uncanny beast: he wants the earth. The necessity that will always exist for timber will however necessitate in the future great forest reservations in all countries where forests can thrive. So there is hope. A forest is the finest thing in the world: it is the expression of nature in its highest form; it is so full of beauty and of variety.[1]

In China, Augustine Henry had seen and collected many new trees. He realised that these beautiful plants had great potential as ornaments for gardens elsewhere, and he set about trying to persuade other collectors to introduce some of them.

DR HENRY'S MAPLE

John Besant, Keeper of the National Botanic Gardens, Glasnevin, from 1922 until 1944, paid tribute to Augustine Henry's botanical work, noting that if Henry

had done no more than make known the marvellous riches of China he would have achieved more than most men ... Happily so many plants bear his name that, while trees and shrubs are cultivated, his memory will remain in every garden and arboretum for long years to come.[2]

From the numerous trees labelled *henryi, henryanus* or *augustinii*, often but not always indicating the species' discovery by Augustine Henry, I have chosen a delicate maple, and a splendid linden. Neither the maple nor the linden is well-known and planted widely. There are trees of Henry's maple in some of the larger Irish gardens, Glasnevin, Birr Castle and Mount Usher. The linden is much rarer, and the finest tree is in the demesne at Birr Castle.

Henry's maple, ***Acer henryi*** (Figure 4),[3] is a handsome, open tree, that may grow about ten metres tall. Its beauty is apparent from the moment the buds start to unfold in spring. The flower spike emerges while the young leaves are still curled like the tentacles of a strange brittle starfish. The flowers are small, without any great brilliance and last for only a few days, but look closely at them - the tiny stamens are bright yellow, fading to a pale creamy-green after they have shed their pollen to the wind. The male flowers wither and fall away, and the females form the fruits ('keys'), which are tinged with red when immature and hang in elegant clusters.

The unfurling leaves and stalks are also flushed with red, changing slowly to pale green. Each leaf is composed of three elliptical leaflets, held on a slender stalk that is about ten centimetres long.

Henry sent the first samples of his maple to the Royal Botanic Gardens, Kew, where they arrived in March 1889. He had collected the specimens during the long journey he made in the summer of 1888 to the country north-west of Yichang. He did send seed to England but none was sown, so it was Ernest Wilson's privilege to collect the seeds for garden introduction.

THE DOVE TREE

Ernest Wilson went to China as a result of Dr Henry's attempts to stimulate others to collect the plants that he had discovered. The two men met at Simao in September 1899. Wilson had travelled by way of Hanoi, to obtain directions and advice from the man he later described as 'this scholarly Irishman'. He had left London with a set of secret instructions, that stated:

the object of the journey is to collect a quantity of seeds of a plant the name of which is known to us. This is the object - do not dissipate time, energy or money on anything else.

4. *Acer henryi*

In furtherance of this you will first endeavour to visit Dr Augustine Henry and obtain precise data as to the habitat of this particular plant and information on the flora of central China in general.[4]

The 'particular' plant had been seen by Henry on 17 May 1888 near a village called Mahhuanggou. It was one of the strangest sights he had encountered - a solitary tree in full bloom, waving its 'innumerable ghost handkerchiefs' in the wind. Henry gathered specimens that were pressed and dried. He sent them to Kew along with some fruits which were collected later in the season by one of his Chinese collectors. The plant was identified at Kew as ***Davidia involucrata***,[5] a tree discovered by a French missionary, Father Armand David.

The tree greatly impressed Henry. He wrote that it is 'worth any amount of money ... Davidia is wonderful'. In 1897, he began to urge the Director of the Royal Botanic Gardens, Kew, to send an expedition to collect its seeds. The Director, Dr William Thiselton Dyer, suggested that Henry should go himself, but Henry eventually persuaded Dyer that he could not lead such an expedition, and that a full-time collector was necessary. Harry Veitch, the nurseryman, was prevailed upon to sponsor the expedition and Ernest Wilson was despatched to China in 1899.

Wilson succeeded in his secret mission, and sent a large number of *Davidia* seeds to Veitch. But he was pipped at the post! Father Paul Farges, another French missionary, sent seeds to the Paris nursery of Maurice de Vilmorin, and the first dove trees to grow in Europe were germinated in Paris from Farges' collection.

Davidia involucrata, the handkerchief tree or ghost tree or (more mellifluously, I think) the dove tree, hardly needs to be described. In full flower it is spectacular, a flutter of green and white as the leaves and flowers are stirred by the breeze. The great white bracts look like petals but they are not petals; they protect a sphere of numerous petal-less male flowers composed of red-anthered stamens, and a solitary female flower composed of a single ovary.

The fruits of the dove tree are like walnuts, except that they dangle on long stalks. The red squirrels that inhabit the National Botanic Gardens, Glasnevin, love to eat them, and visitors sometimes pocket a few! Each fruit has a very hard, woody centre and when ripe takes two years to germinate; two winters are required to break dormancy. If sown while still green but almost ripe, the fruit will germinate in six months. Patience is a very necessary virtue for gardeners with a passion for this gorgeous tree - after germination it can take 20 years for the young plant to flower.

It is worth waiting for. In Augustine Henry's words, the dove tree is 'a wonderful, strange and beautiful tree ... [over which it] would be worth taking an immensity of trouble'. And as long as the white dove-bracts hover beneath its branches in Ireland's gardens, Augustine Henry will not be forgotten.

A BRISTLING LINDEN

Along with many other plants, Dr Henry sent pressed specimens of several lindens (or limes) that were native in central China to the Royal Botanic Gardens, Kew, during the late 1880s. There is no native Irish lime; the lime trees commonly seen in demesnes and along town streets are the hybrid lime (*Tilia* x *vulgaris*), the offspring of the small-leaved lime, *Tilia cordata*, and the large-leaved lime, *Tilia platyphyllos*. Other lindens, from North America and eastern Asia, have been planted in Irish gardens, but none is as common as *Tilia* x *vulgaris*. Among the least familiar, sadly, is the species that bears Augustine Henry's name.

Ignaz von Szyszylowicz, a Polish botanist who was an authority on *Tilia* and who worked as a volunteer assistant in the Hofmuseum in Vienna, received some duplicate specimens of Dr Henry's Chinese lindens and using these gatherings, described and named several new species. One was called after the sender, *Tilia henryana*. Two other species from the same batch were also named by von Szyszylowicz, *Tilia oliveri* and *Tilia tuan*.

Tilia henryana[6] was originally known only as pressed specimens. Dr Henry did not apparently send seeds to Europe. The credit for introducing this beautiful tree goes, again, to Ernest Wilson. He observed trees growing in the wild in Hubei, including a 'gigantic [one] 80 feet tall and 27 feet in girth with silvery new growth'. None of Wilson's seedlings seems to have become established in Irish gardens - I do not know of any old specimens of Henry's lime, nor was any recorded by Mary Forrest in her survey of Ireland's principal gardens. However, in 1938, the sixth Earl of Rosse obtained seeds from Lushan Arboretum and Botanical Garden, Jiangxi, and at least three seedlings were raised. Two of Lord Rosse's trees grow on Mount Palmer within the demesne at Birr Castle, and there is one in the famous arboretum at Headfort House, Kells, County Meath.

Henry's lime blooms at the end of the summer, several months after the common lime - this may explain why seed is not available from established trees, the autumnal frosts preventing the fruits from developing fully. The sweetly scented flowers are tinged with pink, and hang in branched clusters well below the foliage. Each flower is about one and a half centimetres across, larger than those of the European hybrid. The glory of *Tilia henryana* is the foliage. The heart-shaped leaves can be as large as a fully splayed hand, and when young are flushed pale copper and pink. The margins are ornamented with bristles, each of which is an extension of a vein, and these long bristles are the principle character by which *Tilia henryana* can be recognized. The leaves are largest on young plants and on vigorous shoots, and as the pink flush fades, the upper surface become dark green while the lower side is silvery-grey.

There is no reason, apart perhaps for a dearth of seed or bud-wood for grafting, why Henry's lime should not be a familiar tree. It is attractive and, as far as we can tell, not too large for medium-sized gardens. Certainly its springtime foliage and sweet perfume are positive points in its favour. Would that this tree could become better known, and not just as a memorial to Dr Augustine Henry who so enriched us by his hobby, plant collecting.

A COFFIN TREE

As the scholarly Irishman demonstrated, it is not necessary to be a professional plant-hunter or explorer to discover new plants or to bring new flowers into cultivation. The amateur can be modestly successful too. One of the most remarkable amateur plant-hunters in the Orient was Charlotte Isabel Wheeler Cuffe, grand-daughter of the Reverend Sir Hercules Langrishe of Knocktopher, County Kilkenny. She married Otway Wheeler Cuffe, who was heir to another Kilkenny baronetcy, and they lived for many years in Burma. Sir Otway was a civil engineer in the Public Works Department, and often travelled to remote places inspecting engineering projects during and after construction. On some of these trips, Lady Cuffe accompanied her husband.

Charlotte was an enthusiastic gardener and also an artist of considerable ability. She sketched Burmese landscapes and made a record in watercolours of the plants she saw on her travels. Sometimes she also collected seeds and living plants.

About 1910, Charlotte Wheeler Cuffe sent seeds and lily bulbs to her cousin, Baroness Prochazka, who was living in the Cuffe family home outside Kilkenny. Pauline Prochazka gave these to the Glasnevin Botanic Gardens, and thereby initiated contact between Charlotte Wheeler Cuffe and Frederick Moore. Encouraged by Moore, Charlotte took a deeper interest in Burmese plants and regularly sent material to Glasnevin; in return Moore sent tropical plants to her.

In 1914, during a trip into hitherto almost unexplored country in the north-east of Burma, Lady Cuffe learnt about a tree that was highly prized by the neighbouring Chinese for making coffins, because it yielded a scented and extremely durable timber. The only plant she saw was a young, dead tree, but she told Sir Frederick Moore that it was probably a sort of cypress. The coffin tree was even then extremely rare in the wild having been felled in vast numbers for coffins.

Lady Cuffe persuaded a contact in the Customs Service to obtain plants for her. In October 1915 she wrote to Moore saying that the saplings were on their way to Maymyo, where she lived, but nothing more is recorded about the trees and none reached Glasnevin.

Four years later, two professional collectors, Reginald Farrer and Euan Cox, visited the same place - among other plants, including a sparkling *Deutzia* that we will encounter in the next chapter, they succeeded in finding seeds of the coffin tree and their variety is now well-established in cultivation. While at first Farrer and Cox's juniper was regarded as a distinct species, it is now considered to be a mere variety, *Juniperus recurva* var. *coxii*, of the widespread Himalayan juniper, *Juniperus recurva,* that was introduced into Europe in 1830.

This juniper is a most handsome plant, especially when immature, for as it ages the foliage turns dull blue-grey and the tree loses some of its charm. When young, the slender branchlets hang in curtains from the weeping limbs; in the early 1980s I often admired the superb young specimen at Annes Grove, County Cork. The minute leaves, a few millimetres long, are arranged in whorls of three and point towards the tips of the shoots. They are closely pressed to the twigs and obscure them.

The finest form of the Himalayan juniper, ***Juniperus recurva 'Castlewellan',***[7] was raised at Castlewellan, County Down. The original tree still thrives in that garden, but, being mature, it lacks some of the grace of younger specimens; it is a venerable and still shapely tree. This juniper is suitable for small gardens. It is hardy and enjoys the moist Irish climate. As a selected garden variety, the Castlewellan juniper has to be propagated by grafting or from cuttings. The form collected by Farrer and Cox is also characterised by weeping branches, but the Castlewellan juniper was not raised from their seeds.

A GOLDEN CYPRESS

The arboretum at Castlewellan was created by the Annesley family. The walled garden dates from the middle of the eighteenth century, and some of the large trees within the demesne were planted in the early 1800s. The superb collection of unusual trees and shrubs, sheltered in the walled garden, was not started until about 1870 by the fifth Earl Annesley. In 1903 he published a book of photographs depicting some of his prized plants, many of which remain in the garden today. In 1967 the Forest Service of the Northern Ireland Department of Agriculture acquired the Annesley demesne and it has now been developed into a fine forest park. The walled garden with its marvellous trees and shrubs forms the centre-piece of this National Arboretum.

Hugh Annesley, the fifth earl, realized that the climate of Castlewellan was mild. The sloping site, facing towards Slieve Donard and the Mountains of Mourne, means that cold air drains away and frosts are not severe. Inspired by the gardens of Cornwall, especially the garden of Tresco Abbey in the Isles of Scilly, he planted many southern hemisphere species; these have flourished and now are some of the rarest specimens in the collection.

Over the years, young plants were raised from seeds gathered in diverse parts of the world and from the plants already established at Castlewellan. Some of the seedlings have grown into unique and unusual specimens that have been selected and propagated as Castlewellan cultivars - the juniper is one example.

One of the finest Castlewellan plants is a golden Monterey cypress, *Cupressus macrocarpa* **'Keown'**[8]; the cultivar name commemorates a former head forester, John Keown. The original seedling was selected by Keown in 1956 out of a pan of seedlings raised from seed collected in the arboretum. It was planted in the walled garden where it developed into a well-clothed tree, compact, bushy and oval in outline and about ten metres tall. In spring and early summer the feathery foliage is lime-green, verging on gold.

Like other golden varieties of the Monterey cypress - there is one named 'Donard Gold' which originated nearby in the Slieve Donard Nursery at Newcastle - it is slightly tender and can be damaged especially by cold easterly winds. Keown's cypress is a gem, providing a fresh colour that lightens dark garden corners. It grows rapidly, yet is suitable for sheltered gardens of medium size.

LORD CLANBRASSIL'S SPRUCE

There are two other evergreen conifers that are ideal for small gardens. My first choice is the Clanbrassil spruce, *Picea abies* **'Clanbrassiliana'**,[9] which also originated in County Down, not far from Castlewellan, over two centuries ago.

Down is well endowed with fine gardens. Coastal parts of the county have an especially congenial climate that has enabled gardeners to experiment with unusual plants. There is a long and worthy tradition of gardening in the area stretching back into the seventeenth century, and probably beyond. Sir Arthur Rawdon's garden at Moira, which blossomed in the 1690s, was situated 30 kilometres to the north-west of Castlewellan. Rawdon's influence lingered, and gardens were created in renowned demesnes including Castle Ward on Strangford Lough, and at Tollymore on the slopes of the Mourne Mountains.

Tollymore is now a forest park, but it retains many of the follies and some of the trees placed there by the Earl of Clanbrassil in the last few decades of the eighteenth century. Lord Clanbrassil was as eager a collector of trees as his contemporary, John Foster, and Tollymore contained a fine collection at the turn of the eighteenth century, including the original Clanbrassil spruce.

Lord Clanbrassil's spruce was the first dwarf conifer. It is not a true dwarf, but it is a very slow-growing tree; after about 15 years it will be hardly a metre tall. One season's growth is about five centimetres, and young trees form compact, conical plants. In spring the young shoots are bright green and they slowly darken as the summer wanes. The leaves are needle-like, rarely more than a centimetre long, and closely packed on the short shoots.

The original plant (or perhaps an early offspring) can still be seen in Tollymore Forest Park. It is over five metres tall with a circumference of almost 13 metres. It is not a handsome specimen as the lower part of the main trunk is bare. In younger trees the trunk is concealed by branches. I know several fine plants, the best being in the demesne at Abbey Leix, County Laois.

John Loudon, the eminent horticulturist and garden chronicler for whom David Bishop worked, recorded that Lord Clanbrassil found the spruce at Moira, the Rawdon estate, in the last half of the eighteenth century. It was said to have been a stunted seedling growing in a collection of Norway spruces, but Loudon suggested that it might have originated as a witch's broom. The Clanbrassil spruce was well-known by the beginning of the 1800s and John Templeton obtained a young plant from Tollymore on 22 August 1804. As it has to be propagated by taking cuttings or by grafting, a slow process, it is probable that the original plant was noticed in the mid-1700s.

THE KILMACURRAGH CYPRESS

My second evergreen tree is a slender form of Lawson's cypress, ***Chamaecyparis lawsoniana* 'Kilmacurragh'**,[10] from County Wicklow. Lawson's cypress has spawned a legion of cultivars, many of which are so alike that they cannot be told apart even by expert dendrologists. The Kilmacurragh tree is easily recognized, as it forms a column not unlike an Italian cypress. The flat fan-like shoots are held on erect branches and are closely arranged around the main trunk. The shoots are green, darkening with age, and the minute scale-like leaves have a blue bloom on the underside. While it has a pencil-thin habit like the Italian cypress, the Kilmacurragh variety is hardy and will stand the Irish climate unlike the Italian species. There are fine specimens in various gardens, including Castlewellan and the John F. Kennedy Park, but the original plant disappeared many years ago from Kilmacurragh.

Kilmacurragh lies in the eastern foothills of the Wicklow Mountains, near Rathdrum. In the last few months, following years of unhappy uncertainty, the garden has been acquired by the Department of Arts, Culture and The Gaeltacht, successor to the Office of Public Works as custodian of Ireland's heritage, and is now part of the system of gardens with important plant collections linked to the National Botanic Gardens, Glasnevin. The old walled garden still houses a forestry research nursery. In bygone years Kilmacurragh was the home of the Acton family, and Thomas Acton embellished the demesne with rare and exotic plants. Like so many gardeners in the middle of the nineteenth century he was fascinated by the Himalayan rhododendrons. They were very fashionable. It was probably at Kilmacurragh that David

Moore saw the plants he reported to Dr Joseph Hooker of Kew on 11 March 1867:

> I saw last week 11 kinds of your rhododendrons all growing freely in the open air in County Wicklow. They have been planted out five years and are growing vigorously. *R. falconeri* is five feet high. *R. barbatum* was in full flower. *R. thompsonii* with many flower heads nearly ready to expand. *R. wallichii* ...[and] *R. edgeworthii* are all about to flower! The late weather did not affect them in the least, but they grow in one of the most favoured spots on the east coast of Ireland.[11]

Long after Thomas Acton's death, the old head gardener retained a pride in these rhododendrons, and Lady Moore recalled that, when one or other of the more unusual species flowered, a postcard was sent -'Let yez come soon, rosydandry falconyera or lowther is an admiration'. She added that this summons was always obeyed with pleasure.

The mansion has been decrepit, roofless and gaunt for decades. The arboretum has seen happier times, but trees are remarkably persistent, surviving some neglect without appreciable damage. Indeed, the garden has reached that state of decadence that some find depressing but others find exhilarating. It is not an utter wilderness, rather it is like the mature forest that clothes the hill slopes of some far-distant land. The rare 'rosydandries' tower overhead, uplifted on trunks of cinnamon and dove grey. Plants that are more familiar as small shrubs have grown into trees, and superb conifers of immense size grace vistas that once ended at a fine house. One of the biggest trees of *Prumnopitys andinus* known is hidden between the house and the walled garden, and there are many other fine specimen trees. A remarkable pink-flowered *Magnolia campbellii* and the rare southern beech, *Nothofagus moorei* (named after David Moore's brother, Charles), still shelter in the walled garden. An avenue of yew trees, no doubt planted centuries ago, leads to the pond. In early spring in front of the tumbledown mansion there is a carpet of pale purple crocuses, demonstrating that delicate plants can survive neglect better than man's solid artifacts.

Kilmacurragh always was a wild garden, a garden in the style of William Robinson. Therefore there is nothing inappropriate in its present state, nothing that cannot be rectified by careful restoration. Rehabilitation work has been carried out by the garden's several custodians, including most recently Bill Dolan, and I hope the garden's latest managers will not be tempted to make Kilmacurragh too neat and tidy. It would then cease to hold the delight that such old places have, and the mystery which comes from a peaceful ebb into venerable old age. Each corner turned reveals yet another surprise, even though the plants have been growing there for a century or more. Young gardens and young plants do not have the same dignity, but of course new saplings have to be planted for future generations and to ensure a sequence of beauty.

Frederick Burbidge liked Kilmacurragh as much as he admired Straffan. To see such a garden, 'a delightful old pleasaunce', with 'the cool lush grass, and the flowers, and the noble trees against the sky ... is to feel that Pan is not yet dead, and to be assured in one's heart that there is something Arcadian left to us in the world after all'. The green column of

Kilmacurragh's cypress reminds me of its avenue of 'rosydandries' and Irish yews, a tunnel of dark green splashed with crimson flowers and scarlet berries, of its magnolia with pink wine-glass flowers, its bluebells and that ephemeral carpet of pale crocuses.

FIRE-BUSHES IN FAIRYLAND

Visions of another garden that is almost completely vanished, are conjured up by two fine flowering trees. They tell of a man whose garden contained plants that are attempted only by a few fool-hardy, brave gardeners. How sad, for nothing has so utterly changed in Ireland that they cannot be grown today.

Sir John Ross-of-Bladensburg was the Arthur Rawdon of the 1890s. He was a contemporary of Thomas Acton and a good friend of Frederick Moore who so often was the catalyst for adventures in Irish horticulture. John Ross was a native of Rostrevor, a sedate sea-side town on Carlingford Lough, enfolded by the southern slopes of the Mourne Mountains. Perhaps he acquired his love of gardening from his mother who was descended from John Foster, the founding father of Glasnevin. A soldier in his young days, Ross later served on the staff of the Lord Lieutenant of Ireland. In 1901 he became the Chief Commissioner of the Dublin Metropolitan Police.

At his family home in Rostrevor, Sir John planted a garden that was a plantsman's paradise - he called it 'Fairyland'. It was mild, protected from the cold wind by mountains and trees. He found that he could grow tender southern hemisphere plants out-of-doors, and took a special interest in the extraordinary *Protea* family - for example, *Dryandra formosa* from Western Australia bloomed at Rostrevor in 1910.

The most spectacular trees in Rostrevor were the Chilean fire-bushes, which belong to the same family as *Protea* and *Dryandra*. Ross grew several different forms. One plant that had been raised from seed produced deep orange flowers. Another tree had red flowers and ribbon-like leaves up to 30 centimetres long; it blossomed a fortnight earlier than the other variety. This long-leaved form was obtained by Sir John in 1892 from Lord Sheffield of Sheffield Park in Surrey. In 1939, Hugh Armytage Moore of Rowallane discussed the Rostrevor fire-bushes and noted that the long-leaved variety could be propagated by removing the suckers that were produced in abundance. Moore believed that the two forms were not distinct species but different garden varieties.

The long-leaved Chilean fire-bush, **Embothrium coccineum 'Longifolium'** (Figure 5),[12] has leaves that vary in shape from slender, pointed ones that look like scimitars, to shorter, broad ones that are produced on spur shoots. In June the trees are covered with a blaze of red flowers which cluster along the branches and the short spurs. The strange beaked fruits ripen in autumn, turning yellow and orange as they mature.

5. *Embothrium coccineum* 'Longifolium'

The flowers are formed from four petals joined into a tube surrounding the long, protruding style. Nectar is produced in abundance, for in its Chilean homeland the fire-bush is pollinated by nectar-sipping hummingbirds. In this country there are no such birds, but the fire-bush flourishes and sets seed. It grows rapidly and can form substantial trees with hefty trunks, half a metre or more in diameter. It is not as tender as stated, for I have seen plants in gardens in the Sperrin Mountains, and a seedling in my own garden in Celbridge survived the arctic winter of January 1982.

The finest fire-bushes in Ireland are undoubtedly in Glanleam garden on Valentia Island off the coast of Kerry. There are good trees at Castlewellan and Mount Usher, and the plant is worked into the red, white and blue scheme of the Jubilee Avenue at Mount Stewart.

Few trees can provide flowers of vivid scarlet in such profusion. The long-leaved variety, first recognized at Rostrevor, is the form I would choose, but the other cultivars are as desirable for gardeners who dream of hummingbirds.

SIR JOHN'S *EUCRYPHIA*

Among the treasures at Rostrevor were several Australian and South American species of the autumn-flowering genus *Eucryphia*, including *Eucryphia lucida*, an evergreen tree from Tasmania. It has simple leaves and pure white, scented flowers. Nearby grew its Chilean cousin, *Eucryphia glutinosa* which has deciduous, divided leaves. In 1926, Sir Frederick Moore and Lord Headfort visited Rostrevor, shortly after Sir John Ross's death; they noted that the Tasmanian tree was eight metres tall and one of the finest plants in the garden. The Chilean one was about ten metres tall. These two species interbred at Rostrevor.

It is clear from studying the record of the Slieve Donard Nursery and especially an account of *Eucryphia* written by Leslie Slinger that the story of **Eucryphia x intermedia 'Rostrevor'**[13] is not simple. John Rodgers, gardener to Sir John Ross, found several seedlings that were intermediate between *Eucryphia glutinosa* and *Eucryphia lucida* and promptly named the hybrid after himself - *Eucryphia rodgersii*. Without waiting to see which was the best of the hybrid seedlings, several were passed to other keen gardeners, including Lord Aberconway. At Bodnant, the Aberconway's garden in North Wales, these bloomed in the mid-1930s, and flowers from one seedling were exhibited at the Royal Horticultural Society in 1936, gaining an award of merit. This Bodnant clone was named 'Rostrevor'. Regarding the abandoned name *Eucryphia rodgersii*, Leslie Slinger commented

> ... someone took it upon themselves to change the name to 'Rostrevor' and it finally finished up with *Eucryphia* x *intermedia*. This, I think, is unfair to the discoverer as he was surely entitled to name it as he wished and everyone should have accepted his decision.[14]

About 1938, the Donard Nursery offered plants of Rodgers' hybrid *Eucryphia*, but the supply was limited and the price could only be had 'on application'. In 1942, the same *Eucryphia* was listed as *Eucryphia intermedia (Rodgersii)*

Eucryphia 'Rostrevor' possesses characteristics that are intermediate between its parents. It is more or less evergreen and has simple leaves as well as divided ones with two or three leaflets. The leaves are dark glossy green with a striking white undersurface. Like its parents, it has pure white flowers. Inside the saucer of overlapping heart-shaped petals are numerous stamens with white filaments and pink anthers.

The Rostrevor *Eucryphia* is more hardy that its Tasmanian parent, but it is not at all common in gardens. This hybrid tolerates lime-rich soil, and flowers for a long period with the main flush of blossom in late summer. It thrives in a sheltered situation in full sun.

MOUNT USHER'S *EUCRYPHIA*

The hardy *Eucryphia* species and cultivars have one most desirable trait - they flower at the end of summer when few other shrubs are in bloom. In addition most of them are evergreen. At Castlewellan there is an avenue of *Eucryphia*, which is a picture in bloom. Two fine varieties have been selected at Castlewellan, including a late flowering cultivar *Eucryphia* x *nymansensis* 'George Graham',[15] which was first marketed by the Slieve Donard Nursery in 1970.

This hybrid has two Chilean species as parents, *Eucryphia glutinosa* and *Eucryphia cordifolia*. It arose in at least three separate gardens at the beginning of this century. At Nymans in Sussex it was raised about 1915 by Colonel Leonard Messel, and it is from this garden that it takes its botanical name. The hybrid was also produced at Castlewellan for there are large trees of it in the walled garden, including the original plant of 'George Graham' now around 15 metres tall; these could not have been derived from Nymans. It was also reared at Mount Usher in County Wicklow by Edward Walpole.

The Mount Usher variety, **Eucryphia x *nymansensis* 'Mount Usher'**,[16] was grown from seed harvested from a plant of *Eucryphia cordifolia* that had been hand-pollinated. It is not known if pollen from *Eucryphia glutinosa*, the other parent, was deliberately used, or if the hybrid was a natural accident. This was in 1916, the first year in Mount Usher that these two species had flowered at the same time. Three seedlings were raised; one looked very like *Eucryphia cordifolia*, but the other seedlings were clearly hybrids. The three saplings were planted beside the tennis court, where they thrive today. The plant that was selected as 'Mount Usher' is now also about 15 metres tall, and is a splendid sight in September when its flowers are open. 'Mount Usher' has toothed, evergreen leaves, composed of five elliptical leaflets. The branches sweep to the ground, and will produce roots if they touch the soil. The blossoms are formed from four white petals that are slightly crinkled and silky in texture. As in 'Rostrevor', the stamens have pink anthers and white filaments.

Eucryphia 'Mount Usher' was propagated and introduced by Watson's Nursery of Killiney. It is a hardy evergreen, and will grow well in soil containing lime.

TOM SMITH'S *LABURNUM*

While *Eucryphia* is the best late-flowering tree, laburnum is hard to beat for early summer colour. Its chandeliers of yellow flowers have attracted gardeners for many centuries, and we know that Lord Granard planted laburnum at Castle Forbes, County Longford, as long ago as the 1680s. In more recent times it has been fashionable in large gardens to create laburnum walks, with trees trained into arches, so that the flower spikes dangle into the tunnel providing a shower of yellow for a few short weeks

Laburnum comes into bloom in May - 1983 was a peculiarly late year and most trees did not flower until early June. In the National Botanic Gardens, there is a tree of the so-called Scotch laburnum that comes into leaf very late and blooms when all the other laburnum trees have blown and gone.

The late-flowering variety is **Laburnum alpinum 'Newryensis'** (Plate 3),[17] which was introduced by Thomas Smith of Daisy Hill Nursery in the early 1900s. Its history is difficult to chart but it was described in the nursery's 1923 catalogue as a new, robust kind bearing long racemes of clear yellow flowers. Each sparsely hairy leaf is composed of three elliptical leaflets held on a slender, long stalk. The flower spikes are up to 50 centimetres long. Each blossom is like a miniature pea flower and bright yellow without any markings in the throat. The tree produces large quantities of seed which are poisonous - this is not a plant for a garden in which young children play.

The Newry laburnum was probably selected from a batch of saplings. Nurserymen, even today, often pick out plants which they think are different, but on careful study and after years of cultivation these sometimes prove to be so close to other forms that they cannot be distinguished with certainty. However, I think the Newry laburnum is distinct and can be cherished. When I wrote this book in 1983, I knew only the one plant in Glasnevin which came from Daisy Hill Nursery in 1930. I am happy to report that it has since been propagated and distributed to other gardens, but Newry's laburnum is still a rare thing.

Thomas Hood wrote these lines which might well be engraved on a stone beside any old laburnum tree, but especially beside the one from Newry with the crooked trunk that grew hidden in a quiet corner in the National Botanic Gardens.

> I remember, I remember,
> The roses, red and white,
> The vi'lets and the lily-cups,
> Those flowers made of light!

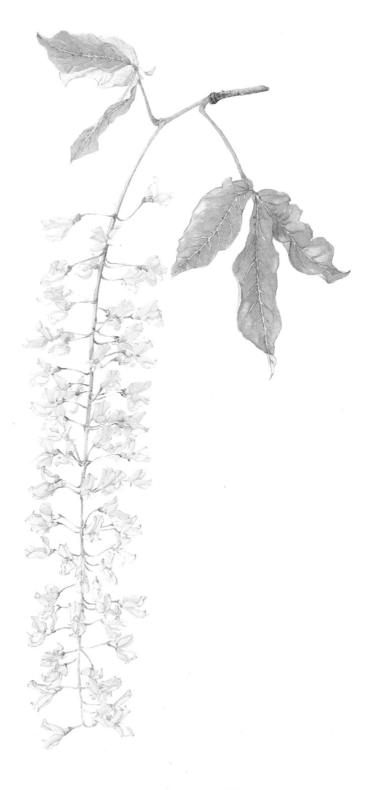

3. Laburnum alpinum 'Newryensis'

The lilacs where the robin built,
And where my brother set
The laburnum on his birthday, -
The tree is living yet![18]

Henri Correvon, an eminent Swiss gardener with a passion for alpine plants, was one of the many people who visited Daisy Hill Nursery. He was impressed by Tom Smith, that 'connoisseur and true amateur of flowers and one of the most skilful growers'. Correvon left Newry thoroughly amazed by the selection of plants growing at Daisy Hill - 'a plant lover could pass there many hours with much profit and enjoyment'. Although he spent a whole day in the nursery he wished that he had had time to study the plants more closely. William Watson, curator of the Royal Botanic Garden, Kew, found that the collection was comprehensive, and that it contained plants not growing in Kew. It is sad to have to record that Daisy Hill Nursery closed in 1996; its name will not be forgotten as long as good plants are cherished.

Thomas Smith received many honours from fellow horticulturists including the Victoria Medal of Honour of the Royal Horticultural Society of London. It is a mark of his stature that the name Daisy Hill was known throughout the world as a place of pilgrimage for plant lovers. He died in 1919 and his son continued to supply fine plants to gardens throughout Ireland. Today Daisy Hill Nursery is remembered as the home of many good garden plants, including 'Our Pat', a double-flowered primrose, the purple *Hebe* 'Autumn Glory', *Cotoneaster newryensis*, eponymous cultivars of *Eucryphia* and *Cytisus*, and the rose 'Daisy Hill' - the rose and the *Cotoneaster* will be planted anon in this imagined Irish garden. There is also the lovely October cherry, already planted in the winter garden.

A SILVER BIRCH

Trees may be grown for their fine flowers, elegant shapes or autumn colour, while the bark of some trees guarantees them a place in an arboretum. *Arbutus* has a red bark that glows, especially in the late evening sun. The bark of eucalypts provides almost endless variety - some species have bark that peels away in crackling strips, while others possess a patchwork of salmon, grey and cream on their smooth trunks. Such trees add to a winter garden, as much as they contribute to the summer scene.

The tree prized for its white bark is the Himalayan birch, and one of the finest forms, ***Betula utilis* 'Trinity College'**,[19] was raised in the College Botanic Garden at Ballsbridge, in Dublin, over a century ago.

In 1881, Sir Joseph Hooker, Director of Kew Gardens, sent some seeds of Himalayan plants to the College, including those of a birch. Frederick Burbidge was the curator at the time, having succeeded Frederick Moore in 1879. The young birch saplings were planted in Ballsbridge and developed into shapely trees. The trunks were enveloped in almost pure white bark, as if someone had carefully applied whitewash and brushed the bole every day to keep it clean. The leaves of this birch are larger than those of our native species; they have toothed margins, and long tapering points, and about ten pairs of veins. The upper surface is dark green, while the lower side is pale green and there are prominent tufts of hairs in the axils of the veins.

Burbidge sent specimens of the bark to the Royal Horticultural Society in 1899. He wrote that 'we have three trees, the larger 20 feet high and we rate them very highly not only for their silver-stemmed beauty, especially during winter, but especially because they were born and raised from seeds which Sir J. D. Hooker ... sent to the gardens eighteen years ago'. Those three plants no longer exist, but offspring grow at Castlewellan, Mount Usher, and (in a sadly mangled state) at Glasnevin. There is a young tree in the experimental botany garden that Trinity College established over 25 years ago near Palmerston Park.

The birches of the Himalayas have not been studied critically. They vary considerably, much as the rhododendrons vary in the same region. As more material is collected from isolated areas, a better understanding of this variation will be built up, and the botanical status of the College birch will be firmly established. At present, it is seen to lie between *Betula utilis* and *Betula jacquemontii*, but these may be extreme forms of one species. The plant's status and scientific name are irrelevant when the beauty of its silver trunk is seen. Plant it against a dark evergreen and the bark will gleam in the winter sun.

In one sense this is another memorial tree, a remembrance of a lost garden. The College Botanic Garden at Ballsbridge vied with Glasnevin as one of the great gardens of Ireland and it was one of the best botanical gardens in the world. Under James Mackay, John Bain, Frederick Moore and Frederick Burbidge, it was a garden of outstanding plants. It was also a nursery for gardeners - David Moore and his brother Charles were trained there before they assumed responsibilities elsewhere, David at Glasnevin and Charles in the Royal Botanic Garden in Sydney. After Frederick Burbidge's death in 1905, the College Garden gently waned. Parts of the garden were ceded piece by piece when an adjacent property needed more land, or when the interest in the relevant lease came up for renewal, and by the 1960s less than half the original ground was left. The university decided it could not support even this more modest garden on such a valuable piece of real estate, and despite vigorous protests from the late Professor David Webb, the College Botanic Garden, Ballsbridge, was finally dismantled in 1966. The plants have been replaced by two concrete hotels, a pathetic fate for any garden. But history was simply repeating itself - the earlier botanical gardens belonging to Trinity College all ended up as building sites!

THE BIG-CONE PINE

Trinity College has a long history of excellence in botany. One of its graduates, Dr Thomas Coulter, enlarged our knowledge of the plants of Mexico and California. He was a native of Dundalk, and after graduating as a doctor of medicine in Dublin went to study botany in Paris

6. Pinus coulteri

and Geneva. In 1824, he was engaged as a doctor to an English mining company that was about to reopen some derelict Mexican silver mines. Tom lived in central Mexico for six years, working as a doctor and also as a mine manager. During his spare time he indulged his interest in natural history, collecting plants, insects and reptiles. In 1831 he left Mexico and began a journey to California which had long been his cherished destination. About October he reached Monterey, and used this small military settlement as his base for exploring southern California.

Dr Coulter made two lengthy trips. On both journeys he passed through the wooded hills that overlooked the missions of San Luis Obispo, La Purissima and Santa Barbara. On these hills remnants of the woodland survive today, including trees of the big-cone pine, which has the botanical name ***Pinus coulteri***,[20] in honour of its discoverer. Tom Coulter was proud of this remarkable tree for he brought one of its huge cones home to Europe in 1834. He showed it to his botanical friend, Aylmer Bourke Lambert, whose amanuensis, David Don, described and christened the pine, basing his work on the single cone.

Dr Coulter later displayed the big cone at a meeting of the Royal Dublin Society in January 1836, along with samples of other Californian trees, including the redwood. Tom kept the cone with his vast herbarium of dried plants, and in 1840 handed the entire collection to Trinity College. Today that cone rests in the Botany School.

When Thomas Coulter discovered the big-cone pine he was almost certainly accompanied by David Douglas, the Scottish plant-hunter. The two men met in Monterey and worked together during the winter of 1831 and 1832. They both enlisted in the local militia, and went fishing and shooting together. Douglas collected seeds of Coulter's pine and sent them to England late in 1832. Plants were raised from Douglas's seed in the Royal Horticultural Society's garden at Chiswick. There was a young big-cone pine in the Trinity College Garden at Ballsbridge in 1843. It is claimed that seeds collected by Coulter were germinated in Glasnevin by Ninian Niven, before 1838; Dr Coulter did present several lots of seed to Glasnevin in 1836, but the names of the plants are not recorded.

The big-cone pine is a fast-growing and short-lived tree in this country. None of the original introductions survives in Ireland or Britain. There are mature specimens in Castlewellan, Mount Usher, and the John F. Kennedy Park, and a young sapling was planted this year outside the County Museum in Dundalk as a memorial for Thomas Coulter. A tree in the demesne at Powerscourt, County Wicklow, was the tallest in these islands, but sadly it fell in a ferocious storm during 1993. The pine has very long needles arranged in groups of three. Its cones are its glory; they may be as much as 50 centimetres long, and are covered with great hooked scales (Figure 6). No other species of pine produces cones as large as those of Dr Coulter's pine.

V

Shrubs from distant lands

Rhododendron edgeworthii - Abelia triflora - Buddleja crispa
Maddenia hypoleuca - Deutzia purpurascens **'Alpine Magician'**
Cotoneaster newryensis - Cotoneaster astrophoros - Cotoneaster bradyi
Itea ilicifolia - Viburnum henryi - Viburnum utile
Rhododendron augustinii - Rhododendron auriculatum
Rhododendron burmanicum - Olearia traversii - Olearia **'Henry Travers'**

Wild thyme and pine-trees from their barren hill
Transplant, and nurse them in the neighbouring soil,
Set fruit-trees round, nor e'er indulge thy sloth
But water them, and urge their shady growth.

Joseph Addison: 'Virgil's Fourth Georgic'

Master Jon's fourteenth-century garden contained only a few shrubs. Box may have edged the formal beds, while rosemary, lavender and bay grew within. Most mediaeval garden plants were annual and perennial herbs. Flowering shrubs did not have a place in those gardens and several centuries had to pass before they became prominent features in pleasure grounds.

After the voyages of Christopher Columbus to the Americas at the end of the fifteenth century, there was a rapid expansion of knowledge about remote lands. Voyages of discovery led to the exploration of new continents and to the importation of many exotic plants into Europe. At first these were mere scientific curiosities, but slowly some found their way from botanic gardens into the gardens of the nobility and rich merchantmen. Gradually plant collecting itself became fashionable and syndicates organized expeditions to collect seeds and living plants.

By the end of the seventeenth century, flowering trees and shrubs were essential in the gardens of Irish gentlemen. The Earl of Granard had lilacs and laburnum at Castle Forbes, County Longford. Lord Massereene grew Spanish jasmine along with exotic pines and firs at Antrim Castle. Sir Arthur Rawdon had parsley-leaved elder and flowering currants in his demesne at Moira. When the Reverend John Keogh compiled his strange book on Irish plants, based mainly on plants grown by Lord Kingston at Mitchelstown, County Cork, before 1735, there were shrubs such as barberry, butcher's broom, jasmine, medlar, myrtle, roses (white, red and damask), bladder senna, tamarisk and vines. In the middle of the 1700s the variety was even greater, and Irish people living or travelling abroad were sending new plants directly to their friends at home. Arthur Dobbs, governor of North Carolina, told his cousin, Judge Ward of Castle Ward in County Down, that he was trying to procure seeds of American plants and in the meantime enclosed 'some of the seeds of a sensitive briar which grows upon our black hills. Touch of a whip will make the whole bush close up, so I hope it will grow upon your rocky hills' - Dobb's sensitive plant is not related to our wild roses and brambles, but is a member of the pea family.

From nurserymen's catalogues published in Dublin in the 1780s, gardeners were able to select flowering shrubs in quantity, and many different garden varieties were available. Edward Bray, for example, listed lilac 'in sorts', as well as thorns, honeysuckle and jasmine. John Foster grew four different species of broom, two distinct varieties of the strawberry tree, the common white and the yellow summer jasmines, and a host of other shrubs.

By 1800 it took only a year or two for newly discovered plants to reach gardeners. Nurserymen who obtained seeds from itinerant botanists and collectors exploited the novelties as rapidly as they could, selling new plants quickly to gain the maximum price. The botanic gardens aided the diffusion by distributing their new plants to other gardens and to their favoured friends.

In the nineteenth century the botanic gardens in Belfast, Cork and Dublin received many packets of seeds and boxes of living plants from Irish people who were working overseas, or who had emigrated to new settlements. The records of plant donations to Glasnevin show that army and naval officers often had time to gather seeds, and government officials in the colonies collected plants during their travels

EDGEWORTH'S RHODODENDRON

One of the most able and respected members of the Indian Civil Service in the 1840s was Michael Pakenham Edgeworth, the youngest son of Richard Lovell Edgeworth of Edgeworthstown, County Longford. Pakenham was born to Richard and his fourth wife Frances Beaufort; he was a half-brother of Maria, famous for her books, especially the novel *Castle Rackrent*. After spending his schooldays at Charterhouse, Pakenham went to the University of Edinburgh in 1827, where he studied oriental languages and attended the botanical lectures of Professor Robert Graham. Having graduated, he went to India where he distinguished himself, gaining the approbation of his superiors and the respect of the native people. In 1842 he returned home on leave, and in 1846, after his marriage, he went back to India for a few more years.

On the return voyage in October 1846, Edgeworth stopped in Aden. While the steamer was coaling, he had two hours 'herborizing' in the hills and ravines, and in that short time he collected over forty plants, including a number that he thought were new species.

Michael Pakenham Edgeworth was a highly competent botanist. His publications include a book on pollen, and an account of Indian species of the carnation family (Caryophyllaceae). He was a friend of Dr Joseph Hooker, son of the Director of the Royal Botanic Gardens in Kew, who dedicated a lovely white rhododendron to

> my accomplished and excellent friend, M. P. Edgeworth Esq., of the Bengal Civil Service who has long and successfully studied the botany of the Western Himalayas and of north-western India generally.[1]

Edgeworth's fine rhododendron, *Rhododendron edgeworthii*,[2] inhabits the dense forests of the hills of Sikkim, Burma and western China, growing at altitudes over 2,000 metres. It can be an epiphyte, growing attached to the trunks and branches of trees and rooted among the mosses and ferns that also thrive in these aerial gardens - but it is not a parasite. Joseph Hooker discovered the shrub in Sikkim, and it was introduced shortly after he returned from his momentous journey to the Himalaya in the late 1840s. By 1862 *Rhododendron edgeworthii* was growing at Kilmacurragh in County Wicklow.

It is one of the less hardy species, thriving best in the milder gardens as at Mount Stewart, Mount Usher and Fernhill near Dublin. Edgeworth's rhododendron can be grown with ease in a cool greenhouse. In May it sends forth fragrant, trumpet-shaped flowers which are white with a pale pink flush especially on the buds and on the outside of the trumpet. The five petal lobes are slightly crumpled in appearance. The stamens have woolly filaments and the dark brown anthers stand out against the white of the flower. The style curves from the trumpet and ends in a prominent red stigma.

The leaves of Edgeworth's rhododendron are handsome. The upper side is glossy and dark green, with the veins deeply impressed. But turn the leaf over, for the underside is covered with a golden-brown felt that extends over the stalks and onto the young shoots.

This rhododendron has played a significant part in breeding garden varieties. It was one of the parents of the well-known house-plants with highly scented white flowers, including 'Lady Alice Fitzwilliam' and 'Princess Alice'. It is not the only Himalayan flower that commemorates Michael Pakenham Edgeworth. *Primula edgeworthii*, from the cool, moist hills of Sikkim, is a much-prized, late winter-blooming primrose, although Dr John Richards has pointed out that, regretfully, the species should be named *Primula nana*.[3] A maidenhair fern is named after Edgeworth - *Adiantum edgeworthii* come from the tropics and produces little plantlets at the tips of its fronds. *Edgeworthia*, a genus of shrubs with strangely pliable twigs and bark that is used for making high-quality paper, was named in his honour by Carl Meisner. *Edgeworthia chrysantha* is a fine, early spring-flowering shrub, with extraordinary, hanging clusters of fragrant, lemon-yellow flowers.

ODOURS FROM THE SPICY SHRUB

M. P. Edgeworth sent Indian seeds to Miss Beaufort (perhaps his aunt) in Dublin, who gave them to the Glasnevin Botanic Gardens in August 1841. She donated more seeds, probably also from Edgeworth, in 1854. In 1846, Pakenham Edgeworth sent seeds to Glasnevin on behalf of another Irishman, Edward Madden. At that time, Madden was a major in the Bengal Artillery, although he later rose to the rank of lieutenant-colonel. Madden often mentioned Edgeworth in his letters, so they were probably good friends. Certainly they shared a strong interest in Indian plants.

Edward Madden's gifts of seeds and plants to the Glasnevin Gardens were more numerous than those of his fellow-countryman. Between January 1841 and April 1850 over 500 packets were received from the Himalaya, including fruits of several palm trees. Bulbs of Indian lilies and orchid plants were despatched by Madden in the late 1840s. One of the most significant packages arrived in Dublin on 21 March 1847 and yielded seeds of that most fragrant, flowering shrub, *Abelia triflora*.

Abelia triflora (Plate 4)[4] comes from the mountains near Simla; Madden noted that it grows on the warmer slopes of the Shallee Hills. The species extends into Kumaon where it was discovered about 1830 by Robert Blinkworth, a correspondent of the Danish botanist, Nathaniel Wallich, who was curator of the botanic garden in Calcutta. While Blinkworth collected the original dried specimens, Edward Madden sent the first seeds to Europe. They were germinated in Glasnevin and the young shrubs flowered in the summer of 1852. David Moore distributed plants to other gardens and in 1860 noted that the original plants in Dublin were already four metres tall. Moore commented that *Abelia triflora* was 'one of the very finest of our hardy free flowering shrubs'. An original plant still grows in the National Botanic Gardens in front of the modern fern house.

This shrub will be noticed by its fragrance long before the small flowers can be closely examined. The strong, sweet perfume will diffuse through the garden on still, warm days. Few shrubs have such a pervasive scent, a joy for a perfumed garden. The flowers are clustered in posies at the tips of the shoots. In bud they are rosy pink, but when open the petals are pure white. The sepals persist after each blossom has withered, thereby prolonging the beauty of the shrub; the fluffy, red-tinted sepals often mingle with a second flush of flowers. Indeed, *Abelia triflora* usually has some flowers on it from June until November, with the main display in late June and early July.

Edward Madden's seed packets provided Glasnevin with several other fine plants, some of which will appear later in this book of Irish flowers. The Belfast and Kew gardens also received parcels from Madden, but Glasnevin seems to have been the most successful in raising and introducing good garden plants from his gifts.

4. Abelia triflora

MADDEN'S BUTTERFLY BUSH

Edward Madden was born somewhere in Ireland in 1805. His mother lived in Kilkenny in 1841 and he often visited Ireland when on leave from the Indian Army. Madden served in the Bengal Artillery from about 1830, and for the first decade he does not seem to have had any interest in botany. We do not know what aroused his interest in botany, but like his contemporary and friend, Pakenham Edgeworth, he made several valuable contributions to the literature on Indian plants.

As a military man, Major Madden was meticulous in his preparation for plant-hunting treks into the mountains. He was highly practical, and for the benefit of less experienced and more fool-hardy explorers he recorded some rules:

> Let your tent be only of such a weight that one strong man can carry it well, even when soaked with rain. Let your cups, jugs, plates, dishes be of metal; with these only may you defy fate and falls; and as for provender to adorn them, an ample supply of tea, sugar, Carr's biscuits, hermetically sealed soups and bouilli, fowls, sliced bread re-baked into everlasting rusks, with a liberal allowance of beer, wine and brandy, the latter precious article insured against damage by being decanted into curacao or other stone bottles. Nor ... must a liberal proportion of tobacco be excluded from the category; be assured Molière was not far wrong when he said 'Quoique puisse dire Aristote et toute la Philosophie, il n'y a rien d'égal au tabac' - at all events when jaded by a severe walk, and all other creature-comforts out of sight.[5]

He was firmly against bringing large parties of servants and porters; a group of three able-bodied men was quite sufficient, and he suggested getting new porters each day. Thus provisioned and aided, Madden walked many miles through the hill country around Simla and Almorah, collecting plants. Progress could be slow - on 11 September 1845 he travelled only 'ten or eleven miles, which took us eight hours, being much delayed by the constant halts of the coolies, by my own rests and search for plants, and, after quitting the forest, by a very difficult path'.

In 1847 Madden explored the Snowy Range near Almorah, and on his return in October wrote to David Moore saying that

> neither fatigue, danger nor admiration of the stupendous and sublime scenery (and they all abounded) prevented my gathering a few seeds of which I have thé pleasure to enclose specimen parcels, the advanced guard of a larger body which I will dispatch and parcel as soon as possible.[6]

The two lots arrived within four days of each other on 19 and 23 January 1848. It is probable that among the collection was a lovely butterfly bush, **Buddleja crispa**,[7] collected near Almorah at elevations between 1,800 and 2,500 metres.

Madden's butterfly bush flowered at Glasnevin in 1854 for the first time. It forms a tall shrub, and is grown against a wall in the National Botanic Gardens although this is not necessary. It is hardy, and performs best if pruned in the spring so that vigorous young shoots are stimulated. It will flower from late July until the first frosts of winter. The heart-shaped leaves have long tapering points and prominent marginal teeth. The young foliage, shoots and flower heads are clothed with a white felt like lamb's wool. The broad spikes of pale lavender blossoms contain hundreds of tiny flowers about half a centimetre across, each with four convex petals and a bright orange eye. The flowers are delightfully fragrant and on warm days the whole bush is covered with butterflies.

That was the story of the discovery and introduction of *Buddleja crispa* - until I examined some of the Edgeworth family's paper. When Christine Colvin and I were preparing an article on Maria Edgeworth's garden, Mrs Colvin sent me a copy of a list of seeds 'sent over by Pakenham June 1841'.[8] Among the plants listed was *Buddleja crispa*. Did Michael Pakenham Edgeworth's seeds germinate at Edgeworthstown? If they did, he should be credited with the introduction of the butterfly bush, and indeed with several other wonderful shrubs including the scented *Daphne bholua*.

Edward Madden retired from active service in 1850 and took up residence in Edinburgh. He was elected president of the Botanical Society of Edinburgh and in his presidential address spoke about the plants of the Himalayas. He died in Edinburgh in 1856, leaving elegant shrubs as his living memorial.

IN HONOUR OF MADDEN

Like Michael Pakenham Edgeworth, Edward Madden's name is perpetuated in a white flowered rhododendron, *Rhododendron maddenii*, and a genus of shrubs. Like Edgeworth, he was a friend and correspondent of Joseph Hooker, who gave the name *Maddenia* to some plants from eastern Asia that are related to the cherries (*Prunus*). Hooker described two species of *Maddenia* from India, and in the early 1900s Ernest Wilson discovered three more species in western China which he introduced into European gardens.

At Glasnevin, on the stone wall beside the *Buddleja* collection there is a shrub of *Maddenia hypoleuca*,[9] one of Wilson's species collected in 1901 and again in 1907 in the west of Hubei province. It is one of those plants labelled 'only of botanical interest' by nurserymen and thereby damned to unjust obscurity. What a waste!

Certainly the spike of dark red flowers is not showy. The petals are inconspicuous but the stamens have creamy filaments and anthers. They wither quickly and are followed by black, uninteresting fruits. However the splendour of *Maddenia hypoleuca* is its foliage. The young shoots are exquisite. The unfurling leaves are startling, iridescent red, and when the sun catches them they glow and sparkle. As the leaves mature the colour changes slowly to a deep bronzy-green and then dark, dull green. When fully developed the oval leaves have prominently impressed veins, and underneath they are bright silvery-grey bloom.

Maddenia hypoleuca is a vigorous shrub, and is pruned heavily each year at Glasnevin to keep it within bounds. I have not seen one grown as a free-standing shrub, but I have no doubt it would be elegant and I can imagine the breeze ruffling those lovely green and silver leaves. It is a plant of much more than 'only botanical interest'.

AN ALPINE MAGICIAN

What a damnable phrase, frightening to the ordinary gardener because it suggests not even faint praise! I am sure there are countless other lovely plants condemned to obscurity by it, including a handsome *Deutzia* now rescued from this damnation.

One spring day, checking some labels in the National Botanic Gardens, Glasnevin, I chanced to be fossicking in a slightly overgrown shrubbery. One of the shrubs was in bloom, and attracted my attention because of the striking combination of colours. Five brilliant yellow anthers sparkled inside a cup of rich plum-purple, and around the cup were five, slightly frilled, bright white petals. The shrub had a history, and I was intrigued enough to have a look at the relevant books.

The story on the label was that the shrub was *Deutzia* aff. *discolor* Farrer 846, and I could easily interpret this. Reginald Farrer, a tireless traveller who was also a vivacious author, had collected seeds of a *Deutzia*, which was similar to *Deutzia discolor*, and distributed them under his collection number 846. In fact he also gathered a specimen in bloom, pressed and dried it, and this is preserved in the Royal Botanic Garden, Edinburgh. Examination of the original specimen, confirmed by checking the Glasnevin plant, indicates that the shrub should be named *Deutzia purpurascens* var. *likiangensis*.

Farrer gathered 846 in copses under Hpimaw Hill in the remote mountains of eastern Burma on 16 April 1919, at about 3,000 metres altitude. The published field-notes described the shrub as 'a bush with arching sprays in May of purple-centred flowers in various shades'; not an enthusiastic description. Reginald Farrer's own handwritten field-notes, preserved on the specimen in Edinburgh, were more glowing.

> Shrub among the rest slender & delicate. Outsides & centres of blossoms deep plum-purple like that of a Gravianum ardentissimum Odonto-hybrid with white margin round outside of each reverse of the white segment.[10]

The strange phrase 'Gravianum ardentissimum Odonto-hybrid' was short-hand for an orchid (*Odontoglossum*) hybrid with rich plum-purple flowers.

5. *Deutzia purpurascens* 'Alpine Magician'

Seed was collected in the autumn, sent to England, and distributed to gardeners. Euan Cox, Farrer's companion on the expedition to Burma, grew the plant, and ten years on, Seed published this description: 'although perfectly hardy this is not of importance, as it is not so good as the best of our garden Deutzias. The colour is inclined to be muddy.' That was the end of *Deutzia* aff. *discolor* Farrer 846 - Cox might just as well have written that it was 'only of botanical interest'.

Any packet containing seeds gathered in the wild from a group of plants described as having flowers 'in various shades' will inevitably produce seedlings of varying quality. The Glasnevin seedling that I chanced upon certainly did not have muddy flowers, and deserved better. I had it propagated at the National Botanic Gardens and at Teagasc's horticultural research centre at Kinsealy. By 1995, plants were available for showing at the Chelsea Flower Show on the stand, jointly staged by the Irish Garden Plant Society and the National Botanic Gardens' Education Society, celebrating the bicentenary of the National Botanic Gardens. *Deutzia purpurascens* **'Alpine Magician'** (Plate 5)[11] was a show-stopper. Over night, almost, this long-ignored shrub became desirable - the ultimate accolade was that a young plant was presented by An Taioseach, Mr John Bruton, to H. R. H. The Prince of Wales during the prince's visit to the Republic of Ireland in the summer of 1995.

'Alpine Magician' forms a shrub about two metres tall. Like any *Deutzia*, it benefits from selective pruning to maintain a succession of flower-bearing shoots. It blossoms in May.

But why did I call it 'Alpine Magician'? Lady Moore described Reginald Farrer as 'this Alpine Magician', and I borrowed her epithet. Others have called him eccentric, provocative, malicious, sensitive, excitable, tireless, fearless. His books and articles are as enjoyable a legacy to gardeners, as are his plants, for they are pugnacious essays, often full of 'fantastic language' that, to quote Professor William Stearn, 'enrich and enliven the literature of horticulture.' We will meet Reginald Farrer again.

A CHINESE PUZZLE FROM NEWRY

The remote region that Farrer and Cox visited in 1919 on the borders of eastern Burma and western China, is an area of immense mountains, deep valleys, and great rivers. The mountains have a rich flora, and many excellent, hardy garden plants have their wild habitats in the woodlands and alpine meadows of the region. The whole area has been a 'Mecca' for plant-hunters since the early decades of the present century.

Among the shrubs that inhabit these places are species of *Cotoneaster*; we have many different species and varieties in our gardens, and most produce spectacular displays of red berries in autumn. This is a complicated genus, containing species that reproduce 'normally', in other words sexually, forming fruits (berries) only after pollination, and also other species that produce fruits containing viable seeds without the need for pollination, that is asexually.

The technical term used to characterize a species belonging to the latter, asexual group is apomictic. When the seeds of an apomictic species are germinated, the seedlings will be identical to the parent - a useful characteristic from the gardener's point of view. When seeds from a 'normal' species are germinated, the seedlings can display substantial variation.

We cultivate many *Cotoneaster* species that are apomicts. Some botanists are not inclined to dignify these by calling them species, but it is traditional to give them Latin names, as if they were 'good' species. One such plant has long been named ***Cotoneaster newryensis***,[12] because it 'originated in the fertile nurseries of Mr Thomas Smith at Newry'. Perhaps this misnomer should not have been allowed, but it was published, and so must remain in use.

As I remarked in *A prospect of Irish flowers*, some garden plants have histories that defy research. Their names appear in nursery catalogues, apparently having come from nowhere, and attempts to trace them back to their wild habitats frequently fail. *Cotoneaster newryensis* is such a plant. For a time it was believed to be 'a giant form of *Cotoneaster simonsii*', that rather stiff shrub, which is now widely naturalized in Ireland, with shiny, oval leaves less than two and a half centimetres long and orange-red, often egg-shaped berries. In works written during the 1930s and 1940s, this shrub was set down as a hybrid. The Swedish botanists, Dr Karl Flinck and Dr Bertil Hylmö wrote wishfully that 'perhaps one day ... *Cotoneaster newryensis* ... can be proved to be [an] apomictic species ... found by an industrious collector in China's so difficultly accessible mountains.' To some extent that wish has come true for Jeanette Fryer and Dr Hylmö now suggest that *Cotoneaster newryensis* hails from the provinces of Yunnan and Sichuan in western China, and it is treated as a good species, not a mere garden variant, in their account of *Cotoneaster* published in *The European garden flora*.

The fundamental question remains: where did Tom Smith get it from? He never visited China, yet he must have raised the plant and distributed it, at least to the French nursery of Barbier & Co., before 1908. In the trade catalogue issued by Barbier, dated Autumn 1908 - Spring 1909, *Cotoneaster newryensis* is offered for sale at one shilling and sixpence a plant, one of the most expensive in the list. And, the National Botanic Gardens, Glasnevin, purchased its original plant from Barbier and not from Daisy Hill Nursery. The mystery remains, frustrating our story.

Cotoneaster newryensis forms a handsome shrub, vigorous, with erect branches and semi-evergreen foliage. The elliptical leaves are more than two centimetres long, leathery, becoming hairless and shiny above while remaining hairy underneath. The flowers are among the largest in the genus, clustered in groups of five to eleven. The five petals are pink, and concave, and the individual flowers do not open wide, staying tulip-shaped. Each flower contains 20 stamens with white filaments. The barrel-shaped fruits are red when ripe, each with usually three nutlets inside.

7. *Cotoneaster astrophoros* (top) & *Cotoneaster bradyi*

AIDAN BRADY: *IN MEMORIAM*

The origin of another of the many *Cotoneaster* cultivated at Glasnevin is not so obscure. In 1962 young plants of thirteen different *Cotoneaster* were received at the National Botanic Gardens from Dr Bertil Hylmö. One of these, numbered Hylmö 9108, proved to be a hardy, deciduous shrub. The dark green, oval leaves are clustered in groups of three or four on short spurs. The flowers are also clustered on these leafy spurs and, because they tend to be obscured by the young foliage, they are relatively inconspicuous. In bud one of the five pale red, slightly ragged petals overlaps the others. The individual flowers do not open fully but, like those of *Cotoneaster newryensis*, remain almost tulip-shaped. There are between twelve and 16 stamens with red filaments topped by pale amber anthers. At Glasnevin, *Cotoneaster bradyi* blossoms in the middle of June. In autumn, this shrub is spectacular, its branches studded with large, glossy, bright maroon-red berries which, alas, are soon eaten by birds. The flesh of the berries is cream, and each berry usually contains three golden nutlets.

For many years at Glasnevin this shrub was labelled *Cotoneaster horizontalis* but it was obviously not that species. Later it was given the jawbreaking tag *Cotoneaster* sp. nov. aff. *splendens*, meaning it was an unnamed new species similar to *Cotoneaster splendens*. Finally, after study by Jeanette Fryer, who recognized the shrub as an unnamed Chinese species, we decided that this was an appropriate plant to commemorate Aidan Brady who had been Director of the National Botanic Gardens from 1968 until his death in 1993. Thus, Jeanette and I named it **Cotoneaster bradyi** (Figure 7).[13]

The story of *Cotoneaster bradyi* was not a mystery. Dr Hylmö had sent to Glasnevin a species which had been raised in Sweden from a batch of seed collected by Dr Karl August Harald ('Harry') Smith high in the mountains between Taining (Ngata) and Mao-niu (Ndrome) in western Sichuan, China, on 30 September 1934. Dr Harry Smith (1889-1971) was a Swedish botanist of Irish ancestry, who visited China three times in 1921, 1924 and 1934.

THE STAR-BEARER, A CHINESE GEM

An English plant hunter, Frank Kingdon Ward, declared that it was a worthy pursuit to reveal the plants hidden in the world's most isolated places so that gardeners can share the joy of discovery and delight in the beauty of mysterious lands. Many of his hard-won shrubs blossom each summer in Ireland's gardens, at Annes Grove near Mallow, at Headfort in County Meath, and at Glasnevin.

Nowadays there are very few places left on the globe where plant collectors have not trodden, so insatiable are gardeners for novelties. And in that quest for plants concealed in remote mountains, plains and valleys, China has been a prime destination. Thanks for revealing and then collecting China's beautiful and abundant flora goes, as I will shortly explain, to the Irish doctor, Augustine Henry, in whose wake went Ernest Wilson, George Forrest, Reginald Farrer, Frank Kingdon Ward, Harry Smith and a host of others.

Those are now familiar names in the annals of horticulture, but there is a little-known chapter in the history of plant hunting in the mountains of western China that involves a native Chinese botanist and an Irish gardener. In the mid-1930s, plans were laid for an expedition to the almost inaccessible mountains of that part of China, in the province of Yunnan, where a series of immense valleys and deep gorges have been scoured into the folded rocks of eastern Himalaya by the great rivers Mekong, Salween and Irrawady. In the valley bottoms it is steamy and warm, with lush subtropical forests, while on the highest peaks there are alpine meadows, and at the saddles and passes the climate is temperate and there can be discovered the plants that revel in the mild gardens of Ireland.

The person who instigated this expedition to Yunnan was the sixth Earl of Rosse who was then beginning to enrich the plant collections at Birr Castle in County Offaly, his family seat. Michael Rosse cajoled other gardeners to share the costs and, consequently, the likely bounty from Yunnan. Thus began the plant-hunting expeditions of a young Chinese botanist.

In Beijing, Professor Hu of the Academy of Sciences was in charge of the expedition, and he selected Tse Tsun Yu to undertake the long and arduous journey. Yu departed for Yunnan in 1936. By May the following year, Professor Hu reported to Lord Rosse that the expedition had penetrated the Tibetan wilderness where no white man had ever ventured and was about to explore the adjacent region. Thousands of plants had been collected already and a vast gathering of seeds was on its way to Europe. That year, Japan invaded China but Tse Tsun Yu was far away from the war zone and continued collecting. The Yunnan expedition yielded almost 3,000 lots of seed in 1937, and several hundred kilos of specimens and seeds were despatched to the Royal Botanic Garden in Edinburgh whence the seed was to be dispersed to Birr Castle, Glasnevin and other gardens.

In June 1939, Professor Hsen-hsu Hu wrote again to Lord Rosse telling of the hardships and perils that Tse Tsun Yu and his party had endured during the first expedition. Six coolies had fallen to their deaths as they attempted to cross a snow-bound pass, but the work would go on. Yu was indeed ready again to set out for Yunnan for another year's collecting, and his particular quarry was a *Magnolia* named after Augustine Henry. By the end of 1939 the situation in China was increasingly difficult; the cost of living, wrote Dr Hu, was soaring like a sky-rocket due to the war and the funds for plant hunting were now insufficient. But Tse Tsun Yu was 'wild' in his enthusiasm, even though the shortage of money meant that he lived a very spartan existence, one that no white man would endure. Professor Hu was forced to leave Beijing in January 1941, complaining bitterly about the Japanese forces of occupation, and the ensuing chaos prevented any further letter reaching Europe for five years.

On 22 April 1946, having returned to Beijing, Dr Hsen-hsu Hu was able to tell Lord Rosse about the botanical discovery of the century, a new conifer, a gigantic tree almost 100 feet tall, but there were only three living specimens then known. Thus came to Ireland the first news of the dawn redwood, *Metasequoia glyptostroboides*, which is now a familiar garden plant. In the meanwhile, Tse Tsun Yu's seed had germinated in quantity at Glasnevin and Birr Castle, to the delight of John Besant, Director of the National Botanic Gardens, and of Michael Rosse. New shrubberies were planted in both Glasnevin and Birr to accommodate the hard-won plants. Today, Tse Tsun Yu's seedlings have grown into mature trees and shrubs. At Birr Castle there is a host of his collecting, birches, wild pears, junipers, golden rain trees (*Koelreuteria* species), mountain ashes (*Sorbus* species) and pines. Some bear no Latin names beyond the generic name because they have not been identified yet.

In the summer of 1984, three Chinese botanists came to Ireland as guests of the National Botanic Gardens. By chance, the leader of the delegation was Professor Hu Qiming, the great-nephew of the Beijing professor who in the 1930s had supervised the expedition of Tse Tsun Yu. We had hoped that Professor Yu himself could have made the journey, but he was an old man and too infirm to make such a long trip. In his letters to me, written in impeccable English, Tse Tsun Yu had told how he wanted so much to walk through the gardens in Glasnevin and Birr, to see the plants that were raised from seeds he had collected half a century earlier. What tales he surely could have told about each and every one. Sadly, this venerable old man, a great and courageous botanist, died in July 1984, a few weeks after his colleagues had returned to Beijing with their accounts of the gardens of Ireland and photographs of his plants. Thanks to Tse Tsun Yu and his nameless colleagues, some of whom perished on those arduous expeditions, we can delight in the floral riches of western China, in silver-leaved pears, cherries that weep white petals, and in particular in a graceful evergreen *Cotoneaster* that sparkles with a myriad of stars.

Harry Smith was the first botanist known to have seen this particular *Cotoneaster* in western Sichuan near Ta-ch'ien'lu on 24 October 1934, but his specimens have neither flowers nor fruits, so presumably Smith did not gather seeds. Three years later near the lamasery, high in the mountains about 3,100 metres above sea level, at Washin in Yunnan, Tse Tsun Yu collected the same *Cotoneaster*. Yu's pressed and dried specimens which were in the consignment sent by Professor Hu to the Royal Botanic Gardens, Edinburgh, do include berries and were originally identified as *Cotoneaster buxifolius* var. *vellaeus*. No-one else is known to have gathered or seen this shrub in the 1930s, so Jeanette Fryer and I believe that Yu was the source of cultivated plants of the *Cotoneaster* that we have named **Cotoneaster astrophoros** (Figure 7, p.76), the star-bearer!

There are two old plants of the star-bearer in the National Botanic Gardens. The precise origin of these two shrubs is now lost, but hundreds of packets of seeds including several species of *Cotoneaster* came to Glasnevin from Tse Tsun Yu's expeditions. The one in the rock-garden tumbles over the stones, its graceful, arching branches cloaked with tiny, silver-rimmed leaves and sparkling with a brilliant profusion of white, starry blossoms during the latter weeks of June. The red, barrel-shaped fruits have honey-coloured flesh and because they are not popular with birds there are always some left on the bushes throughout the winter.

The mystery about this shrub is how it came to the attention of the Slieve Donard Nursery. A *Cotoneaster* for which a succession of different names was used including *Cotoneaster microphyllus*, and described as producing 'bright red berries ... more freely ... than any other dwarf evergreen type', was being sold by the Donard Nursery from 1953. Later, the *Cotoneaster* was given the cultivar name 'Donard Gem', but it turns out to be none other than *Cotoneaster astrophoros*. Whether Glasnevin was the source of the Slieve Donard Nursery's stock is not recorded, but it is not unlikely. In its new guise the shrubs can still retain the Donard's name - *Cotoneaster astrophoros* 'Donard Gem'.[14]

A GLOBE-TROTTER'S SHRUB

As I have mentioned, China has been the source of a regiment of shrubs that are well-suited to Irish gardens, and some of these have direct connections with Ireland, more direct even that Tse Tsun Yu's collections at the behest of the Earl of Rosse. My next choice is a plant that does not produce bright flowers and gaudy berries, but for all that, is an attractive, modest shrub.

Itea ilicifolia (Figure 8)[15] looks like the common holly when not in flower. Its leaves are the same shape and size and are armed with prickles, but they are thinner in texture. When the young shoots and new leaves appear in late spring, they have a bronzy hue. The mature leaves are a deep, glossy green above, and beneath are pale green with a greyish gloss. The fragrant flowers open in late July and early August; they are arranged in a slender curving inflorescence, like a large graceful catkin. The individual blossoms are only five millimetres across, with five green-white petals, alternating with the stamens. When a shrub is healthy and in full bloom, it looks like a waterfall of pale green, and its perfume invades the garden.

Itea ilicifolia was discovered by Augustine Henry at Yichang. It grows on the cliffs of the famous Yangtze Gorge, upstream of Yichang, and extends westwards into Sichuan province.

8. *Itea ilicifolia*

In his diary for Easter Monday, 26 April 1886, Dr Henry noted the arrival of the steamer from Shanghai with several 'globe-trotters on board'. On 27 April he wrote 'Warm, went up river with Captain and globe-trotters'. He was not apparently impressed by these tourists, but things changed and in the following ten days he became quite friendly with one globe-trotter, Lord Kesteven. They went for walks in the countryside, and while Kesteven shot snipe and woodcock, Henry botanized. Later in the year, after Lord Kesteven had returned to England, Dr Henry sent him seeds of *Itea ilicifolia*. Kesteven reciprocated by sending a pepper-mill to Yichang.

The seeds germinated and the shrub was planted in Kesteven's garden at Casewick House in Lincolnshire. It survived in the open-air, and flowered long before seeds were sent to Veitch's nursery by Ernest Wilson.

Lord Kesteven remained a close friend of Augustine Henry. They visited French forests together, and Henry's excursion to the western United States of America in 1905 was sponsored by Kesteven. He was one of that very select group of people who received seeds from Henry during his work in China, and *Itea ilicifolia* is one of the few plants that Dr Henry discovered and introduced.

THE PATUNG VIBURNUM

As I write this a small sprig of another Chinese shrub, another of Henry's plant, ***Viburnum henryi***,[16] is lying on my desk. It is wonderfully fragrant, and the perfume floats around the room, the scent of honey fresh from the honeycomb. Once again the individual flowers are small, no more than six millimetres in diameter; each has five creamy-white petals. They are arranged in an open panicle that is broadly conical in shape.

Viburnum henryi forms a compact shrub, as its branches are erect. The foliage is sparse and the leaves are leathery and dark green. The shrub blooms in late June, but the real splendour of *Viburnum henryi* is the crop of coral-red berries which decorates the branches in late summer; they change to black when they are fully ripe.

This is usually described as an evergreen shrub but *Viburnum henryi* is almost fully deciduous in Glasnevin and will behave similarly in colder gardens. The young leaves are bright green and appear in late April. In milder areas it will hold its leaves throughout the year and the old ones will fall as the new foliage develops.

This is one of the plants discovered at Patung by Dr Henry's native collector. Henry himself collected it later in Sichuan, and Ernest Wilson introduced it in 1901. There are several species of *Viburnum* from central China grown in our gardens, including one found by an earlier Irish resident of Yichang.

THOMAS WATTERS' VIBURNUM

One of the European diplomats whom Dr Henry met while living in central China was fellow Ulsterman, Thomas Watters. By a remarkable coincidence he was the brother of Henry's sweetheart, Martha Watters, who had met Augustine when he was a student in Galway. He proposed to her and she declined. Yet they remained good friends and corresponded for many years. Henry carefully noted each letter that he received from her as well as the dates of his replies.

Thomas and Martha Watters were the children of the Reverend Thomas Watters, minister of Regent Street Presbyterian Church in Newtownards, County Down. Young Thomas was a brilliant scholar and developed an interest in Chinese Buddhism, a subject that he researched while in China. He was a member of the British Consular Service from 1863 to 1894, and in 1878, a few years before Dr Henry arrived, was appointed acting consul in Yichang. Watters was stationed in that city when Charles Maries, the first of Harry Veitch's collectors, was working in the area.

Like Henry, Watters developed an interest in the local flora but unlike Henry he did not pursue it relentlessly. He collected some of the useful plants growing at Yichang and sent specimens to Henry Hance, a colleague in the Consular Service who actively tried to stimulate interest in the flora of China among members of the diplomatic corps. Watters also responded to an appeal from the Royal Botanic Gardens, Kew, for material relating to the economic botany of China.

Perhaps, in response to the Kew request, Thomas Watters collected *Viburnum utile*,[17] the twigs of which the Chinese used in the manufacture of pipe stems. He sent specimens to Hance in 1880, but the *Viburnum* was not described as a distinct species until dried material was received at Kew several years later.

This useful shrub is evergreen, retaining at least some of its leaves through the Irish winter. The leaves are arranged in opposite pairs on the thin, weeping shoots. When young, they are bright green and glossy on the upper surface, and there is a grey felt on the lower side. The flat, round clusters of flowers appear in May and June at the tips of the shoots. The buds are waxy and red, opening to reveal pure white petals. The whole inflorescence is about ten centimetres across although the individual flowers are less than a centimetre in diameter.

Viburnum utile is hardy and reaches three metres in height. It is not widely available, but it is easy to propagate from cuttings and tolerates limy soil.

Thomas Watters also collected the Chinese primrose, *Primula sinensis*, at Yichang. He was an inveterate traveller and an expert photographer. He photographed cities and sites in many countries but none of his photographs were published. One of his friends, E. T. C. Werner, remembered Thomas Watters as 'quiet [and] unostentatious ... a genial Irishman with a good sense of honour ... a kind-hearted gentleman of vast learning and extreme modesty who was insufficiently appreciated in his lifetime'.

THE BLUE RHODODENDRON

China is a vast country and Thomas Watters was able to make only a minute contribution to our knowledge of the floral treasures that grow there. Dr Henry and his paid local helpers collected about 150,000 dried specimens, and, during 20 years, discovered hundreds of new species. Despite the work of people like Dr Henry, Ernest Wilson, George Forrest and China's own botanists, new plants remain to be discovered and undoubtedly new garden plants are there for future explorers to unearth.

Of the many plants that bear witness to the work of Augustine Henry, the blue-flowered *Rhododendron augustinii*[18] is probably the most accessible. It is one of the few that will tolerate lime, for its natural habitats are on the limestone soils of Hubei province.

There are many colour forms of Henry's rhododendron and the finest is one with bright blue flowers that is known in Ireland, informally, as the Mulroy or Leitrim variety. It was distributed by Lord and Lady Leitrim, from their garden on the shore of Mulroy Bay in the north of Donegal. It is grown in several gardens including Fernhill. Unlike the forms commonly seen, the blooms do not have a lavender tint, but are a clear blue.

Rhododendron augustinii is hardy and forms a substantial shrub up to four metres tall. The flowers are funnel-shaped, about four centimetres long and broad. There are five petal lobes and the largest, upper one is often spotted with brown or orange dots. The ten stamens have blue filaments and the style, which is longer than the stamens, protrudes from the flower in a gentle curve.

Dr Henry did not discover this shrub; like the wych hazel and *Viburnum henryi* it was collected, in the first instance, by Henry's Patung collector. Augustine Henry described this man as an 'ignorant peasant'. He occasionally made mistakes for which Henry had to apologize, and he perpetrated one of the greatest botanical hoaxes of all time, a trick that was executed with 'panache and an inverted sort of intelligence'. The story is worth telling.

The man from Patung supplied two specimens of a new plant, one of which was included among many other specimens sent to London in 1887. In March 1888, Daniel Oliver, one of the most respected botanists at Kew, described a new genus based on the sample. The plant was named *Actinotinus sinensis*. In June 1889, after re-examining the material, Oliver realized that it was a trick, and that the specimen consisted of flowers from a species of *Viburnum* stuck into the bud of a horse-chestnut. The hoax was carefully executed. Daniel Oliver corrected his mistake, admitting that *Actinotinus* 'proves to be based upon a trick played upon us by one of Dr Henry's Chinese collectors'. Henry apologized to Oliver, noting that he had retained a duplicate of the hoax and would examine it to see how the trick had been played. The Patung collector either had an impish sense of humour, or disliked someone, for a careful examination of the list of plants, identified at Kew, shows that other hoaxes were received, but noticed before botanists got 'egg on their faces'.[19]

LADY CUFFE'S RHODODENDRON

There are numerous rhododendrons with Irish associations, and in restricting my choice, I have unavoidably omitted many species and cultivars that are of outstanding quality. But there is one other rhododendron which I believe deserves a place in my Irish garden, and that is *Rhododendron burmanicum*.[20] I have included it for no better reason than this - it was discovered by that plucky little lady, Charlotte Wheeler Cuffe.

It is another of the half-hardy species that grow happily in the mild, coastal areas; it may be seen in Rowallane and Mount Stewart, for example. It is an evergreen shrub, and can reach two metres in height but is usually not so tall. The leaves are dark green above, and the underside is golden-brown due to a multitude of small amber scales which can be seen with a hand-lens. The flowers are butter-yellow, and occur in groups of from four to ten, at the tips of the shoots. They are funnel-shaped, and about five centimetres across, with five rounded lobes and a narrow tube. The outside of the flower is covered with more amber scales.

This delicate rhododendron was found on Mount Victoria, western Burma, in May 1911 by Charlotte Wheeler Cuffe and her companion Mrs Winifred MacNabb. The two ladies saw it growing above about 2,700 metres and near the summit of the peak, but on their first visit they did not collect any plants. They returned to Mount Victoria in May 1912 and procured some young plants of this species and also of a white flowered one. The saplings were carefully packed and sent to the Botanic Gardens in Glasnevin. When the yellow shrub bloomed in May 1914, Sir Frederick Moore saw that it was a new species and sent specimens to Kew. It was described and named by Dr John Hutchinson.

Charlotte Wheeler Cuffe was most impressed with Mount Victoria. She took photographs of plants and the marvellous scenery when she visited it in 1912. A number of watercolour sketches survive showing the view from the summit, and the alpine meadows glowing with blue and yellow and white flowers. Near the summit she saw carpets of blue buttercups and great bushes of the yellow rhododendron. From the summit, at around 3,000 metres, she could see the mountain chain curve northwards towards Tibet.

HENRY TRAVERS' DAISY BUSHES

Many of our finest shrubs come from the Orient, especially from the great mountains of Burma, Tibet and India. But Irish gardens contain plants from every continent, and the mild climate allows us to grow many species from the Antipodes, in particular trees and shrubs from the islands of Tasmania and New Zealand.

The Irish played a minor role in the discovery and exploration of those distant lands, but emigrants who went to live in the new colonies sometimes took an interest in the strange flora and fauna, and a few Irish men and women helped to introduce plants into European gardens. Undoubtedly the greatest horticulturist to take an interest in Australasian plants was Lord Talbot de Malahide. He brought numerous species from Tasmania and cultivated them with consummate skill at Malahide Castle. Milo Talbot also sponsored a superbly illustrated book in six volumes on the unique plants of Tasmania.

The first European contact with Tasmania and New Zealand occurred in 1640 when these distant lands were visited by the Dutch navigator Abel Tasman. Almost one and a half centuries passed before a European settlement was established. The earliest settlers were convicts, but by the middle of the nineteenth century the majority of emigrants were honest folk. Among the Irish people who took the long sea voyage to the other side of the globe and who settled in New Zealand was William Henry Locke Travers.

William Travers was born on 9 January 1819 at Castleview near Newcastle West, a few kilometres from Limerick. His father was Captain (later General) Boyle Travers of the 56th Regiment and his mother was Caroline Brockman, niece of the Reverend Thomas Locke who lived at Castleview. Travers was educated at the College of Saint Servan in France and, at the age of 17, joined the Spanish Legion to fight in the Carlist Wars. For a short time he was aide-de-camp to the Duke of Vittoria. He returned to Britain in 1838 to study law, and was called to the Bar in 1844. In 1843 he married Jane Oldham in Cork, and the couple had a son and daughter. In 1849, William Travers and his young family emigrated to New Zealand where he continued to practise at the Bar. From 1854 he sat in the New Zealand parliament.

Travers was keenly interested in natural history and was one of the chief promoters of the New Zealand Institute. He collected plants during his travels in the South Island and sent many valuable specimens to Kew.

In 1864, the Australian botanist Ferdinand Mueller dedicated a book on the vegetation of the Chatham Islands to William T. L. Travers, 'by whose personal exertions our knowledge of the vegetation of New Zealand has been so extensively advanced'. Indeed, Travers met the costs of an expedition to those islands, which lie 1,000 kilometres east of Christchurch. The expedition was undertaken by his son, Henry, who set sail in October 1863 and returned several months later with a substantial collection of plants. Mueller based his book mainly on Henry Travers' specimens. Although Travers was not the first person to visit the Chatham Islands, many of the native plants had no Latin names and had not previously been described in botanical works. His haul included *Geranium traversii* and several daisy-bushes, species of the genus *Olearia*, including *Olearia traversii* and *Olearia semidentata*.

The climate of the Chatham Islands is mild, windy and moist, not unlike that of Kerry and Cornwall. The local plants have evolved in isolation and many are unique although they often are closely related to species that grow on the main islands of New Zealand. Because of the climatic similarities between Ireland and the Chatham Islands, many of the islands' plants thrive in our gardens.

Travers' daisy-bush, *Olearia traversii*,[21] was named by Ferdinand Mueller in honour of the young naturalist and 'his enlightened father'. It was described as the noblest plant found on the islands, where it grows over ten metres tall. The Maoris call it ake-ake. It is a remarkable shrub for it is extraordinarily resistant to salt-laden, ocean gales. I have seen it growing in gardens on Achill Island and the Burren coast of County Clare where it was unaffected by the exposed situations - other plants including *Escallonia macrantha* were burnt and stunted, but Travers' daisy-bush grew erect and unspoilt. Its flowers are minute and of no value whatsoever - they look like small groundsel flowers. The leaves are beautiful, bright green and extremely glossy above, and with a pale fawn felt on the stems and lower side. This difference in colour and texture is most attractive, and in the wind the leaves glitter and flash like the finest poplars.

Olearia traversii was introduced to Europe in 1887, and an original plant grows on Tresco in the Isles of Scilly.

CHATHAM ISLAND SPLENDOUR

During his expedition, Henry Travers collected specimens of another Chatham Island daisy bush, which were identified as *Olearia semidentata*, a splendid species that was eagerly sought by keen gardeners in Britain and Ireland during the late 1800s and early 1900s. Captain Arthur Dorrien-Smith of Tresco went all the way to the Chatham Islands to collect it and brought plants to the Isles of Scilly in 1910. However, Henry Travers sent young plants labelled *Olearia semidentata* to Glasnevin in 1906 and they survived the long journey along with many other rare New Zealand plants. Thus *Olearia semidentata* was apparently introduced to Ireland before it was grown in Britain.

This new daisy bush were quickly propagated and then distributed from Glasnevin to other gardens and nurseries. It was being propagated at the Slieve Donard Nursery during the early 1910s, and in 1916 the Donard Nursery exhibited *Olearia semidentata* at the Royal Horticultural Society in London and received an award of merit for it. Twenty years later, Leslie Slinger reported that there was a plant three metres tall and nine metres in circumference, covered with countless purple flowers and always in bloom, growing near Newcaslte in County Down.

But was the plant received at Glasnevin the true *Olearia semidentata*? In its native habitat, *Olearia semidentata* grows in peaty and boggy ground and is rarely more than a metre tall. In Ireland it flourishes in sandy soil, providing that it is in full sun, and can be five metres and more tall. It is not completely hardy, but it is apt to die more quickly from sun-stroke than frost - Milo Talbot suggested that it should always be planted with its roots in the shade. There are other differences, and in Ireland the very floriferous shrub grown as *Olearia semidentata*, which is invariably propagated by taking cuttings, very rarely produces seeds - until 1995 I would have said that it never sets seed, but I was shown indubitable seedlings by Dr David Robinson in his garden on Howth. Thus, I believe that the garden plant, represented in Ireland probably by a single clone, is best considered to be a cultivar, perhaps a hybrid, rather than the pure species, and it is now named *Olearia* **'Henry Travers'**.[22]

This daisy bush has leathery, elongated, glossy green leaves with a white-felted underside and crinkle-toothed margins. In the early summer 'Henry Travers' lives up to its name, bearing numerous flowers like those of the wild ox-eye daisy. The outer rays are pale mauve, while the inner disc is a deeper purple. Lord Talbot grew this handsome shrub at Malahide Castle, and recorded that when his largest plant was only one metre tall he removed over a thousand dead flower-heads from it. *Olearia* 'Henry Travers' will bloom from June until the first frost in November or December.

Henry Travers, who was born in 1844, studied law and practised as a barrister in New Zealand, but retired early so that he could devote more time to natural history. He grew native New Zealand plants in his garden in Wellington and sent many species to Glasnevin in the early 1900s. His letters to Frederick Moore record some of the difficulties that he experienced in collecting them. A consignment despatched in May 1908 included Chatham Islands' most famous plant, the giant forget-me-not, *Myosotidium hortensia*, which has bright green leaves like a giant spinach, and stunning blue flowers.[23]

VI

A border of hardy flowers

Paeonia cambessedesii - Agapanthus campanulatus 'Mooreanus'
Lilium henryi - Macleaya cordata - Cardiocrinum giganteum
Romneya coulteri - Phlox drummondii - Abutilon vitifolium
Cortaderia selloana - Allium giganteum - Allium babingtonii

'Tis there's the daisy and the sweet carnation,
The blooming pink and the rose so fair,
The daffodowndilly, likewise the lily,
All flowers that scent the sweet, fragrant air.

Richard Milliken: 'The groves of Blarney'

William Robinson, that irascible Irish doyen of gardeners and potent author, was a champion of the flower border. Gardens that contained only a few varieties of flowers, planted in thousands, or hundreds of thousands, held no pleasure for William Robinson. 'During all time', he wrote, 'the simple border has been the first expression of flower gardening'. He argued that there was no better way to grow perennials; a border of hardy flowers was graceful, varied and a delight to all the senses. Robinson advocated that a border should be permanent, furnished with plants that would grow for many years, rather than flowers that lasted for a single, short summer and then had to be replaced with new plants. He advised that the flower border should contain plants that bloomed in succession, giving colour from late winter until the year's end.

Annual and perennial herbs with clear Irish associations are not as numerous as shrubs and trees, and there is no obvious reason for this imbalance. The selection I have made is cosmopolitan - the only continent not represented is Australia.

MISS GEOGHEGAN'S PEONY

I have already noted that the privilege of introducing a new plant into cultivation is not the sole prerogative of the professional explorer or collector. The real amateur, the garden-lover away on holiday, a diplomat on an embassy to a foreign land, the lady who loves flowers, can discover plants not known in gardens. One such person was Miss Frances Geoghegan of Donabate in north County Dublin.

6. Paeonia cambessedesii

7. Paeonia cambessedesii

Fanny Geoghegan went on a visit to Mallorca (Majorca) about 1895, and decided to bring some of the native plants to Ireland, including roots of a wild peony. This settled down in a Fermanagh garden and flowered. Later, Miss Geoghegan showed her Balearic peony to Frederick Burbidge of Trinity College Botanic Garden, who dismissed it as a species common in Spain. When she had to move her house, Fanny Geoghegan offered plants to Frederick Moore for the collections at Glasnevin. He accepted the roots and was delighted to discover that the peony was a most unusual species which was found only in the Balearic Islands. The peony was painted and an illustration published in the *Botanical magazine* in 1907.

Miss Geoghegan recorded the story of her peony for Frederick Moore.

I did not see the peony growing. An old man got it for me from a rocky inaccessible sort of place on Cape Formentor ... I sent it to my sister in 1896 to County Fermanagh where it grew well and four or five years ago she gave me a small bit of it which is now a well-grown plant.[1]

Miss Geoghegan's peony, named **Paeonia cambessedesii** (Plates 6 & 7),[2] is a most beautiful plant. It is low growing, reaching perhaps half a metre in height. The stems and young shoots are crimson. The upper surface of the leaves is a lovely green with a remarkable silvery-grey sheen, while the lower surface is rich crimson. These colours are best developed in plants that are grown outside. It is one of the first peonies to flower, producing large, solitary blooms that are rose-pink, but as they age the crumpled petals fade to a softer, paler pink. In the centre of the saucer-shaped flower is a cluster of stamens with bright yellow anthers and purple filaments. One of the distinguishing characters of *Paeonia cambessedesii* is the group of six or seven carpels, more than in other peonies The pods ripen in late summer, bursting open to display ruby-red seeds and black seeds - the red ones are not fertile but the black germinate readily.

There is no other peony as compact and handsome. Alas, its short flowering season is too fleeting, but the silver-washed leaves, the crimson stems and the startling ruby seeds help to prolong its beauty. It grows well out-of-doors in Dublin; what I believe is Miss Geoghegan's original still flourishes in the rock-garden at Glasnevin, having lived there for a century. *Paeonia cambessedesii* also thrives in a cold greenhouse where it will flower in April. This lovely plant was virtually unknown to gardeners in the early 1980s, but is now more often available at plant sales and some nurseries stock it. Fanny Geoghegan did us a great service when she brought it to Ireland, to bloom for the first time by the 'winding banks of Erne'.

KEIT'S BLUE LILY

Another small and attractive, yet elusive plant is a blue African lily, **Agapanthus campanulatus 'Mooreanus'**,[3] which came to Ireland in the late 1870s from Natal. I have not seen the genuine plant, but include it here in case a gardener may grow it and recognize it.

What passes today for *Agapanthus* 'Mooreanus' does not match the early descriptions, and various sources indicate that the name is given loosely and inaccurately to hybrids of quite different origins.

Agapanthus has been grown in Europe for several centuries and the blue umbels are familiar to most gardeners. It is grown in tubs and in warm, sunny borders, and blossoms in late summer. The flowers are grouped at the summit of a long stalk, in a grapefruit-shaped head, and the individual flowers range in colour from deep blue to snow-white. The flower stalk can be as much as a metre tall, and the strap-like leaves may reach the same height.

In the late 1870s - the exact date is uncertain - bulbs of a variety of the African lily with short stems and erect, narrow leaves were received at Glasnevin. The flowers were dark blue. This plant was named *Agapanthus umbellatus* 'Mooreanus' but recent work on *Agapanthus* in its native South Africa, suggests that 'Mooreanus' was a form of *Agapanthus campanulatus*.

According to Lady Moore, the bulbs of the dwarf African lily came from a German botanist who had been a student in Glasnevin. This can only be Julius Wilhelm Keit,[4] who was not a student but one of the senior gardeners in Glasnevin during the directorship of David Moore. Keit was the son of a master soap-maker from Dresden. He worked in several German gardens, before moving to Basle and then Paris before, in the autumn of 1864, joining the staff of the well-known Belgian nurseries belonging to Jean Jules Linden. In 1866 Monsieur Linden secured for Keit a post with the Dublin Exhibition Palace and Winter Garden Company to manage the Winter Garden of the International Exhibition. When the company went into liquidation the following year, Keit went to England, but he returned to Ireland at the beginning of June 1868 as propagator in the Glasnevin Botanic Gardens. David Moore had great respect for Wilhelm Keit; he assisted Moore in pioneering work on raising hybrids of the insectivorous pitcher plants, *Sarracenia*, and Moore recommended Keit for the vacant curatorship of the Natal Botanic Garden. He was appointed, and on 14 November 1872 took up his new position in Durban.

Once he had settled in, Wilhelm Keit remembered his friends in Dublin. In July 1874, Moore received a case of tree ferns, and in March 1878 a collection of bulbs. Another collection of rare and unnamed bulbs arrived in February 1882, three years after David Moore's death and the appointment of his son, Frederick, to the post of curator at Glasnevin. It is not certain which consignment of bulbs contained the dark blue African Lily, but Keit suggested that it should be named after one of the Moores.

By 1884, this bulb was widely known - which suggests that the collection arrived in Dublin in 1878. George Nicholson included it in his *Dictionary of gardening* as 'a new variety with [dark blue flowers], shorter, narrower and more upright leaves than the species; it has a dwarf habit. Perfectly hardy'. Plants were sent to Kew, where they survived in the open on the rock-garden, sending up numerous spikes of deep violet-blue flowers. *Agapanthus campanulatus* 'Mooreanus' is said to come true from seed, but this has led to the original form becoming lost, or at least obscured among a plethora of pallid blue hybrids. I hope the dark plant can be recovered and returned to our flower borders.

Meanwhile, there is a fine, modern cultivar named 'Midnight Blue' which was selected by Philip Wood and introduced about 1968 by the Slieve Donard Nursery; the name is descriptive. And there is also a very hardy, dwarf, white blossomed cultivar named 'Lady Moore' that seems to have come into English gardens from Lady Moore - otherwise, its history is not known, but some distant association with Wilhlem Keit's plant is a possibility.

DR HENRY'S LILY

The African lily belongs, in a broad sense, to the lily family (Liliaceae) but it is not a true lily.[5] There are many different lilies (*Lilium* species) and innumerable artificial hybrids for it has been, and continues to be, a fashionable genus. For the ordinary gardener, lilies have one disadvantage; the majority only thrive in acid, lime-free soil. Dr Henry's lily, from the limestone hills of central China, is a notable exception.

Lilium henryi[6] is a glorious orange lily. It can grow to two metres or more tall, topped with a great open truss of pendant flowers. The individual blossoms have six fleshy petals which are curled outwards and upwards like the folds of an exotic turban. On their inner surfaces the petals are covered with fleshy papillae and are spotted with green. The curved stamens project from the flower encircling the style and stigma on to which they shed dark orange pollen.

In the wild this lily only grows about a metre tall, but in one suburban garden in Dublin, I have seen plants not less than three metres in height.

Augustine Henry discovered his lily in two places in the vicinity of Yichang. One colony grew on the grassy slopes and cliff faces on the right-hand bank of the Yangtze Gorge between the villages of P'ing-shan-pa and Shih-pi-shan. His second site was on the eastern side of a great mound of conglomerate rock called The Dome. When Henry left Yichang in March 1889 he brought some bulbs with him. He sent them to Charles Ford, curator of the botanic garden in Hong Kong, who despatched half of the consignment to Kew. *Lilium henryi* flowered in London in the summer of 1889.

On his arrival at Yichang in 1900, Ernest Wilson was dismayed to discover that Henry's lily had been almost exterminated in the sites where Henry had seen it. Luckily he found plants in an area about 50 kilometres to the south of Yichang. In his monograph on the lilies of eastern Asia, Wilson remarked that it was

> particularly fitting that such a notable addition to our gardens should bear the honoured name of a pioneer who has done so much to acquaint a sceptical world of the rich floral wealth of interior China.[7]

ROSES AND POPPIES FROM CATHAY

Chinese flowers have been cultivated in our gardens for several hundred years, and while most of the common ones are relatively recent arrivals here, some have been available for centuries. Dr Henry, indeed, was not the first Irishman to take an interest in China's wild plants, nor was Thomas Watters the first diplomat to gather seeds and specimens

One of the most remarkable European expeditions to China took place between 1792 and 1794. It was the embassy sent by King George III to the Emperor Qianlong. The Ambassador Extraordinary and Minister Plenipotentiary was Lord Macartney, a native of County Antrim, who had a distinguished diplomatic career. He was a man of integrity and tact, unkindly described as one of the 'bog-gentry of northern Ireland'. His secretary and 'Minister Plenipotentiary in the absence of the Embassador' was another Irishman, Sir George Staunton, from Cargin in County Galway. Sir George's eleven-year-old son, Master George Thomas Staunton, was also among the ambassador's retinue, nominally as his page. This remarkable boy learned Chinese during the ten-month voyage, and was the only member of the party able to converse with the emperor.

Lord Macartney's embassy was a grand affair. There were almost 100 officials, with a military escort, a band, and numerous attendants. It left Portsmouth on 26 September 1792 in the warship, H. M. S. *Lion*, and the East-Indiaman *Hindostan*, accompanied by a tender. The voyage took the embassy to the Canary Islands, Rio de Janeiro, south of the Cape of Good Hope and across the Indian Ocean to Java. Eventually on 16 August 1793 the party disembarked at Tong-chow-ju for the final, short, overland journey to Beijing. One of the problems which exercised Lord Macartney's tact was the ceremony of kow-tow, the nine prostrations before the emperor, performed even in his absence before anything 'emblematical of his Chinese majesty'. The embassy refused to do this, unless Chinese officials of equal rank performed the same ceremony in front of a portrait of King George. In the end, the emperor agreed to accept the same homage as that which the embassy would perform before their own sovereign. The audience took place in the garden of the emperor's summer palace at Jehol.

> The emperor's approach was notified soon after daylight, by instruments of music. His Imperial Majesty was preceded by persons loudly proclaiming his virtues and his power. He was borne by sixteen men in a triumphal car, followed by his guards, officers of the household, standard and umbrella bearers, and a band of music.[8]

Lord Macartney, with his page, interpreter and secretary, was given a place of honour on the left-hand side of the throne.

> His Excellency appeared in a suit of velvet richly embroidered, decorated with a diamond badge and star, the Order of the Bath, and over this, a long mantle of the same order. The minister plenipotentiary [Sir George Staunton] being an honorary doctor of laws, of the university of Oxford, was habited in the scarlet gown of that degree.[9]

9. *Macleaya cordata*

The ambassador knelt on one knee before the emperor, as agreed, and presented him with a jewelled casket containing King George's message. Master Staunton was then presented to the emperor; they spoke together in Chinese and the emperor was 'so charmed with the converse and the elegant manner of this accomplished young gentleman, that he took from his girdle his areca-nut purse ... and presented it to him with his own hand'.

The embassy was politely dismissed several days later without achieving its full purpose, and on 7 October the whole party left Beijing to rejoin the ships at Guangzhou (Canton). Most of the long journey was made by the great canals of eastern China. Sir George Staunton remarked that 'the gentlemen of the Embassy were not, as before, restrained from little excursions', and they were able to venture onto dry land to observe local agricultural techniques and to collect plants.

Lord Macartney and his company reached Guangzhou in mid-December and remained there for a short time before moving to Macao. They sailed for England on 17 March 1794 and reached Portsmouth safely six months later.

The results of the embassy may not have been totally pleasing from a diplomatic viewpoint, but the two gardeners who accompanied the party, and Sir George Staunton himself - he was a trained physician - succeeded in assembling several hundred dried plant specimens and they also gathered seeds of perhaps a dozen plants. Some of the seeds were presented by Staunton to the Royal Gardens at Kew and among the seedlings raised was a lovely, late summer-blooming, white rose which today is known as Macartney's rose, *Rosa bracteata*. It is slightly tender and is rather rare in Irish gardens.

Another of Staunton's plants is the plume poppy, **Macleaya cordata** (Figure 9).[10] The King's gardener, William Aiton, attributed its collection to John Haxton, but stated that it was introduced by Staunton - Haxton was engaged personally by Sir George as a gardener and botanist. The plume poppy is one of the finest herbaceous perennials in our gardens. It grows up to two metres tall and its stems are furnished with large, heart-shaped leaves that are elegantly sculpted into sinuous lobes. They are soft, grey-green in colour and compliment the tall plumes of pale buff flowers that rise above the foliage in August and September. The flowers are not like those of ordinary field poppies - there are no showy petals, just a fluffy cluster of numerous stamens and small, creamy white sepals. But each flower spike is composed of numerous individual blossoms, and the effect is of a great feather. The plume poppy will flourish in a sunny place in good soil, either as a clump by itself, or within the scheme of an herbaceous border. But the true *Macleaya cordata* is a rather rare plant; its flower buds are cream, quite fat, and enclose at least 25 stamens. The very commonly grown, rampageous plume poppy is either a selected form of *Macleaya microcarpa* which has smaller flowers with no more than twelve stamens, or the hybrid between these species, *Macleaya x kewensis*, although they may be labelled *Macleaya cordata*. Sir George Staunton's plume poppy is altogether a more desirable garden plant as it does not tend to be so invasive.

A MUSICAL LILY

Let us return to lilies. Edward Madden also collected them. He sent bulbs from the Himalaya to Belfast and Glasnevin botanic gardens, including *Lilium wallichianum*, which arrived in Dublin on 10 April 1850 and flowered a few months later. Although he sent bulbs of Wallich's lily, of his greatest gift to our gardens, the giant lily, **Cardiocrinum giganteum**,[11] he only managed to export seeds. These arrived in Dublin in 1848 and took two long years to germinate. David Moore liberally distributed seeds and seedlings. In 1851, the giant lily flowered for the first time in these islands at Lamorran Rectory near Truro in Cornwall, and in 1852 bloomed at Glasnevin.

The scientific name of this lily, *Cardiocrinum*, alludes to the gigantic heart-shaped leaves that form a rosette out of which the huge spike of flowers rises like an obelisk. The leaves are bright, glossy green. In early summer the lily is a superb foliage plant, especially when planted in the dappled light of a tree-shaded border - the spots of sunlight glint off the shining leaves. By July the giant lily is at its prime. Augustine Henry saw it in China: 'in open glades it may be spied miles away across the valley with its gorgeous turrets of flowers'. The flower spike is stout and soars to three or four metres, carrying white trumpets that perfume the whole garden. The blossoms are like those of the white Madonna lily, but much longer; the outside of each flower is suffused with purple, while they are purest white inside. This princely lily is monocarpic - once it has flowered the plant dies, but it perpetuates itself by forming offsets around the base of the spent bulb and it produces copious quantities of seeds.

Dr Nathaniel Wallich discovered the giant lily in 1825, but Edward Madden was the first person to succeed in sending seeds to Europe so that the plants could be grown in gardens. In its native country, *Cardiocrinum* inhabits damp forest glades at altitudes between 2,500 and 3,000 metres. In winter the bulbs lie dormant under a covering of snow, so it is very hardy. In the wild, the lily grows in rich, black, peaty loam, and in our gardens requires the same sort of conditions. It benefits greatly from a liberal top-dressing of compost in the spring, or as Alexander Wallace succinctly put it - 'Giganteum literally revels in muck'.

I may exhaust superlatives and metaphors in writing about this plant, but it is unequalled. One can dream that its white flowers grace the meadows of that celestial paradise, where its flowery trumpets are sounded by an angelic choir. And that idyllic vision is not pure fantasy, for Edward Madden recorded that the hollow stems of the exhausted lily were made into musical pipes in Kumaon!

There is a rather painful story about Madden's lily which should be retold. This plant was very precious in the early years after its introduction, and it was greatly prized in Glasnevin where the bulbs were carefully nurtured in a specially prepared border behind the glasshouse. One year, when Frederick and his brother David were lads, they made some toy swords out of plant stakes, and attacked the great lily as it bloomed. The lily lost! The boys' father, David senior, was furious. Many years later, after he retired as Keeper of the Botanic Gardens, Sir Frederick Moore recalled that while 'we did not break our swords upon the lilies ... later our swords were broken on us, and my brother and I had good cause to remember' Major Madden's gift.

THE MATILIJA

From ancient times, lilies have been symbols of purity, their white flowers signifying a chaste existence. Poppies in this century have come to symbolize death and destruction followed by a renewal - the scarlet petals of the wild poppies that flowered on the battle-fields of Flanders are memorials for fallen soldiers. But poppies are not always blood-red, and in our gardens when the white trumpets of the giant lily wither, the white flowers of the matilija, the Californian tree poppy, open.

The botanical name for this perennial poppy, **Romneya coulteri**,[12] was coined by William Harvey of Trinity College, Dublin, in honour of two friends. The second (specific) name, *coulteri*, commemorates his predecessor as curator of the College's herbarium, the botanical explorer Dr Thomas Coulter. The first (generic) name, *Romneya*, was a tribute to an eminent astronomer, the Reverend Dr Thomas Romney Robinson. Harvey was unable to use *Coulteria* as the generic name because it had already been suggested for a tropical member of the pea family, nor could he christen the poppy *Robinsonia* as that had been devised by the Genevese botanist, Augustin-Pyramus de Candolle, for a plant from Juan Fernandez Island, the legendary exile of Robinson Crusoe.

Thomas Coulter discovered the matilija while he was in California in 1832. He left Monterey in March and travelled along the road that linked the missions, passing through San Luis Obispo where the big-cone pine grew, and on to San Gabriel which is now consumed in the suburban sprawl of Los Angeles. From San Gabriel he went south-eastward towards the Colorado River. The trek took Thomas and his companions through the flat and desolate Colorado Desert, where they found neither water nor fodder for the cattle they were driving.

It is not known where or when Coulter found the poppy. In a letter that he wrote to his friend Alphonse de Candolle from his camp on the banks of the great red river, Coulter said that 'This is truly the Kingdom of Desolation.. here is nothing - nothing'. However, he noted that he had gathered some interesting plants before reaching the desert, including lupins, poppies and some strange crucifers. The matilija was probably one of the poppies, as it grows in the area south of Los Angeles.

Dr Coulter did not describe any of his Californian or Mexican plants, but he left the dried specimens sorted and labelled. Harvey discovered the poppy in the vast pile that Coulter left. Although William Harvey named *Romneya coulteri* in 1844, it was not introduced into gardens until the early 1870s, and it flowered for the first time in Ireland at Glasnevin in the late summer of 1877.

The matilija is not totally hardy; its stems are cut back to the base in winter, but it has a persistent rootstock from which it sprouts each spring. In mild areas it does not die down in winter, and flowers in early summer, rather than in August. The stems and leaves are grey-green. The smooth, beaked buds burst open to release the delicate petals like crumpled silk. The saucers of pure white are formed by five overlapping, heart-shaped petals, and in the centre is a boss of stamens with maroon filaments and golden anthers that quiver in the wind like a globe of molten gold. The delicate perfume has been likened to the fragrance of old hock!

One could hardly hope to be immortalized by a more graceful flower. William Robinson described it as 'the fairest ... that ever came to our land from that country of flowers, California'.

A TEXAN ANNUAL

While Thomas Coulter was making his parched way to the Colorado River, Thomas Drummond was in the eastern part of North America, beginning his last journey in search of plants for our gardens. I have mentioned him as one of the Scotsmen who took charge of Irish botanic gardens in the 1820s. For about two and a half years, until the end of 1830, Drummond was curator of the fledgling botanic garden on the banks of the River Lagan in Belfast. He had taken this post during the summer of 1828, not long after returning from his first expedition, under Sir John Franklin, to the eastern side of the Rocky Mountains and to Hudson Bay. Thomas Drummond was probably a restless soul, unhappy at being confined to one garden. He was also prone to argue with his superiors and had a 'fatal propensity for strong drink' and so was dismissed from his post in Belfast, but he did not forget the Botanic Garden and later sent seeds from North America to Belfast.

In April 1831, having promised not to 'take fermented Liquors for a year', Drummond arrived in New York from Scotland. He was sponsored by several private garden owners and by Glasgow and Edinburgh botanic gardens. Dr William Hooker, who was Professor of Botany in the University of Glasgow at the time, was his chief patron and the person to whom Drummond sent seeds for distribution to other gardens.

Drummond worked in the eastern states, especially around New Orleans in Louisiana until 1833, when he moved west to Texas. The life of a plant collector in the early 1800s was not easy and the next few years demonstrated this with great clarity. There was chaos in Texas; serious floods, political unrest and an epidemic of cholera made life difficult. Thomas Drummond caught cholera, but he dosed himself with opium and survived. He almost starved to death because the party he was with was so weakened by the disease that they could not obtain food. Nevertheless, Drummond made a small collection of plants and animals, and eventually settled at Galveston Bay for the winter. Again, he nearly starved. 1834 was no kinder. He reached San Felipe in April, too late to join a party of surveyors that was heading into the interior. Luck was on his side this time, for those men were massacred by Indians. He

10. *Phlox drummondii*

became ill again with bilious fever, diarrhoea and boils during the autumn, but recovered and moved to Florida. In February 1835 en route by sea from Apalachicola to Key West, Florida, sometime between 9 February and 11 March 1835, he died in unexplained circumstances in Havana, Cuba.

Despite the hardships he endured, this dauntless Scot collected and introduced a number of fine plants, some of which bear his name - on his first expedition to the Rockies he gathered, for example, a mountain avens with yellow flowers and it is named *Dryas drummondii*. A Texan annual species of *Phlox* was also named after him in the hope that 'it would be a frequent memorial of its unfortunate discoverer'.

Although my hardy flower border should contain perennial herbs, I think this lovely annual, **Phlox drummondii** (Figure 10),[13] deserves a place in every garden. It is so easy to grow from seed sown in the spring. The seedlings are planted outside in early summer and they bloom for weeks on end, through July and August. Any packet of seed will yield a rainbow of phlox; there are pink and scarlet flowers, blue, purple, white, orange, plain and striped. Drummond's phlox grows about 20 centimetres tall, and is ideal for the front of a border. The leaves clasp the stems, and are hairy, greyish-green. The flowers are like those of the perennial phlox, with five petal lobes forming a flat ruff at the end of the long floral tube. In bud the petals are coiled into an inverted cone.

Phlox drummondii can also be sown in late summer and the plants kept in a cold greenhouse during the winter; they will bloom in March. Favourite forms may be perpetuated by taking cuttings in late summer, but abundant variety is a characteristic of this little phlox and this is encouraged only by raising it from seeds.

Thomas Drummond sent seeds of the phlox to Hooker who passed a sample to Belfast Botanic Garden. It flowered in Belfast in the summer of 1835, but it is only one of many new American plants that were raised in Ireland in the early 1800s.

CAPTAIN COTTINGHAM'S *ABUTILON*

Private gardeners occasionally had the pleasure of being the first to flower novelties. One gentleman who did this was Captain Edward Cottingham, who lived at Bellfield in Drumcondra, one of Dublin's northern suburbs, a short distance from Glasnevin. He was a justice of the peace, a magistrate and a keen gardener. In the 1840s Cottingham served on the council of the Royal Horticultural Society of Ireland. No description of his garden survives, but in 1835 he presented some greenhouse plants to the Glasnevin Botanic Gardens, so he had broad interests and grew tender as well as hardy plants.

Cottingham had a contact in Chile, who sent seeds to Dublin. In 1836, Edward Cottingham raised a fine, large-flowered tree mallow, **Abutilon vitifolium**.[14] He planted it out-of-doors and it soon flowered. In 1840, James Mackay sent a specimen of Cottingham's *Abutilon* to London and a small plant of it was donated to the Royal Horticultural Society's garden at Chiswick.

Abutilon vitifolium is hardy, but may be cut back by severe frost. It grows rapidly and can form a substantial shrub in a few years. Because its branches are soft-wooded and because it becomes lanky, this plant is best treated as a large herbaceous perennial. As its name suggests the leaves are vine-like, with a large central lobe and two smaller side lobes. Well-grown plants bloom profusely throughout the summer. The flowers can be porcelain blue with a tinge of purple or pure white, and they resemble those of a single hollyhock. The five petals form a shallow cone-shaped cup, about six centimetres broad, that envelops the central column of stamens and branched style.

Captain Cottingham's original plant had white flowers 'with a slight tinge of blush'. It greatly impressed Irish gardeners and the Royal Horticultural Society of Ireland awarded him a gold medal for his introduction.

PAMPAS GRASS

In the 1830s, John Tweedie collected seeds and herbarium specimens on the eastern side of South America, in the Argentine, for Dr William Hooker who was the focal point of botanical and horticultural circles in the British Isles at that period. Tweedie was Scottish and had worked in Edinburgh Botanic Garden at the beginning of the century. He emigrated to Argentina in 1825 'under contract to be gardener to the Scotch colony of Monte Grande'.

He took up plant hunting as a means of gaining some extra income, although his family shop supported him, his wife and their six children. Tweedie also worked as a landscape gardener, and laid out the garden of Santa Catalina in Buenos Aires.

John Tweedie corresponded with Hooker and also with Ninian Niven, curator of the Glasnevin Botanic Gardens from 1834 until 1838. Niven may have known Tweedie in Scotland before he left for the Argentine. Tweedie was also friendly with the Earl of Arran, who served as a diplomat in South America and whose daughter lived near Glasnevin. Lord Arran sometimes received seeds from John Tweedie and these were passed to Glasnevin Gardens.

Niven and his successor, David Moore, obtained many packets of seeds from Tweedie, as well as boxes of orchids and cacti. From a collection of seed gathered on the Argentinean pampas, Moore raised a fine, tall grass. Seedlings were put outdoors and survived. Three summers later, in 1842, the grass flowered to the delight of David Moore. He distributed plants to other botanic gardens, and the pampas grass became a familiar sight in gardens.

Some may despise the pampas grass, ***Cortaderia selloana***,[15] because it is now so common, but it is a useful, 'architectural' plant for herbaceous borders. The long, thin leaves arch gracefully, like a cascading fountain, providing an unusual texture for gardeners with an eye for form. The pampas grass is usually planted as an isolated specimen in the middle of a lawn, but I prefer to see it in the border among other plants. It does have one serious drawback - the leaves have edges as sharp as a surgeon's scalpel and can lacerate one's arms and hands. The beautiful cream or pink fluffy plumes and the green fountain of leaves are ample compensation for a few drops of blood.

At first John Tweedie was not impressed by the ubiquitous grass - 'tho interesting to some, I don't much mind it', he wrote. At that time, 1835, he was on one of his treks across 'those vast plains ... where nothing but grasses were to be met with'. Yet, in 1838, when he sent seeds to David Moore, he described the pampas grass as

> the most showy plant of any class in this country, the flower stem six to twelve feet high, with large spikes of twelve to eighteen inches appearing like white sheets hung on poles and seen at a distance of many miles in our flat plains ... [16]

The pampas grass has another Irish connection. The French botanist Charles Lemaire recognized that it represented a new genus and suggested the name *Moorea* for it. This was Lemaire's tribute to David Moore. Alas, other botanists did not adopt that name and it languished in obscurity until an orchid was named *Moorea* after Frederick Moore. By that time the pampas grass had acquired its present name, *Cortaderia selloana*, and to avoid confusion both applications of *Moorea* were rejected. The orchid was renamed *Neomoorea* and the pampas grass retained *Cortaderia*. Such are the fickle fortunes of botany.

William Hooker paid tribute to John Tweedie by naming a genus after him - of it more will be said later. 'And some there be, which have no memorial', certainly not a plant named after them.

MERV'S ONION

Edmond O'Donovan[17] was an ardent supporter of the Fenians and a newspaper correspondent - indeed he was a famous war correspondent and there is a memorial, a brass plaque, to him and six other war correspondents in St Paul's Cathedral, London. His botanical memorial is a sumptuous onion once described as 'an expensive monster' - it does not bear his name but the species was described from bulbs he brought to England from Merv.

Where is Merv? I looked in my atlas to find out if Merv was marked on any of the maps and was amused to find this entry - 'Merv - see Mary'. I found that Mary, otherwise Merv, is situated in the desert where the Murgab River disintegrates into streams that vanish into nothing. This is the 'back of beyond' in the deep south of Turkmenistan, in what used to be called Soviet Central Asia, about half way between the southern tip of the Caspian Sea and the western edge of the Hindu Kush. Merv is on an ancient caravan route linking the Persian city of Mashhad (Meshad) and Buchara (Bohkara) in modern Uzbekistan. Nowadays a railway line links Merv with the Caspian port of Krasnovodsk to the west, and with Buchara and Samarkand to the east. The Iranian border is about 150 kilometres away, and the frontier with Afghanistan perhaps 250 kilometres; Teheran lies to the west and Kabul to south-east. In other words, Merv is not the kind of place that nineteenth century tourists were likely to visit unless they have been besotted by Edward Fitzgerald's 'The golden journey to Samarkand' -

> For lust of knowing what should not be known,
> We take the Golden Road to Samarkand.

- and utterly lost their way. How then did Edmond O'Donovan find his way there and, moreover, bring back an onion?

In the crazy world of nineteenth century international relations, Merv was not such an unknown place. Edmond O'Donovan went there as a war correspondent, and his subsequent book, *The Merv oasis. Travels and adventures east of the Caspian ...*, was voted Book of the Year 1882. The Russians, having just beaten the Turks in a short war during 1879, turned their attentions eastward to subdue the Turkmens, and O'Donovan went to report on this minor Asian skirmish for the *Daily news.*

Edmond O'Donovan was the third[18] son of the famous Irish topographer, John O'Donovan whose brilliant Ordnance Survey letters penned in the middle of the last century provide such a wealth of detail about Ireland and Irish antiquities. Edmond was to become his father's equal as a correspondent. He was educated 'under the ferula of the Jesuits' in Belvedere College, Dublin, before proceeding to the Museum of Irish Industry, Dublin, where he won a prize in natural philosophy. Although a Roman Catholic, Edmond O'Donovan went on to Trinity College, Dublin, but he never graduated. Instead he became embroiled in the Fenian movement, and with his special interest in rifles and military engineering, he travelled about Ireland teaching men to use rifles. Three times he was arrested and was released from prison only after the intervention of Sir Thomas Aiskew Larcom. When the Fenian rising of 1867 was aborted, O'Donovan fled to Paris because 'it was now more convenient [for him] to live out of British territory than within.' One the Irish colony in Paris, J. Augustine O'Brien Shea, summed up Edmond at this period:

> A gay but purposeful stripling he was well read, quick of perception and brimming with vitality ... He could sketch, shoot, lecture, botanize, quote Milton, handle conic sections, sleep on a table and was master of minor accomplishments too numerous for my memory to retain ... The study of Arabic was Edmond's passion ...[19]

He was, like his brothers, an 'adventurous young [man], full of vitality and high spirits', and his quest for adventure led him to travel far and wide. In 1870 Edmond enlisted in the Légion étrangère, fought briefly in the Franco-German War but was wounded and captured. While interned in Bavaria, he sent despatches to newspapers in Dublin and London. O'Donovan reported from the Basque province on the Carlist uprising in Spain during 1873, and in 1876 he went as correspondent for the *Daily news* to the Balkans when Bosnia and Herzegovina rebelled against the Turkish rulers. Following that assignment he was applauded as an excellent war correspondent, and was asked by Sir John Robinson to represent the *Daily news* in Afghanistan. Thus began O'Donovan long trek to Merv.

Edmond with his native servants travelled from the Caspian Sea through Persia before crossing the 'wild Turcoman desert' and reaching the oasis of Merv on 2 March 1881. O'Donovan was compelled to remain in Merv until the end of July, initially because he was suspected of being a Russian spy; he was held 'as a kind of political hostage'. By dint of his own efforts, diplomacy and courage, he eventually convinced the Turkmens that he was a newspaper correspondent, and then he managed to extricate himself from Merv, and flee back across the Persian frontier. When Edmond returned to London, he addressed the Royal Geographical Society and wrote his celebrated book, *The Merv oasis*.

What about the onion? On 4 August 1881, en route for Mashhad and six days after leaving Merv, O'Donovan and his companions halted beside a stream in the foothills beyond Chaacha. A caravan from Mashhad approached bringing telegraphic bulletins for O'Donovan from Teheran. Having recorded the event in his book, Edmond went on to describe the abundant wild flowers about their halting place. There was among these a 'peculiar' onion, the flower stalk of which, he noted, grew to a height of four feet - the Turkmen called the onion *deli guzella*. He collected some of the huge bulbs and brought them to England. Indeed he seems to have collected seeds and plants elsewhere on this escapade, because early in 1882 he presented 'a large quantity of bulbs and seeds from Merv' to Frank Miles, the popular society artist and friend of Lily Langtry and Oscar Wilde. The Merv onion bloomed in Miles' garden during 1884 and was illustrated one year later in *Curtis's botanical magazine*.

By the time the onion blossomed in England, Edmond O'Donovan was probably dead. He had gone to Sudan, again as a correspondent, and there perished during November 1883 when the Egyptian army commanded by Colonel Hicks Pasha was annihilated in an ambush at El Obeid. O'Donovan's treacherous orderly, Gustav Klootz, who had deserted, searched the battlefield and found Edmond O'Donovan's dispatch case with scattered pieces of blood-stained notes. O'Donovan Pasha has no known grave, but every year the violet, cricket-ball flower heads of the Merv onion serve as a reminder of this adventurous, indeed reckless Dubliner who was hailed in Merv as the 'beneficent Sahib of the excellent British Government, the spreader abroad of the Christian religion'.

This perennial herb grows happily in Irish gardens, and blossoms in July. It forms a large bulb and the striking flower head rising out of the earth without any leaves being apparent. The foliage is a grey-green rosette of sword-shaped leaves that begin to emerge in late winter; usually the foliage is entirely withered when the flowering stem erupts. ***Allium giganteum,***[20] to give the Merv onion its botanical name, is a silent memorial to Edmond O'Donovan, war correspondent and botanical collector.

BABINGTON'S LEEK

My last herbaceous plant, for the present, is another member of the onion tribe, and it has a very ancient history. Botanists have suggested that it was cultivated in western Ireland long centuries ago as a pot-herb, and that it was brought here by prehistoric gardeners from southern Europe. Today this wild leek, ***Allium babingtonii,***[21] grows wild in the coastal areas from Clare to Donegal and on the Aran Islands; it is also found in Cornwall. Babington's leek was discovered by William Thompson and Robert Ball on the Aran Islands about 1834. It was named after the English botanist, Charles Cardale Babington, who occasionally visited Ireland - we will cross his path again.

I am including *Allium babingtonii* for a couple of reasons. I have grown it myself and although it is not a pretty plant, it is handsome and easy to cultivate. In deep gravel it sulks, growing no more than about thirty centimetres tall - it does not flower nor increase. But in heavy clay it thrives and has leaves a metre long. It looks like a slender leek but has large honey-coloured bulbs. The leaves are a soft, greyish-green, and have serrated margins. The few flowers that it deigns to produce are pallid purple. The round flower-head appears in July on a long stalk that can be two metres tall in good conditions. About half of the flowers in each head are replaced by bulbils which will fall off and root - unless you want a forest of Babington's leek, it is best to remove the heads before they mature!

E. A. Bowles cultivated this leek in his rock garden, and admired its grey leaves. In one of his delightful books he said that 'I love to see it towering up there against the sky behind the Orange tree and the large Asparagus ... its glaucous leaves and stems contrasting so well with their deep green tones'.

Babington's leek might not be to everyone's taste, but it intrigues me, as it has intrigued other botanists. Professor William Stearn, who has studied the European onions and leeks (*Allium* species), concluded that *Allium babingtonii* is a form of the widespread species *Allium ampeloprasum*, and that the Irish plant is 'probably a relict of former introduction from the Mediterranean as a pungent seasoning plant'. Possibly it came from Iberia and survives in the remote west because of its prolific, flavoursome bulbils which in the Aran Islands were used as garlic. Like the crocuses on the lawn at Kilmacurragh, it has outlived its original cultivators, and will undoubtedly outlive us.

The crocus and leek remind me of the last words of Charlotte Grace O'Brien, whose family created Dromoland on the Fergus estuary in County Clare.

I will puzzle botanists of another generation, and when my bones are dust and my good spade rust, when my house is pulled down and my garden asphalt and bricks, my extra special wild briars and my daffodils will still linger on the hillside and scent the bloomy air for generations that know me not, nor mine.[22]

VII
A heather garden

Calluna vulgaris 'Clare Carpet' & 'County Wicklow'
Erica mackaiana 'Plena' - *Erica* x *stuartii* 'Irish Lemon'
Erica x *stuartii* 'Stuartii' - *Erica erigena* 'Irish Dusk'
Erica carnea 'Eileen Porter' - *Erica cinerea* 'Glasnevin Red'
Erica cinerea 'Colligan' Bridge' & 'Joseph Murphy'
Daboecia cantabrica 'Praegerae' - *Daboecia cantabrica* 'Charles Nelson'
Cassiope fastigiata - *Gaultheria myrsinoides*

> **Summer brings low the little stream**
> **The swift herd makes for the water,**
> **The long hair of the heather spreads out,**
> **The weak white cotton grass flourishes ...**
> **Flowers cover the world.**

Anonymous (c. 900 A.D.): 'Maytime'

The people of bygone ages were not as simple-minded as we like to think. Today scientists laboriously accumulate reams of data to prove what country folk learnt by experience over centuries. Irish farmers learned over generations to assess the fertility of land by observing the plants that grew naturally on it. In Kerry the formula used was *an t-or fe'n aiteann, an t-airgead fe'n luachair agus an gorta fe'n bhfraoch* - gold under the furze, silver under rushes and famine under heather.

Heathers generally grow on the poorest land whose soil will not raise crops. They inhabit the gentle, peat-covered slopes of the mountains and the deep quaking bogs of the west. Fraoch or ling is one of the most abundant wild plants, covering vast expanses of countryside, from the very edge of the ocean to the summits of the high hills. It is the flower of ling that paints the mountains purple in late summer.

At this point I should declare an interest. For more than 25 years, since my student days, heathers have fascinated me. At home in Fermanagh, I studied the strange colony of the white Cornish heath, *Erica vagans*, that grows on a remote hillside overlooking Lough MacNean, hundreds of kilometres from its Cornish home.[1] I spent a summer sampling and mapping the little colony, and out of that work has developed a passion for these plants. If I seem over-enthusiastic, I can only plead that every gardener surely has his or her favourite flowers.

Heathers are among the easiest plants to grow, although some are quite difficult. Many people think that heathers are dull and that they can grow only in acid or peaty soil. On the contrary, heathers are endlessly variable and there are many cultivars which are happy in a garden with limy soil. A garden planted with nothing but heathers is colourful throughout the year.

For my imagined heather garden, I have also chosen plants that belong to genera other than *Erica* - the true heathers. The common ling, sometimes called Scottish heather, is the only species in the genus *Calluna*. Saint Dabeoc's heath from Connemara has a generic name mutated from that of the saint - *Daboecia*. A heather garden can contain other genera of the heather family (Ericaceae), and to whet your appetites, I have included two exotic plants, a *Cassiope* from the Himalaya, and a *Gaultheria*, formerly named *Pernettya*, from the high Andes.

LOUGH DAN'S LING

Any watchful person walking on the moorlands and hills in late summer will see that the ling, *Calluna vulgaris*, is not uniform in habit or flower colour. The blossom varies from rich mauve to pure white - white-flowered ling seems to abound in coastal areas and is regarded by the superstitious as a lucky plant. Most heathers are bushy with upright branches, but I collected cuttings from ling growing on the coast of County Clare which have produced plants that show no sign of growing upwards. In my Celbridge garden and at Glasnevin the bushes remained low, hugging the ground and tumbling over rocks and peat blocks. One of these heathers has beautiful soft foliage that is bright emerald-green in summer. It has wispy shoots of pale pink blossoms and I have named it *Calluna vulgaris* **'Clare Carpet'**.[2]

The leaves of ling are tiny and tightly appressed to the wiry stem, like the leaves of a cypress. The individual flower is composed of two whorls of separate segments. The outermost segments called sepals are the largest; in most flowering plants the sepals are small and green but in *Calluna* they are brightly coloured. Inside this calyx is the whorl of four petals which are smaller but the same bright colour.

Occasionally a heather plant arises that deviates from the fixed pattern of its fellows. Such a mutant was collected before 1933 near Lough Dan which nestles on the eastern slopes of the Wicklow Mountains not far from Roundwood and a short distance over the hills from Glendalough. Its flowers are made up of many more than eight sepals and petals. Such multi-petalled forms are usually called double-flowered heathers. The Lough Dan plant was noted by Miss Meta Archer who collected cuttings for propagation. She gave material to various nurseries, including the famous heather nursery of Maxwell & Beale in Dorset, England. The plant was increased and about 1933 introduced to gardeners as *Calluna vulgaris* **'County**

Wicklow'.[3] Miss Archer wanted the heather named 'Meta Archer', but this did not happen.

'County Wicklow' is a fine plant in late summer, laden with large, puffy blossoms of pink which almost entirely obscure the foliage. The flowers last for many weeks. Indeed, sprigs of this heather picked on a cool morning and placed in the freezer will remain fresh for months and can be taken out for use in bouquets and vases.

WILLIAM McCALLA'S HEATHER

The traditional image of heather is a plant with small needle-like leaves and purple bell-shaped flowers, and this is the general form of species of *Erica*. The sepals are small, green and quite inconspicuous. The four petals are joined to form a flower that is like a small urn. The flower-bell betrays its composition by four minute recurved lobes at its mouth. Inside there are eight stamens and the stigma, style and ovary.

There is only one species of *Erica* known to have double flowers like those of *Calluna* 'County Wicklow'. This is Mackay's heath, *Erica mackaiana*,[4] which was discovered simultaneously in Ireland and Spain in 1835, and even today has not been found in any other region. The cultivated double-flowered one, ***Erica mackaiana* 'Plena',**[5] was collected in August 1901 near Roundstone in Connemara by Dr F. C. Crawford. At first it was thought to be a new species and was named *Erica crawfordii*, but later it was realized that it was an aberrant form of Mackay's heath. In 'Plena' the stamens are replaced by numerous petal-like segments that fill the very plump little bells - some flowers are so fat they burst along the petal seams. This is another marvellous garden plant, producing vast numbers of bright pink, barrel-shaped flowers, which are usually white beneath where the petals are shaded from the sun. Many people have trudged over the bogs near Roundstone trying to rediscover this plant without success, but in 1969 Dermot Burke gathered a few small plants of Mackay's heather from the side of the road, and when they flowered in 1970 he noticed that one was double-flowered just like Crawford's plant.

Erica mackaiana is a singularly inappropriate name for this heather. The species was so named as a compliment to James Mackay of Trinity College Botanic Garden in Dublin, but he did not discover it, although he had visited the area several times. It was first noticed by William McCalla, a keen, 21 years old, amateur naturalist, whose father, a retired Scottish soldier, ran the inn in Roundstone. William noticed that this heather differed from the cross-leaved heath, *Erica tetralix*, which is abundant throughout Ireland. In September 1835, when Charles Babington - of the leek - visited Galway and called on McCalla, the two botanists walked across the bogs and looked at the heather. Babington confirmed McCalla's opinion, and later described and named the new heather.

William McCalla was employed in 1836 as an assistant botanist in the Irish Ordnance Survey, working under David Moore. He passed some of Moore's data to other naturalists -

Babington and William Thompson were the alleged recipients - and was promptly dismissed. Then he was engaged by several Dublin professors, mainly Dr John Scouler of the Royal Dublin Society, to collect specimens of plants and animals. Scouler made elaborate plans to send McCalla to New Zealand as a plant collector, but McCalla procrastinated and Scouler abandoned the scheme, saying that William McCalla was a coward. McCalla returned to Connemara and taught in a local school. He contracted cholera in 1849 and died on 2 May aged 35. His grave, marked by an inscribed slab of limestone, stands at the foot of Errisbeg Mountain, a lonely monument to a young naturalist whom Scouler described as 'this wild man I have caught in Connemara'.

DR STUART'S HEATHER

One of the peculiarities of the heather that William McCalla found is that it does not appear to reproduce sexually in Ireland; it does not set seed. In Spain, seedlings are abundant. Contrariwise, in Spain *Erica mackaiana* does not hybridize with the cross-leaved heath, while in Ireland plants of hybrid origin are abundant throughout the areas of Connemara, Mayo and Donegal where *Erica mackaiana* and *Erica tetralix* grow.

The hybrids arise when the flowers of the cross-leaved heath are pollinated by pollen from Mackay's heath. The progeny of this mixed marriage was known as *Erica* x *praegeri*, after the Irish naturalist Dr Robert Lloyd Praeger. A change in the rules governing plant names, and confirmation of the parentage of a most peculiar heather, mean that the hybrid must be called *Erica* x *stuartii*.

Stuart's hybrid can be spotted on the moorlands in early summer by the brightly coloured young shoots. In June on the shores of Lough Nacung in Donegal, I have seen plants with bright yellow or orange tips. By August the vast majority of such plants look like ordinary heathers - plain green. David McClintock was the first to point out this characteristic of hybrid heathers, and the lovely coloured shoots of these plants are now exploited by heather growers to extend the enjoyment of heather gardens. Varieties are available with pink, bronze, orange or yellow summer foliage.

In 1966 David McClintock visited Lough Nacung and collected cuttings of various heathers. When the young plants began to show their form and colour, one was noticed with lemon-yellow shoots. David selected this plant for further propagation, and it is now widely available as ***Erica* x *stuartii* 'Irish Lemon'**. The bright colour does not fade until mid-summer and the contrast between the lime-green foliage and lavender flowers is startling. There is a sister cultivar, called 'Irish Orange', which has some red on the yellow tips giving it an orange hue. David McLaughlin of Omagh has recently added 'Irish Rose' to this gathering of colourful heaths from Lough Nacung's shores - the long, new growths are pink.

Erica x *stuartii* received its name in recognition of the discovery by Dr Charles Stuart of a remarkable variety of the hybrid. When visiting Connemara in 1890 he found one heather with small, tube-shaped flowers that are beetroot-red. The stamens protrude from the mouth of the bell. At first it was thought to be a hybrid between the cross-leaved heath and the Irish heath, *Erica erigena*, but in 1977 a sport was noticed that had flowers showing all the characteristics of the plant called *Erica* x *praegeri*. Thus the identity of Stuart's plant was revealed and the older name *Erica* x *stuartii* had to be adopted for all the plants of the hybrid.

Dr Stuart's strange little heather was propagated and is widely cultivated. The two-coloured flowers are most attractive. Its full name is the unwieldy ***Erica* x *stuartii* 'Stuartii'**.[6]

Both these heathers, *Erica mackaiana* and *Erica* x *stuartii*, are more variable than is generally realised. A number of good forms are already in cultivation, and others may become available in years to come. Cuttings root very easily so plants can be increased rapidly.

IRISH DUSK

Mackay's heath belongs to a group of plants that grow in Ireland, south-western France and the Iberian Peninsula but do not occur in Britain. Another heather with this type of distribution is the Irish heath, *Erica erigena* (Figure 11).[7] This has also had a number of names; it was called *Erica mediterranea* and then *Erica hibernica*, and these names are still used by some gardeners and nurserymen.

The Irish heath grows in counties Galway and Mayo, from Errisbeg northwards to the Mullet Peninsula. It flowers in late winter and early spring, when very few other native plants are in bloom. It brightens the hill sides and moorlands in March and April and is one of the great botanical treasures of Ireland. But its claim to being a true native has now been thrown into great doubt. Dr Peter Foss extracted pollen grains of heathers from peat deposits in the areas where *Erica erigena* is so abundant and demonstrated that this heather invaded western Ireland around five centuries ago - its pollen is entirely absent from older peat. The most plausible explanation for this extraordinary discovery is that the Irish heath was accidentally introduced, probably from the Iberian Peninsula, as packing around wine casks.

The best places to see the Irish heath are on the shores of Bellacragher Bay at Mallaranny and the western shore of Lough Carrowmore near Bangor Erris. At Mallaranny it covers many hectares of the hillside from the sea shore to about 200 metres above sea level. The lanky bushes can be two metres tall, and bear small mauve bells with the fragrance of honey. On the shore of Lough Carrowmore, the shrubs are not so tall as they are grazed by cattle, but they flower more profusely. Looking north along the lake margin, there is a band of heather covered in pale flowers in March, with an occasional golden furze among the bushes.

Long ago the swishy branches of Irish heath were used as makeshift sprayers; after being dipped into Bordeaux mixture they were ideal for applying the fungicide to potato crops. The

11. *Erica erigena*

Irish heath will form a tall shrub - the record is held by a plant in David McClintock's garden in Kent. The branches and twigs are brittle and apt to break in heavy snow, but this should not deter Irish gardeners especially as this heather will grow in soil that contains lime. Indeed in the wild it grows in very wet bogs, at the edges of streams and even on lake margins with its roots in the water - why not try it in the water garden?

This heather was collected in Ireland for the first time during 1700 by a Welsh antiquarian, Edward Llwyd, but his find was never published. In 1830 James Mackay rediscovered the species on Errisbeg near Roundstone. The colour of the flowers in the wild populations is remarkably uniform, so that any unusual colour forms are gleefully exploited by heather maniacs like myself. That doyen of heather students, David McClintock, has found and introduced a number of superb heathers, including two cultivars of the Irish heath. In 1966 on the shore of Lough Carrowmore, he spotted two shrubs with salmon-pink flowers instead of the usual mauve-pink ones. David gathered cuttings and both of these plants spawned fine cultivars. Arguably the best is *Erica erigena* **'Irish Dusk'**.[8] It has dark green leaves which set off the clear pink flowers.

White-flowered plants are extremely rare; the first report was in 1852 when David Moore found a white plant in the barony of Erris in County Mayo. After a long hunt, in company with my brother and David Small, two plants were found on the shore of Lough Furnace in March 1983. Undoubtedly the best white-flowered cultivar is 'Brian Proudley', named after an English heather nurseryman. It is an erect, shapely shrub that produces long flowering shoots covered with masses of white bells. The original plant grew in the garden of the late James Walker Porter at Carryduff. John Letts and Valerie Proudley obtained cuttings from this plant in 1968. It was introduced and named by Bert Jones.

PORTER'S HEATHERS

Both J. W. Porter and his wife Eileen made important contributions to heather gardening even though they were both amateur enthusiasts. Walker Porter was born at Ballymacarret, County Down, on Christmas Eve 1889. He studied chemistry at the Royal College of Science in Dublin, and worked as an industrial chemist in the explosives factory at Arklow during the First World War. In 1920, Porter returned to Belfast and began growing heathers as a hobby. He worked for a few years with the Ulster Linen Company and then became a lecturer in the Faculty of Applied Science in The Queen's University, Belfast. He retired as senior lecturer in 1955.

James Walker Porter and Eileen Gee were married on 21 December 1927. On Saint Patrick's Day in the following year, they were walking on Collin Mountain which overlooks Belfast, when they spotted a coloured shoot on a partly burnt bush of ling. Mr Porter collected a cutting and raised his first new heather, a form of *Calluna vulgaris* with terracotta-red foliage which he named 'Saint Patrick' - alas it is not known to have survived in cultivation.

Porter had a great interest in raising plants from seeds, and many of the shrubs that he grew in his own garden had been propagated in this manner. In 1934, he harvested seeds from the winter-flowering heather, *Erica carnea* 'Rubra Praecox' and sowed them. One of the seedlings began to flower in October 1936 and continued blooming for eight months until May 1937. Porter showed the new heather to an English nurseryman who bought a layer for the huge sum of ten pounds. Maxwell & Beale introduced it to commerce, and the cultivar was named after Mrs Porter.

Erica carnea '**Eileen Porter**'[9] is a marvellous garden plant; the Royal Horticultural Society granted the cultivar an award of merit in 1956. It is one of the lime-tolerant heathers, and for the whole of the winter and spring it is covered in bright mauve bells. The little flowers are clasped by cream sepals, and the dark-brown anthers protrude from the flowers. However, 'Eileen Porter' is an enigmatic plant because it does not usually produce pollen, and it may be a hybrid between *Erica carnea* and *Erica erigena*.

Those two species are almost identical. They both bloom in the winter and differ mainly in their growth habit; the former is a prostrate shrub unlike the erect Irish heath. Walker Porter raised several good hybrids between these species, an achievement which few other heather enthusiasts have equalled. One of his hybrids is named *Erica* x *darleyensis* 'J. W. Porter', and two other cultivars bear the names of his sisters, 'Jenny Porter' and 'Margaret Porter'. Jenny has pink and cream tips to the shoots in spring, and Margaret is covered with lovely deep lilac flowers, while their brother has red spring foliage. They are hardy and lime-tolerant.

Most of J. W. Porter's heather seedlings were given to friends, although he kept the best himself. Sadly the majority of the cultivars he named are no longer grown, but as long as 'Eileen Porter' is cultivated, this Irish couple will be remembered.

All gardeners dream of producing a superb new plant, a unique garden variety. Mr Porter dreamt of a double-flowered, white variety of *Erica terminalis*. He did not succeed, but when he died in 1963, his legacy was a collection of five wonderful winter-flowering heathers.

Mrs Porter continued to take an interest in heathers after her husband died. In 1969, while on holiday near Killybegs in County Donegal, she collected two dwarf heathers in the wild. One was *Calluna vulgaris* 'Anne Dobbin', a dumpy ling that is smothered with flowers in summer. The other was a very compact form of the bell heather which is named *Erica cinerea* 'Little Anne', again after her grand-daughter, Anne Dobbin.

BELL HEATHERS

Mrs Porter's dwarf cultivar of *Erica cinerea* is only one of many that have been gathered in Ireland and later introduced into the trade. Most of the wild-collected plants have the typical purple flowers of the species. But, as with other heathers, the bell heather blooms exhibit a range of colours and shades, variations of purple with different proportions of red or blue. The quest for a hardy, pure red heather has been going on for years, although it has not been pursued with the vigour of, for example, blue roses, black tulips, yellow sweet peas or red delphiniums. There are many scarlet and red blossomed species in the high mountains of South Africa but none is hardy in northern latitudes. One of the best hardy, red heathers was raised by chance at the National Botanic Gardens in Glasnevin, and is a cultivar of the bell heather, *Erica cinerea*.

Erica cinerea '**Glasnevin Red**'[10] was found as a seedling, growing among some plants of another cultivar, 'C. D. Eason', in the 1950s. Its small, urn-shaped flowers are dark cherry-red, and it grows into a compact plant with dark green foliage. It is not a robust variety and is susceptible to frost but it did well in trials of heathers at the Royal Horticultural Society's garden at Wisley and received a horticultural certificate in 1967. In 1968 when exhibited at one of the Society's London shows, 'Glasnevin Red' received an award of merit.

THE PURPLE HEATHERS

While 'Glasnevin Red' was a seedling found in a garden, several cultivars of the bell heather have been selected from plants seen in the wild. One of the finest is *Erica cinerea* '**Colligan Bridge**'[11] with long, elegant spikes of bright purple flowers. It grows strongly, and may reach 30 centimetres in height when in flower. The original plant was growing at Colligan Bridge in the Mourne Mountains, and was noticed in 1936 by Brian Mulligan, a native of County Down, who was then working in the Wisley garden. He collected cuttings from the plant and this cultivar was introduced some years later.

Another splendid purple-blossomed bell heather is *Erica cinerea* '**Joseph Murphy**'.[12] This hails from Bray Head, County Wicklow. The flowers are striking, having a florescent quality that makes them stand out much more than usual. The habit is compact. Joseph Murphy collected his bell heather in 1972, during one of his rare holidays in his native land - on the same occasion he also gathered the spring-coloured ling, *Calluna vulgaris* 'Bray Head'. Joe emigrated to England in the 1940s to find work in the Nottinghamshire coal mines. He worked as a miner until it affected his health and then, during the 1960s, he took up a new career as a jobbing gardener. He joined the staff of Tabramhill Gardens and when, as Geoffrey Yates put it,

> Joe was 'converted' from his strong belief that the only way to grow a plant was to use the same methods as the farmer in his home town used to grow his turnips and potatoes, he became the finest potting machine ever invented, potting-up at least 1000 plants every day, in addition to 4000 cuttings per day in the season. When the Javo potting-machine salesman telephoned twice a year on his UK selling tours, he never could understand that Tabramhill Gardens had the best potting machine you could ever wish for, and he had never heard of the Joseph Murphy make. ... The fact was that Joe rarely, if ever, broke down; he never needed servicing, and he ran on a 'fuel' of black tea, bread and butter, and cigarettes.[13]

Joe worked in Tabramhill Gardens for more than ten years, and is now retired. He is a very modest man, one of an army of unsung jobbing gardeners who day after day, decade after decade, make substantial contributions to our enjoyment of gardening by potting and propagating plants. Without loyal workers like Joe, we would all be the poorer. The remarkable thing is that Joseph Murphy, one-time miner, having spotted a couple of handsome wild heathers on a Irish headland, had the good sense to bring home some cuttings.

There are other heathers culled from Irish moors and many make attractive garden plants, but my purpose is not to list them all. Anyone who wishes to make a collection for their own garden can do it easily, using only heathers found growing in the wild. Cuttings root easily, dipped in a peat and sand mixture and popped into a plastic bag. In a few summer weeks roots will form and in a couple of years the plants will be flowering well. Never remove a heather plant from the wild - it will look scruffy and will surely die. A few cuttings taken do no harm, and the wild plant remains to flower for others.

SAINT AED'S HEATHER

My list of heathers with Irish associations amounts to about 40 cultivars and species, and the biggest, brightest and best of the native heaths belongs to a genus that got its name from a little-known saint.

Saint Dabeoc's heath, *Daboecia cantabrica*, is a superb plant, one of the botanical glories of the west of Ireland. It can be found in Galway and southern Mayo, and is especially abundant in Connemara. The flowers on glandular stalks hang from long, curved stems. The leaves are dark glossy green above, and silvery-white underneath. The blossoms are shaped like upturned urns, and are about one centimetre long, the largest flowers of any of our native heaths. The blossoms are generally vivid mauve, but the colour ranges from deep royal purple to pure white - white-flowered *Daboecia* is occasionally found in the wild and has been cultivated since the 1830s. A beautiful ruby form was found in Connemara by Mrs Lloyd Praeger in 1938. Cuttings were given to the National Botanic Gardens in September 1938, and subsequently "Praeger's Variety" was distributed from Glasnevin to nurserymen during 1941. Desmond Shaw-Smith of the Ballawley Park Nursery in Dublin seems to have been the first to list *Daboecia cantabrica* **'Praegerae'**[14] in his catalogue for 1946. I think that a mixed bed of various colour forms of *Daboecia* is the best way to grow this heather.

The presence of Saint Dabeoc's heath in Ireland was first brought to the attention of botanists by Edward Llwyd, the same traveller who found the Irish heath, during 1700. He described it as having flowers like a hare-bell (*Campanula rotundifolia*), and noted that in the west of Ireland it was called *Frych Dabeog*, that is *fraoch Dabeog*, or heather of Dabeoc. James Petiver published an illustration of it in 1703 and it was noted in John Ray's *Historia plantarum* of 1704 as *Erica S. Dabeoci Hibernis*. Carl Linnaeus, the great Swedish botanist who formulated our present system of Latin plant names, gave it the name *Erica daboecii*, thereby, accidentally in my opinion, mutating the name of the saint. This error was perpetuated in *Daboecia* - it should be *Dabeocia*.

Who was Saint Dabeoc? The name Dabeoc, pronounced dav-ock, is the diminutive of another name beginning with the adjective beo meaning lively. The name is probably Aed; beo-Aed becomes Beooc or Beoc. There are several Dabeocs or Aeds in Irish martyrologies, but the best known is Dabeoc of Lough Derg in County Donegal. This is the person favoured by Dr Praeger as the patron of the heather. However, Dr Kathleen Mulchrone pointed out that another Beo-Aed was bishop of Ard Carna in County Roscommon and was renowned for his hospitality.

Dabeoc of Lough Derg was the son of a Welsh chieftain. He lived towards the end of the fifth century when he founded a monastery on Saint's Island which is the traditional site of Saint Patrick's vision of the Otherworld, his Purgatory. Lough Derg was a great place of pilgrimage in mediaeval times and remains today one of the major pilgrimage centres in Ireland, a retreat for penitential devotions.

To return to the heather, Llwyd recorded that in Connacht the young maidens carried around sprigs of it 'as a preservative against incontinency' - *mulericulæ superstitiosæ surculos ejus secum circumferunt adversus incontinentiam*. Over the years the meaning of incontinent has altered subtly, and to understand this phrase we have to return to its original meaning - to be incontinent was to be lacking in self-restraint especially in sexual matters. Thus when Dr James Edward Smith commented that 'Ray tells us... that the Irish girls gird themselves with its long trailing branches as a protection to their chastity [but] with what success he unluckily has omitted to inform us', he realized that there was a credibility gap.

A DOUBLE NELSON

At this point you must forgive an impertinence. There is a unique variety of *Daboecia cantabrica*, now commonly available from heather nurseries, that parallels *Calluna vulgaris* 'County Wicklow' and *Erica mackaiana* 'Plena' in having double flowers. I found it near Carna in 1978. A single plant with dumpy, bloated blossoms was growing - and still grows - by the side of a rough track leading towards the small colony of *Erica mackaiana*. The peculiar shape of the flowers attracted my attention and I examined them closely. Inside, instead of eight stamens and a style, there were numerous petal-like segments. When I dissected a flower, I found about eight concentric whorls of these petals and a mass of green filaments in the middle where the ovary should have been.

In 1980 when visiting Connemara with David and Anne McClintock and Major Walter Magor, I showed them the plant, and we decided to take some cuttings. These rooted and plants are now established in gardens in Ireland and England. We have since discovered that the plant is even more peculiar. The first flowers which open in late May are often perfect with eight stamens and no extra petals. However, the flowers of the second flush are invariably double.

David McClintock and Major-General Pat Turpin, then chairman of the Heather Society, suggested that this new monstrosity should be christened 'Charles Nelson'. I put up some half-hearted arguments against that name, and lost! ***Daboecia cantabrica* 'Charles Nelson'** (Plate 8)[15] has pale purple flowers, which remain on the stalks after withering and turning pale brown - some people do not think these dead flowers are attractive but they can always be removed.

Incidentally, the earliest record of Saint Dabeoc's heath in cultivation dates from 1764. Peter Collinson, a Quaker businessman and keen botanist, received seeds from Spain through the good offices of William Bowles, a native of Cork who lived most of his life in Spain and wrote a natural history of that kingdom. The seeds germinated in 1764 and Saint Dabeoc's heath flowered the following year in Collinson's garden at Mill Hill near Hendon in Middlesex.

MADDEN'S *CASSIOPE*

The three genera already described are only a small fraction of the heath family, which also includes such plants as the strawberry tree (*Arbutus*), rhododendrons and bilberries (*Vaccinium*). Some of the genera are huge - *Rhododendron* contains perhaps 900 species. There are over 730 species of *Erica*,[16] but only about 20 of these occur in Europe; the rest are found in South Africa.

Cassiope is a small genus of a dozen species, from the mountains of Europe, Asia and North America. They are often regarded as difficult subjects for Irish gardens, but once established in a congenial place they will thrive in our climate. In one Dublin garden that I knew very well during the 1980s, several varieties grew in a raised bed against a north-facing wall. Despite the limestone of the wall and the sunless situation, the plants were vigorous and flowered well. Several hybrids have been raised in gardens and are available from nurseries; these bloom more prolifically than the species and are relatively easy to cultivate in acid, peaty soil.

One of the Himalayan species, ***Cassiope fastigiata***,[17] was raised at Glasnevin from seeds supplied by Edward Madden, who found it growing near Almorah and around Simla. In 1845 he described seeing the *Cassiope* near the Changsheel Pass in 'an alpine glade [that was] a perfect carpet of flowers of all forms and colours: the Botanic Garden of Asia'. Seedlings raised from Madden's seed flowered at Glasnevin in 1854, and were used in the preparation of an illustration for *Curtis's botanical magazine.*

Madden's *Cassiope* grows to about 20 centimetres tall. The four-sided branchlets are erect, so the plant has a fastigiate habit like a miniature Irish yew. The leaves are closely appressed to the stems, giving the four-cornered effect; they are minute with a fringe of silky hairs. In late spring the delicate white flowers, like tiny electric lights covered in white glass shades, hang from the shoots on slender stalks; they are about half a centimetre long and have five recurved lobes.

8. *Daboecia cantabrica* 'Charles Nelson'

FROM THE HIGH ANDES

Many garden plants have come from the Himalaya - rhododendrons, gentians, poppies and countless others. The massive range of the Andes in South America has not provided as many, although the potato, which is a native Andean plant, has been the single most important plant to reach Irish gardens. The heath family is represented in the Andes by a few genera, including *Gaultheria* which has a wide distribution being found in eastern Asia and north America, as well as on islands that encircle Antarctica, including the Falkland Islands, New Zealand and Tasmania.

For excellent reasons *Gaultheria* and *Pernettya* were recently united into a single genus; there are no constant characters that can be used to distinguish species of *Gaultheria* from species of *Pernettya*, so the artificial division was abandoned. Unfortunately this means learning new names, and the names of all plants formerly placed in *Pernettya* have had to be altered. In some cases, *Pernettya* only has been amended to *Gaultheria*, but in a few instances, as we will see, both Latin names have changed.

Gaultheria mucronata, formerly named *Pernettya mucronata*, from southern Chile and Argentina is the most familiar species of the redundant genus *Pernettya*. It is an evergreen shrub, reaching about one and a half metres tall, with white, heather-like flowers and large coloured berries because of which it was widely planted in Irish demesnes as a source of food for pheasants. *Gaultheria mucronata* is now naturalized in a few places. There were some selected forms with especially good berries marketed by Irish nurseries, in particular *Pernettya mucronata* 'Bell's Seedling' (to return to its familiar name), but I do not believe the true plant is still available. However, the plant with Irish connections that I have chosen is the species of *Gaultheria*, originally named *Pernettya pentlandii* by the Swiss botanist Augustin-Pyramus de Candolle after Joseph Barclay Pentland.

Pernettya pentlandii (Figure 12)[18] is now placed within **Gaultheria myrsinoides**, a very variable and widespread species, and Pentland's plant is considered to represent just one of many variants within the almost continuous spectrum of variation in the species. Therefore, sadly, his name is no longer used as a botanical epithet. As known to Irish gardeners the plant formerly named after him forms a compact shrub that is evergreen and hardy. The branches tend to spread horizontally so that the shrub rarely exceeds 30 centimetres in height. The leaves are oval with small marginal teeth which are bristle-tipped when young. The flowers are suspended on short, green stalks and look like tiny, translucent, white pearls. When the blossoms wither, the flattened, globose fruits develop; each berry is about one centimetre in diameter and they range in colour from blue-black through lavender and pink to pure white.

Pentland's *Gaultheria* is an easy shrub to grow; like *Cassiope* it requires lime-free soil and the roots should be kept cool and shaded. It can be cultivated in a raised bed or trough.

12. *Pernettya pentlandii,* now *Gaultheria myrsinoides*

Pentland was born in Ballybofey, County Donegal, in 1797, but he was orphaned when a young child and was cared for by relatives. Joseph was sent to school in Armagh and when his schooldays ended he went to the University of Paris. He studied natural sciences and about 1818 began to work with the famous French scientist, Georges Cuvier, professor of anatomy and an eminent scholar in zoology and geology. Pentland acquired a considerable reputation as a palaeontologist and published several papers on fossil animals.

In 1826 Joseph Pentland travelled to South America with Woodbine Parish. Their expedition worked in the Bolivian Andes, where Pentland made numerous observations, paying particular attention to the position of the snow-line on various peaks. He visited Lake Titicaca and mapped its outlet accurately. After returning to England, he was appointed secretary to the British Consul-General in Peru, and went back to South America for a few months.

During the early 1830s, Pentland worked in Paris, but in 1836, Lord Palmerston appointed him Consul-General in Bolivia. He lived in La Paz for almost three years, during which time he collected and dried specimens of the local flora, including his *Pernettya*. Pentland completed his survey of Lake Titicaca and had time to visit some of the famous archaeological sites, including Cuzco.

Joseph Barclay Pentland is not known to have returned to Ireland after leaving to go to university, nor to have sent seeds to any of our botanic gardens. He did send bulbs to England, of which more later. He is a minor figure in horticulture, although several plants were named for him, but he is remembered as an expert on fossils and as an authority on Rome. He lived in the Eternal City for many years after retiring from consular duties, and wrote a series of tourist guides about Italy. Some of his letters survive, but nothing remains in Ballybofey to remind us of this Irish plant collector.

VIII
'The red-rose bordered hem of her' An Irish Rosary

Rosa x *hibernica* - *Rosa bracteata* - *Rosa hugonis*
'Daisy Hill' - 'Handel' - 'Irish Elegance' - 'Souvenir de St Anne's'

Red rose, proud rose, sad rose of all my days
Come near me, while I sing the ancient ways.

William Butler Yeats: 'To the rose upon the rood of time'

Roses and Ireland are inseparable.[1] William Butler Yeats wrote of Ireland's 'red-rose bordered hem', yet centuries earlier, during the reign of Queen Elizabeth I, the little black rose, *roisin dubh*, 'My dark Rosaleen', was the prevailing metaphor for the old Ireland, repressed and blood-stained after the Cromwellian and Elizabethan wars. It is not unlikely, as happened much later with the shamrock, that this impossible and dark floral symbol was the counterpart of the Tudor rose, the red and the white rose of England.

O! The Erne shall run red
With redundance of blood,
The earth shall rock beneath our tread,
And flames wrap hill and wood,
And gun-peal, and slogan cry,
Wake many a glen serene.
Ere you shall fade, ere you shall die,
My Dark Rosaleen!
My own Rosaleen!
The Judgement Hour must first be nigh,
Ere you can fade, ere you can die,

My Dark Rosaleen![2]

In the context of Irish roses, there are no verses about roses as well-known as those of Thomas Moore's love-song.

'Tis the last rose of summer left blooming alone;
All her lovely companions are faded and gone;
No flower of her kindred, no rose-bud is nigh,
To reflect back her blushes, or give sigh for sigh.[3]

Let me digress slightly. The inspiration for the ballad was a rose which Moore saw in the garden of Jenkinstown House near Kilkenny. One version of the story is that Moore was taking part in a festival of amateur dramatics which was held annually during October at the old theatre in Kilkenny. He was staying at Jenkinstown House, and in the garden noticed a Blush China rose still in bloom. This was about 1810. The original rose bush and the garden had vanished by 1950, but Lady Elaine Bellew had propagated this memorable rose, and gave cuttings of the 'Last rose of summer' to various people. A scion from Lady Bellew was presented to the National Botanic Gardens, Glasnevin, in April 1950 by The Thomas Moore Society, and its progeny is still cultivated. Thomas Moore's rose was the China rose called 'Old Blush'.

However the romance of the rose was not an Irish invention - it was an imported conceit. Our earliest native poets in Early Christian times celebrated wild nature, not artificial gardens; their verses include the names of many plants - yew, hazel, ferns, blackberries, sloes and rowan - but there is hardly ever a mention of roses. Not until the romantic rose infiltrated from the east did Irish poets absorb the ineluctable imagery of these plants.

From Classical times, roses figured in love poetry. Verse-translations by the Belfast-born scholar and poet, Helen Waddell, of mediaeval Latin lyrics describe how Ausonius left Rome and retired to Bordeaux to cultivate his garden wherein at daybreak he pondered life.

Tell me now, did dawn come first, or roses?
Or did the Cyprian stain them from one shell?...[4]

... Think you, did Dawn steal colour from the roses
Or was it new born day that stained the rose.
To each one dew, one crimson, and one morning
To star and rose, their Lady Venus one.
Mayhap one fragrance, but the sweet of dawn
Drifts through the sky, and closer breathes the rose.[5]

Thomas Moore also turned his hand to translating the poetry of ancient Greece. Anacreon lived six centuries before the Christian era, and sang the praises of love and women, wine and roses.

Oh! whence could such a plant have sprung?
Attend - for thus the tale is sung.
When, humid, from the silvery stream,
Effusing beauty's warmest beam,
Venus appeared, in flashing hues,
Mellowed by ocean's briny dews:
When, in the starry courts above,
The pregnant brain of mighty Jove
Disclosed the nymph of azure glance,
The nymph who shakes the martial lance:
Then, then, in strange eventful hour,
The earth produced an infant flower,
Which sprung, with blushing tinctures drest,
And wantoned o'er its parent's breast.
The gods beheld this brilliant birth
And hailed the Rose, the boon of earth![6]

The works of Ireland's poets alive in the nineteenth and twentieth centuries contain more allusions to roses and love, to sacrifice and passion. John Boyle O'Reilly (1844-1890), a prominent Fenian who was transported to 20 years' penal servitude in Australia and eventually settled in the United States, wrote these verses.

The red rose whispers of passion
And the white rose breathes of love;
O the red rose is a falcon
And the white rose is a dove.

But I send you a cream-white rosebud,
With a flush on its petal tips;
For the love that is purest and sweetest
Has a kiss of desire on its lips.

THE NATIVE IRISH ROSES

Fourteen species of rose are listed as native in Ireland, and there is a suite of complicated, obscure hybrids including the only rose deserving the title Irish Rose, *Rosa x hibernica*. Roses fill hedgerows and occur in habitats as diverse as sand dunes, woodlands, and limestone pavements - the burnet rose, *Rosa pimpinellifolia*, is one of the great joys of the bleak rockscape of The Burren, County Clare, in western Ireland where it blossoms in shades of white and creams and pinks.[7]

Our native roses have small, ephemeral flowers, so roses were not at first valued for their beauty. They had mundane uses although none that is recorded from Ireland is unique to the island as far as I am aware. Wild and, later, cultivated roses have been for centuries sources of medicines; indeed the name dog rose, *Rosa canina*, merely is a translation of the original Greek name *cynorrodon*, the rose of the dog, which was bestowed because, according to legend, a soldier bitten by a dog cured himself of hydrophobia (rabies) with its root. Dr Caleb Threlkeld, in his Irish flora, recommended the sweet briar; 'the pulp of the hips has a pleasant tartness, strengthens the stomach, cools the heat of fevers, good for coughs, spitting of blood and scurvy.' According to him the hips of the burnet rose have the 'vertues of the other wild roses'. He also suggested that a conserve made from the fruit of the common wild rose was 'a good vehicle for other medicaments.' The Quaker naturalist, Dr John Rutty, in the late eighteenth century, noted that the fruits of burnet rose could be squashed and the juice, diluted with water, yielded a dye that gave a peach colour to muslin and silk, or deep violet when alum was employed as a mordant, but the hip juice would not dye linen or wool.

EARLY GARDEN ROSES

The small number of native roses has been augmented by uncounted exotic rose species, hybrids and cultivars, imported by gardeners. We do not know when the first exotic roses were cultivated in Ireland but we can make some informed guesses. Religious orders from Europe arrived in Ireland to establish monasteries during the late twelfth century, and it is most probable that the monks brought the skills of cultivation and propagation required to perpetuate selected roses, and they probably brought some roses too.[8] The monastery gardens were the earliest well-organized gardens in Ireland, and the first flower gardens. By the close of the thirteenth century, physic gardens, set aside for the cultivation of medicinal herbs, must have existed in the grounds of well-established monasteries such as Mellifont; monastic communities usually had a physician who tended a garden of herbs, including roses. Moreover, by this era, a few beautiful flowers which had acquired roles as symbols of faith were grown for decorating churches on great festivals, especially those of the Virgin Mary; popular flowers included lilies and roses, the latter particularly signifying a paragon -

> *... et Rosa, purpureo vestita rubore decenter*
> *vernans est horti gloria, lateus honos.*

> The rose, fitly clad in blushing purple,
> the glory and glad honour of the
> garden when in bloom.[9]

By the close of the sixteenth century roses were common garden plants. The deeds of the University of Dublin, the College of the Holy and Undivided Trinity founded in 1592, contain references to the cultivation of sweet-smelling plants - roses and lavender are singled out. Harry Holland leased a garden from the college and had to 'set and plant [it] with some herbs'; in part payment of the rent, Holland was obliged to give the College half of 'all the herbs that grow, lavender, roses, fruit of the trees.' An early map of the college shows knot-gardens, perhaps with bowers of roses, so Holland seems to have performed his obligations well.

By the mid-1600s roses were being imported into Ireland and grafted here in quantity. At that period the only rose cultivars available were short-season plants that blossomed once during summer, although by judicious pruning gardeners might manage to get bushes to produce a second, lesser flush of flowers in autumn. An exchange of letter between England and Ireland gives accounts of some of these techniques. 'An honorable person' wrote to Samuel Hartlib in April 1654:

> Upon the way from Youghal to Dublin I had an occasion to oblige an ingenious Gentleman, who hath been a great traveller in the Eastern Countrys of the world and came some years since to settle himselfe in Ireland where he had made himself eminent for Husbandry, in which I hope to be much improved ... One curiosity he hath practised which may not be altogether unworthy your notice, and that is a way to have roses twice a year which he performed by pruning off divers of the branches upon which the roses grow as soone as ever they are gathered and then the same places will shoot forth fresh branches and roses too about autumn.[10]

Hartlib must have told Benjamin Worsley, an army physician, about this, for Worsley wrote to Hartlib on 28 June 1654:

> Beside what you speeke of Roses bearing twice a year, there is a species of Roses call'd the Monthly Rose that beares all the year ... I have had 2 or 3 very good experiments communicated to me about the Husbandry of Roses which I shall communicate to you as I find the success of them.[11]

True to his word Worsley later wrote - with remarkable prescience - that roses were the plants 'I the soonest of any expect advantage from in this country where they are as yet scarce enough' - he himself had imported thousands of young sets.

Roses remained in favour through the eighteenth century, but few garden records listing plants have survived for the period. One interesting set of plans for a garden in the northern part of Ireland prepared during 1763 by the English poet and landscape gardener, Joseph Spence, recommended to Dean Paul, that the

> ... ground should be planted with studs of roses, honeysuckles, & Jessamines &c. - hear a Damask-rose with 2 Jessamine there, A Province, with a couple of white Meserions: a Cabbage rose, with 2 Dutch honeysuckles, in a third part, & a Moss-Rose, alone, in a fourth: & so on, with as much variety as can be.
>
> This Variety might be greatly helped by planting one of the forenam'd red Roses (Damask, Provence, Cabbage, or Moss) with a white rose, in one studd; two whites with a red, in another: & two reds with a white in a third - The same alternatives might be

practis'd with the Munday-Rose; & with the Yellow rose, if you can get ones ...[12]

These roses at the Glebe House near Cootehill in County Cavan were to be surrounded by lawns of wild flowers and, beyond, shrubberies of rowans, strawberry trees, larch and wild cherries.

When the Dublin Society's Botanic Gardens at Glasnevin opened in 1800, roses were on display in profusion; the 1804 catalogue listed 80 different species, cultivars and hybrids including the recently discovered Irish rose, *Rosa* x *hibernica*, and at least one newly introduced Chinese rose, Macartney's rose, *Rosa bracteata*.

A botanic garden was formed in Cork during 1809. Evidently the curator, James Drummond, was a keen cultivator of roses and sent several to the Horticultural Society's garden in London. Two of Drummond's roses were formally described and named - *Rosa dicksonii*, named after James Dickson, a London nurseryman and one of the founders of the Horticultural Society, and *Rosa alpina* 'Speciosa' which was known as Drummond's thornless rose. The histories of the Cork plants are obscure but *Rosa dicksonii* was reputed to have reached Cork through the Botanic Gardens at Glasnevin, and that it had been received there from James Lee of Hammersmith in London.

THE IRISH ROSE

In 1828 Ireland's fourth botanic garden was established in Belfast and, by chance, its first curator was James Drummond's younger brother, Thomas. The Belfast Botanic Gardens owed its origin to the enthusiasm of a group of men whose mentor had been John Templeton, the celebrated naturalist and gardener. Templeton lived at Cranmore, previously called Orange Grove, in Malone, a suburb of Belfast, where he grew many tender plants without the aid of a greenhouse, native wild plants and a collection of roses. His special joy was a rose that he had discovered growing near Holywood in County Down, about ten kilometres north-east of Belfast. This hedgerow shrub was similar to the common dog rose, with single, blushing cream flowers and greyish-green leaves. However, the hips were different (Plate 9).

John Templeton found the rose about 1795. He noticed that the pear-shaped hips were crowned by the persistent sepals and were very dark red, not at all like the scarlet hips of the dog rose, nor the black ones of the burnet rose. He raised young plants from cuttings and in 1797 sent the new rose to two London nurserymen, James Dickson (after whom *Rosa dicksonii* was named) and William Curtis. Five years later the Dublin Society awarded Templeton a prize worth five Irish guineas for his discovery and the rose was presented to the Botanic Gardens at Glasnevin. A description, illustrated with a wood engraving based on a drawing by John himself, was published in the Society's journal, and the rose was named *Rosa hibernica*, the Irish rose.

9. Rosa x *hibernica*

According to the vicar of Holywood in 1819, the Reverend W. Holmes, Templeton's rose formed a 'beautiful bed ... to near an acre in extent, beneath the road to Richmond Lodge'. However, a new road and railway were driven through the site later in the century and the rose was decimated. By the beginning of this century it only survived in one hedge. Progress demanded a wider roadway, and in the early 1960s the last bush was threatened, but it was rescued by Robert Johnston and moved to a small experimental garden belonging to the Department of Botany in The Queen's University, Belfast - a few years ago the same plant was rescued again, and now is in Belfast Botanic Gardens Park.

The Irish rose, *Rosa* x *hibernica* (Plate 9),[13] was cultivated by some keen plantsmen earlier this century, although it is extremely rare today. For many decades it grew in Glasnevin Botanic Gardens, and Lady Moore, wife of Sir Frederick Moore, brought it from Glasnevin to her garden at Willbrook in Rathfarnham, County Dublin. She knew the rose well, and described it growing in 1921 at Rostrevor, County Down, in the garden of Sir John Ross-of-Bladensburg. 'Among these flaunting foreigners', she wrote referring to many exotic roses, 'there is a greatly treasured modest little plant, *Rosa hibernica*'. She also treasured modesty, and it was from Willbrook that Graham Stuart Thomas got his plant of John Templeton's prize-winning rose.

Rosa x *hibernica* is believed to be a hybrid, the offspring of a common dog rose and the spiny burnet rose. It looks more like a dog-rose. One highly valuable, but evidently variable, characteristic of the hybrid is its prolonged flowering season. John Templeton took pains to record this. In 1808, for example, it was in blossom on 15 June although he noted that none of the other native roses was in flower at Cranmore. In 1809, *Rosa* x *hibernica* flowered from 31 May until 13 November. My own experience was different - for five years in my garden at Celbridge, *Rosa* x *hibernica* blossomed only once a season, in the early summer. Indeed, prolonged flowering is no longer mentioned when the Irish rose is discussed by rose experts.

I hope this modest plant will continue to attract some present-day gardeners, for it is extinct in the wild and can now survive only in cultivation. Alas, nurserymen who list the Irish rose usually supply plants which bear no relationship to Templeton's rose, but the last wild plant in Belfast has been propagated so *Rosa* x *hibernica* - in its original form - has a fair chance of surviving as a garden plant.

In August 1986, Catherine and Paul Hackney found a rose near Glenarm, County Antrim, that is similar to Templeton's rose; whereas most of the hips which it produces are like those of *Rosa* x *hibernica*, the Glenarm rose has hairy styles and pink flowers. They have propagated and named it *Rosa* 'Straidkilly'.[14]

ROSES FROM IRISH DIPLOMATIC COLLECTORS

Apart from growing roses and breeding new cultivars, a topic I will return to, a major contribution that Irish men and women have made to roses in cultivation was through their work as botanical collectors overseas.

I have already told the story of the grand affair of Lord Macartney's diplomatic mission to China between 1792 and 1794 to the court of Emperor Qianlong on behalf of King George III. The embassy was a diplomatic fiasco, but the horticultural results were exciting. Macartney and Staunton returned from China with seeds of, among other plants, the plume poppy and perhaps more than one new rose. The handsome *Rosa bracteata* was for a short period popularly known as Staunton's rose but soon the name changed to Macartney's rose - one wonder's why? Staunton and Macartney probably also introduced to England the rose called 'Parson's Pink China' which may be identical with 'Old Blush'.

Macartney's rose, **Rosa bracteata**,[15] is a marvellous shrub although, as I have said, rather rare in Irish gardens. In the wild this is a scrambling shrub, and that is the way I prefer to grow it rather than trained up pillars or against walls, as is usually done. In mild areas Macartney's rose remains evergreen, but the leaves are easily killed by frost and will fall off; indeed very severe frosts may kill this rose. The foliage is bright glossy green. The shoots are thin, clothed in white, woolly hairs, and armed with vicious, skin-catching, hooked thorns. *Rosa bracteata* blooms in late summer - a useful characteristic, although early frosts will curtail flowering. The flowers are pure white, with five, heart-shaped petals that emerge from a tight, hair-encrusted bud, to form a bowl-shaped blossom. In the centre is a boss of lemon-yellow stamens. The perfume is lemony too.

A century after Lord Macartney's unsuccessful embassy, Augustine Henry was living in central China and he spent his spare time plant-hunting in the hills about Yichang on the River Yangtze. As already related, Dr Henry discovered many new genera and species, including a white-blossomed scrambling rose that now bears his name, *Rosa henryi*. Seedlings of this rose were recently raised in the National Botanic Gardens and distributed to several gardens. Henry's most significant contribution was perhaps the discovery of the wild form of *Rosa chinensis*, believed to be one of the parents of the long-blooming series of roses, indeed of modern roses. Likewise he found the single, five-petalled form of the Banksian rose, *Rosa banksiae* var. *spontanea*, in the wild.

FATHER HUGH'S YELLOW ROSE

Another Irish collector in China was John Aloysius Scallan, who was born in Rathmines, Dublin, on 6 September 1851. On entering the Franciscan Order, he was given the religious name Hugh. Early in 1886, Father Hugh left England where he had been teaching, and began life as a Franciscan missionary in China. Little is known about his years in remote parts of China but his obituary did hint at tribulations and dangers; 'once he was almost stoned to death by pagans, once imprisoned, and frequently he was robbed'. Pater Hugo, as he is named in botanical literature, died aged 76 at Tung-yuan-fang in Shensi Province. In 1896 the Keeper of Botany at the Natural History Museum in London received a packet of pressed specimens and seeds from China. The only information about the origin of the plants in this package was contained in a letter, written in Latin, from an Italian missionary, Father Giuseppe Giraldi who had been asked by Father Scallan to forward them to London. The plants had been collected, according to Giraldi, in the mountains of Shangxian province. The seeds were sent to Kew where those from a rose germinated. One seedling, at least, flourished and still grows in the Royal Botanic Gardens, Kew. The rose is vigorous and may attain four metres in height, and strangely will blossom most profusely when planted in a poor soil. The foliage is fern-like and delicate, and the flowers are a clear yellow, like large buttercups. Father Scallan's 'very beautiful yellow wild rose, tall and free' blossoms in May and appropriately was named after him, *Rosa hugonis*.[16]

LADY WHEELER CUFFE'S MYSTERIOUS BURMESE ROSE

Like Dr Henry and Father Scallan, Charlotte Wheeler Cuffe occupied her spare time, when living in Burma, by collecting plants. On several occasions she travelled into remote areas of the country with her husband, and on these treks she collected rhododendrons, orchids and many other plants and, most valuably, she also painted the flowers that she observed. In May 1918 Sir Otway and Lady Cuffe went to northeastern Burma, reaching the village of Kutkai on 16 May - 'We have got back to civilization again' she told he cousin, the Baroness Pauline Prochazka, 'in the shape of a brick bungalow, table and chairs and beds of a solid sort in place of grass and bamboo shanties and folding camp furniture of the lightest and most portable description'. Kutkai was near the Chinese border, about 1,500 metres above sea level. The nearby hills supported an interesting flora. As usual there was an abundance of rhododendrons. Edelweiss grew on the slopes as did some excellent mushrooms. Lady Cuffe found a white rose and collected seed from it. When she returned to Maymyo she planted the seeds she had collected.

Among her collection of botanical paintings, now a treasured possession of the National Botanic Gardens, Glasnevin, is an unfinished but very fine watercolour sketch of this rose[17] which is also described in her letters home. The painting shows the

> ... climbing white cluster rose that I found at Kutkai on the limestone plateau of the Northern Shan States ... a beautiful and curious rose - its peculiarities are the centre style almost like a hibiscus and a strong scent almost more like a lilac than a rose & burnished evergreen leaves ... It had thoroughly established itself by the stream in the rose garden [at Maymyo].[18]

Before leaving Burma, Charlotte promised seeds of her Kutkai rose to Sir Frederick Moore for the Botanic Gardens at Glasnevin. For some years I believed that the Kutkai rose was the familiar, evergreen climbing rose with large, single, white flowers called Cooper's Burmese rose, *Rosa laevigata* 'Cooperi', a variety of the so-called Cherokee rose. However, the watercolour shows that I was mistaken - the Kutkai rose and Cooper's Burmese rose are not the same because the Kutkai rose produces clusters, not solitary blossoms, of creamy-white flowers, each one about a third the size of Copper's Burmese rose.

Lady Cuffe was invited to establish a botanic garden in Maymyo, a small hill-town north of Rangoon. She accepted the task with delight telling Pauline Prochazka, in a letter written on the morning after she had been asked to undertake the job, that 'I couldn't sleep last night with excitement over it (which was very silly of me).' One hundred and fifty acres of jungle were set aside for the botanic garden and Charlotte Wheeler Cuffe worked hard to convert this tangle of weeds into an ordered garden. In 1921, on Sir Otway's retirement, the Cuffes left Burma. The botanic garden had been completed and was a considerable success. Reginald Farrer visited Maymyo in February 1920 and wrote 'I have no doubt it will be a paradise'. A curator was appointed by the India Office, on the advice of the Director of Kew, to take charge after Lady Cuffe departed. He was Roland Cooper, who had worked in the Calcutta Botanic Garden, and was an experienced plant collector. Charlotte Cuffe met him and later wrote to Sir Frederick Moore saying that 'I am handing over my beloved garden ... with great confidence'. With this letter she enclosed a sketch of the white rose from Kutkai which was well-established in the Maymyo garden. She instructed Roland Cooper to collect seeds and send these to Ireland. Cooper fulfilled the commission. In 1923 seeds arrived at Glasnevin, and Lady Cuffe wrote confirming that she had found the rose at Kutkai on a limestone plateau. From Glasnevin, seedlings were distributed to other botanic gardens. But the cluster rose from Kutkai seems to have vanished without trace.

ROSES FROM DAISY HILL

There were apparently few Irish nurseries supplying quality roses in the early and mid-1800s. In 1846, the novelist Maria Edgeworth had to import roses from the United States of America and from England. Rodger, M'Clelland & Co. of Newry stocked *Rosa* x *hibernica*, 'Celeste', 'Reevesiana' and cultivars of *Rosa rugosa* in the 1870s and other nurseries offered roses in small variety. Not until the last decades of the century did our nurseries begin to specialize in roses, and when rose propagation and later rose breeding became well established, Ireland rapidly gained fame for its roses. Around the turn of the century, Daisy Hill Nursery in Newry was second to none and its rose catalogues contained the very best cultivars.

Thomas Smith, the nursery's founder, raised a handful of roses but none of the brash roses that were the progenitors of today's lineages. From Daisy Hill came 'Daisy Hill', and 'Paulii Rosea', recently renamed 'Newry Pink'.[19] 'Narrow Water' was introduced by Thomas Smith and he also marketed Sir John Ross-of-Bladensburg's 'Tipo Ideale' described in 1921 by Lady Moore as 'bright pink with crimson shadows'. 'Tipo Ideale' had been noticed, so the story goes, by Lady Ross-of-Bladensburg growing in a small market garden in Baveno on the shores of Lago Maggiore in northern Italy, not far from Isola Bella, the famous residence of Prince Gilberto Borromeo. The prince evidently knew this rose, although then misnamed *Rosa turca* or *Rosa turkestanica*, because about 1895 he presented a plant to Henri Correvon, the Swiss gardener who, coincidentally, praised Daisy Hill Nursery for its unequalled collections. Lady Ross brought home a plant, and Daisy Hill Nursery propagated it. Eventually this lovely rose, whose petals vary through 'shades of rose, copper, fawn and yellow', was identified as a cultivar of the China rose, *Rosa chinensis*, and today bears the name 'Mutabilis' which Henri

Correvon gave it presumably not knowing that it already had a name.[20]

Rosa **'Daisy Hill'** (Plate 10) is an exquisite, sprawling rose, a seedling from 'Macrantha' raised at Newry around 1900. Thomas Smith probably wrote the original catalogue description himself, which, given his penchant for hyperbole, is restrained:

> Of very vigorous growth, with full double flowers of a delicious shade of pale silvery blush, suffused with peach and deliciously fragrant. Quite one of the finest of Summer flowering garden roses, either as a bush or as a semi-climber.[21]

I saw it for the first time at the Royal Horticultural Society's Wisley garden, cascading over a wall by some steps, and was so impressed by it that I soon bought a plant which quickly filled a large part of a shrub border in my Celbridge garden. This is one of those easy roses - it grows vigorously, yet not too vigorously, and does not need pruning. The individual flowers open almost flat, displaying yellow stamens surrounded by a swirl of petals that are a delicate pink with a hint of cream, and they fade as they age. They are sweetly perfumed. Graham Thomas noted that this lovely rose was used by Wilhelm Kordes as a parent for some of his cultivars.

THE AMATEUR ROSE BREEDER

The history of rose breeding in Ireland is dominated by the dynasties of Dickson and McGredy. Yet I have learned that it is wrong to think of those families as being the only bright lights in the Irish rose industry. There were a few amateurs active in the 1890s and early 1900s although their names are no longer included in the litanies of rosarians.

The pages of antique gardening magazine such as the *Gardeners' chronicle* have to be combed minutely to unearth the amateur rose breeders. George C. Garnett was one, described in August 1881 as 'a most enthusiastic and accomplished rosarian residing in the immediate vicinity of Dublin'. He noticed a white and salmon-rose 'part-coloured or piebald' sport on a bush of 'Letty Coles', a rose with soft rosy pink blooms shaded with intense crimson, to which he had several years previously attempted to bud-graft the creamy-white 'Niphetos'. Mr Garnett sent the sport to Messrs Keynes & Son of Salisbury who propagated it and introduced 'Thomas Gerrard'. Nothing else is recorded about the rose, or Mr Garnett and Mr Gerrard.

Dr James Campbell Hall is a little less of a mystery. He was a member of the National Rose Society and a close friend of Dr O'Donel Thornley D. Browne, a Dublin physician, who frequently contributed to the short-lived monthly *Irish gardening*, and who had a rose named after him. In 1908, Browne described Dr Hall, who lived in Monaghan, as 'our champion rose grower', and evidently he had been breeding roses from around the turn of the century. By 1906 most of his vegetable garden was 'eaten up' with seedling roses, because Hall had been 'bitten with the fever of hybridizing'. In 1908, he had a magnificent success with one seedling which gained a gold medal.

10. Rosa 'Daisy Hill'

But what pleased me most of all was to see my friend Dr Campbell Hall on the warpath. I thought I would be competing against him - but, oh! dear no - he had better ideas in his head than ordinary showing. He was going for the gold medal - the highest trophy a rosarian can win - for a brand new seedling rose raised and cared for by his own brains and hands, and HE GOT IT. It was a triumph we were all delighted at. ... Last year he had bad luck in not hitting the day, but he did not miss this year.[22]

That was Dr O'Donel Browne's colourful account of the annual metropolitan show of the National Rose Society in Regent's Park, London, on 3 July 1908. As for the rose, it is somewhat astonishing that 'Mrs Campbell Hall' is still available from at least one specialist rose nursery in England. I have not grown this rose, but it certainly deserves a place in my imagined flower garden.

'Mrs Campbell Hall', for so the worthy doctor calls this new rose, is a pure Tea rose - a very large, stately-shaped flowers; colour, a rich cream suffused with copper and peach. The edges of the petals in the half-expanded flower reflex in a charming manner, making the bloom most beautiful when looked into.[23]

I know that John Campbell Hall raised and named nine roses,[24] some of which were introduced by Alex Dickson, some by McGredy, and others by the English firm, George Prince of Oxford. 'Mrs Campbell Hall' was marketed by Alex Dickson of Newtownards from 1914.

'No matter how tired I am, if I can only get five minutes with my roses, I am fresh again', was Dr Hall's philosophy. 'To show against him I always feel I am fighting a stern foe', wrote Dr Browne, 'for he will not spare you - but, winner or loser, he is always the same - kindly, genial, and good natured.'

'HANDEL'

Within the ranks of professional rose breeders, the nurserymen who have created Ireland's incomparable heritage of roses, McGredy and Dickson are pre-eminent. It is almost impossible to choose a single rose to represent these remarkable dynasties, but I have my favourites, and they have both been illustrated elsewhere by Wendy Walsh. From the Portadown nursery, I have selected the climbing rose named 'Handel', and from the Newtownards nursery, the lovely old hybrid tea called 'Irish Elegance'.

I remember as a small boy travelling with my parents from Enniskillen to visit grandparents in Belfast, and in those days it was necessary to go through Dunmurray where McGredy had a display garden. There were regiments of roses, reds and yellows and pinks and whites, and even the first of those grey-mauve roses that are miscalled blue. My parents wanted a climbing rose to cover a trellis, and for some reason that I cannot recall, on one visit to Dunmurray they selected 'Handel'.

About a century ago, the second Samuel McGredy, 'the Irish wizard', began raising roses at Portadown, County Armagh, and before long he gained his first gold medal, for 'Countess of Gosford'. Until 1972 Portadown was the centre of the family's highly successful business. **'Handel'**[25] was raised at Portadown by Sam McGredy IV. The pollen parent was a floribunda rose called 'Columbine' which had been released in 1956 by the famous Danish rose breeder Neils Poulsen. The seed parent was a German cultivar named 'Heidelberg', one of many roses raised by Wilhlem Kordes, which was released in 1958. In the late 1950s, Sam McGredy used 'Heidelberg' for several crosses and noticed that the seedlings were consistently good climbing plants. Among the progeny of 'Heidelberg' raised by McGredy were 'Swan Lake'(a vigorous white introduced in 1968) and a scented salmon-pink rose named 'Galway Bay' (which had the very familiar pink rose 'Queen Elizabeth' as its pollen parent), released in 1966.

'Heidelberg' has double, bright red flowers, but its offspring, so Sam McGredy noticed, acquired a tone that was more similar to their pollen parents. From the seedlings raised by pollinating 'Heidelberg' with 'Columbine' he gained a rose with neat, tightly scrolled, conical buds that opened into a semi-double, cupped flower. The ground colour of the petals is cream-white and the edges are flushed with red. Its flowers do vary in colour, according to the weather as they mature, the red flush being more intense and spread over more of the petals in hot weather. Sam McGredy named this beautiful rose after the composer, George Frederick Handel.

'Handel' was first marketed in 1965, and has been lauded in many places, voted the best climbing rose, and remains a favourite among gardeners. It is a vigorous shrub that tends to grow very erect; to prevent the stems become leggy and bare, the growing shoots should be trained horizontally at weekly intervals, and in subsequent years the spur-shoots can be pruned to give a mass of flowers into the autumn.

'IRISH ELEGANCE'

When Samuel McGredy II started raising roses, the Dickson family had already gained their first prizes, and Pat Dickson is the principal rose breeder in Ireland today. Stimulated by the success in 1878 of a Wiltshire man, Henry Bennett, in showing some "Pedigree Hybrids", George Dickson of Newtownards began the following year trying to breed better roses. His two sons, Alexander and George, assisted and after their early, not unexpected failures they did succeed in producing three new roses which were shown in London during 1886. 'Earl of Dufferin' was a sweetly scented rose with large velvety crimson petals shaded with dark maroon. 'Lady Helen Stewart' was bright crimson scarlet and highly perfumed. 'Miss Ethel Brownlow', dedicated to the English novelist, was a tea rose with salmon pink blossoms. In 1887 this first set of seedlings was offered for sale. For the remainder of the nineteenth century, the business developed steadily and by the beginning of the 1900s, Dicksons of Hawlmark were established as a leading international nursery. The Dicksons raised as many as 3,000 seedlings each year, rejecting most of these in their quest for winning roses. They attempted to produce a race of hardy free-flowering plants; in particular, the firm raised a series of single-flowered tea roses which were vigorous and blossomed throughout the summer.

These tea roses bore names with the prefix 'Irish' - the series included 'Irish Beauty' (1900; white), 'Irish Brightness' (1903; crimson shading pink), 'Irish Engineer' (1904; scarlet), 'Irish Fireflame' (1913; dark orange), 'Irish Glory' (1900; light pink), 'Irish Harmony' (1904; saffron-yellow buds, opening creamy-white), 'Irish Modesty' (1900; light orange pink), 'Irish Pride (1903; 'ecru, suffused old rose'), and 'Irish Star' (1903; 'rose du Barii'). In their heyday these roses were eulogized, but they have fallen out of fashion and few can be purchased today; only 'Irish Brightness', 'Irish Fireflame' and 'Irish Elegance' persist in nurseries.

Rosa **'Irish Elegance'**[26] has been described by Jack Harkness as 'that evidence of good taste in Newtownards'. Introduced in 1905, the catalogue entry may be quoted for although it includes the usual nursery hyperbole, it does well describe the rose.

> This we consider the most charming variety of all the single roses we have raised. It is a gem of the first water. In the bud state it is bronzy scarlet, which whilst expanding assumes varied apricot hues which, in contrast, lend to it a charm peculiarly its own. It is of vigorous and erect growth, branching freely, and is a profuse bloomer from early June until the extreme end of the flowering season. The spiral buds, expanding and expanded blossoms are of such exquisite distincture as to always draw attention, even in the midst of our seedling quarters, so that for button-holes or decoration it has distinct features all its own. When known we predict this unique rose will create quite a furore.[27]

The prediction did not come to fruition. 'Irish Elegance' gained a Wisley Rose Award (class II) after trials by the Royal Horticultural Society, but by the 1950s it had lost favour with most rose fanciers although it still had its champions; N. P. Harvey pleaded 'for the old Irish Elegance, one of the loveliest of all singles, the coppery-pink blooms being admirable for cutting'.[28]

As well as the single tea roses, Dicksons initiated their own lineage of double flowered roses. 'Killarney', a silvery-pink, was one of the first, released in 1898. Much more recently, Pat Dickson has developed a unique series of "patio roses", diminutive plants, free flowering, and eminently suited to the modern suburban garden.

SERENDIPITY IN A LADY'S GARDEN

The other remarkable Irish rosarian was Phylis Moore. The greatest Irish gardeners have invariably been individualists, and Lady Moore was not an exception to that rule. She was the doyen of Irish gardeners for many decades, and to her goes credit for keeping alive and distributing 'Souvenir de St Anne's', which is my favourite. This rose has all the character and charm, colour and fragrance that anyone could wish for; it is disease-resistant and blooms from May to December. Yet, 'Souvenir de St Anne's' was not created - it was a serendipity.

Before this century, few ladies has a chance to make their marks on Ireland's gardens. The arousal of more liberal attitudes, leading ultimately to female emancipation, allowed women to assume more prominent roles towards the end of the last century, and to become master gardeners. Today it is taken for granted that women are superb, practical horticulturists, and girls receive training as equals with boys. Yet, a century ago, women were not allowed to attend Glasnevin Botanic Gardens as pupil gardeners, or to become apprenticed in other gardens. Some of the impetus to the removal of the barriers came from writers like Gertrude Jekyll and, in Ireland, from the example of Phylis Moore.

Frederick Moore instituted a training course for lady gardeners in 1896. Lady Moore told the story of its beginning thus. The principal of Alexandra College, Miss Henrietta M. White, and Miss Fanny Currey of Lismore, arrived on a jaunting car at the Gardens and demanded to see the Keeper. They spoke to Moore and 'could not be induced to leave his office' until he promised to pass on the ladies' proposal for a training course to his superiors.

These two ladies belonged to a circle of eminent gardening women, including the Duchess of Leinster and Lady Ardilaun. Lady Ardilaun's garden at St Anne's in Clontarf, on the north side of Dublin, was both renowned and denigrated. Miss Ellen Willmott, a rather stuffy English gardener of great distinction, met Lord and Lady Ardilaun in France and commented in a letter to Frederick Moore that she

> was surprised how very little [Lady Ardilaun] knew about plants and gardening in fact no more than she had known six years ago but she told me her garden at St. Anne's was quite wonderful and that she had worked it up until it was quite first rate in every way.[29]

Miss Willmott remarked that she had heard such different opinions about St Anne's that she was confused, adding the devastating retort that 'whatever be the case it is most fortunate that the owner is so completely satisfied'.

One contrary opinion was expressed in 1884 - a visitor wrote that St Anne's possessed 'the greatest charm for the real lover of good gardening. I can conscientiously say that the herbaceous borders at St Anne's are by far the neatest and best kept I have ever seen.'

Lady Ardilaun, of course, did none of the digging, weeding and planting. She was an expert, as her cousin remarked, in theoretical matters! Ladies could not dirty their hands, much as they would have liked to. One day Lady Ardilaun did pull out a weed and her head gardener 'met me in the very act and looked very pained and hurt, and next day there were men and boys in every border and by-way hunting stray weeds like sleuth-hounds'.

The head gardener was Andrew Campbell, a modest retiring man, 'the best and most estimable', deeply respected by his fellow gardeners. As a plantsman 'he was outstanding, with a sharp eye for novel and unusual varieties.' He raised several cultivars of *Lobelia* and also an important white-flowered Japanese anemone named 'Lady Ardilaun' which I believe is still in cultivation, but extremely rare. These apart, the jewel of St Anne's was a rose.

This rose was a sport on the old Bourbon rose 'Souvenir de La Malmaison'. Campbell noticed that some flowers were almost single, not fully double as was usual. He carefully propagated the sport and produced a 'charming little rose' named **'Souvenir de St Anne's'**[30] which was jealously protected. Lady Ardilaun would not generally give the new rose to other gardeners, but the odd cutting was passed to trusted friends after they had solemnly promised to let no-one else have it. Among this select band were Sir Frederick and Lady Moore, who always appreciated a good plant when they saw it. After Lady Ardilaun's death, her prohibition on the rose gradually lapsed and as early as 1931 Sir Frederick sent cuttings to Thomas Bolas, Lady Londonderry's gardener, at Mount Stewart.[31] However, the rose did not become commonplace and had Lady Moore not preserved it in her garden, Lady Ardilaun's rose could have vanished. Fortunately, Phylis Moore cherished it. She gave it to Graham Thomas, then at Hilling's Nursery, who propagated it and made it available in the early 1950s. And, in turn, Graham introduced me to 'Souvenir de St Anne's'.

A well-grown shrub of *Rosa* 'Souvenir de St Anne's' can be two metres tall and laden with flowers in summer and autumn. I have had it in bloom in late May before any other shrub rose. It is robust and has fine dark green leaves with three or five leaflets. There are few thorns. The buds are shapely cones of deep pink borne on glandular, reddish stalks. The flower is a flat, pale pink rose with a faint perfume. Each bloom has about a dozen petals, and in the centre, with the golden stamens, may be a few small curled petals which add a sculptured quaintness to the flower. Shell-pink blends into cream around the centre and the rose fades to a whiter shade of pink.

St Anne's is now a public park, managed by Dublin Corporation. It contains an international rose trial garden, filled with aspiring new varieties, but at the entrance is a guard of honour of the rose that is the garden's own.

BRING ROSES IF THE ROSE BE STILL IN BLOOM

The influence of Irish roses has been far-reaching. As an aside it is worth noting that Graham Thomas,[32] not so long ago dubbed the *pater familias* of roses, came here first in 1937 to visit Tom Blythe at Daisy Hill Nursery. In one of his books, *The old shrub roses*, Thomas recalled visits to the gardens at Rowallane and Rostrevor as well as Glasnevin where he saw *Rosa* x *paulii* 'Rosea'. At Newry he viewed only the 'sad remnants of Tom Smith's once magnificent collection'. In 1949 Thomas returned to Ireland, and at Mount Stewart he was regaled with 'Mrs Oakley Fisher' and 'Penelope'. At Larchfield in Dublin, the garden of Mr and Mrs Salmon, 'a thousand and more' roses, including 'Le Roi a fleur pourpre', were closely grown in borders - 'It was good to feel that this variety will now become available again thanks to [Mr Salmon's] care'. In Lady Moore's garden, Willbrook at Rathfarnham, he saw the misnamed *Rosa slingeri* which proved to be the double-flowered cultivar of *Rosa xanthina*, and, for the first time, 'Souvenir de St Anne's'. Graham Thomas's passion for roses was nurtured by his contacts with people like Lady Moore, and by Ireland's gardens. It was appropriate therefore that on one of his visits to Dublin in the early 1980s we should happen upon the sumptuous China rose 'Fortune's Double Yellow' in the garden called St Catherine's at Leixlip. This rose was believed to have become extinct in Britain, but soon returned as cuttings.[33]

What are we doing about conserving this heritage, and about explaining it to our fellow countrymen? The blunt answer is nothing. There are international rose trial grounds in Belfast and Dublin, both planted with modern roses; to me, the battalions of new cultivars are bland, uninspiring and tedious, like peas from a packet of frozen peas, all more of the same or, at best, minor variations on themes.

> The Rose of the past is better
> Than the rose we ravish today
> 'Tis holier, purer and fitter
> To place on the shrine where we pray.[34]

The so-called old roses - at least those cultivars that originated in nineteenth century or earlier - are nowadays fashionably old-fashioned and in some countries gardens have been established to house conservation collections of the antique cultivars. There are heritage societies devoted to roses in Australia and South Africa. Irish gardens have even contributed to the restoration of roses to these gardens - as I have noted, 'Fortune's Double Yellow' has been returned to Britain from a old garden near Dublin.

Shamefully there is no garden within Ireland dedicated to growing and conserving the roses that Irish men and women introduced from wild habitats or produced by elaborate breeding programmes. There is no society devoted to this remarkable heritage. There is no garden that interprets Ireland's distinctive contribution to rose gardening, that explains the science of rose breeding and the lineages of plants like 'Handel' or 'Irish Elegance'. Even if such a garden is not formed to preserve Irish roses simply because they were raised in Ireland, it must not be forgotten that older cultivars could contain valuable genes - perhaps for disease resistance or a new colour - that might help enliven a dowdy, tired line in years to come.

We have hitherto relied on individuals to keep alive the older Irish roses. Had Lady Moore not cherished 'Souvenir de St. Anne's', that beautiful shell-pink rose would have vanished. If no-one had bothered about *Rosa* x *hibernica*, the true Irish rose would have become extinct. Had The Thomas Moore Society not propagated and distributed the 'Last Rose of Summer' we would remain ignorant of the rose that inspired an immortal ballad. We cannot afford to depend on individuals any more, because the task is too urgent and enormous.

In 1991 when I was invited to speak at Rose Emerald, the ninth World Rose Convention, in The Queen's University, Belfast, I voiced that opinion, and also argued that we cannot wait any longer; it was time to begin to collect the cultivars produced by Dickson and McGredy and all the other rose breeders, to form a national archive of Irish roses, and to begin propagating and distributing the surviving plants to anyone who will cherish them. If we delay much longer we will lose more of the old cultivars and our successors will not thank us for letting slip the chance to preserve their unique heritage.

> Pour wine and dance if manhood still have pride
> Bring roses if the rose be yet in bloom ...[35]

One of the finest poets of the First World War was a young farm labourer from County Meath who, like Charles Frederick Ball of the Glasnevin Botanic Gardens, volunteered for service and who, like Ball, was killed in that hell. From Francis Ledwidge's exquisite verses about the month of June, comes this stanza and I propose that it should be inscribed at the entrance to the garden that will conserve for future generations the ineluctable roses of Ireland.

> And loop this red rose in that hazel ring
> That snares your little ear, for June is short
> And we must joy in it and dance and sing
> And from her bounty draw her rosy worth.
> Ay! soon the swallows with be flying south
> The wind wheel north to gather in the snow
> Even the roses spilt on youth's red mouth
> Will soon blow down the road all roses go.[36]

> I cast my heart into my rhymes,
> That you, in the dim coming times,
> May know how my heart went with them
> After the red-rose-bordered hem.[37]

IX

An Irish Shrubbery

Forsythia x *intermedia* 'Lynwood Variety' - *Luma apiculata* 'Glanleam Gold'
Griselinia littoralis 'Bantry Bay' - *Pittosporum tenuifolium* 'Silver Queen'
Potentilla fruticosa 'Tangerine' & 'Sophie's Blush'
Viburnum carlesii 'Donard Variety' - *Pieris formosa* 'Rowallane'
Sambucus nigra 'Guincho Purple'
Paeonia 'Anne Rosse' - *Paeonia delavayi* 'Phylis Moore'
Hebe 'Headfortii' - *Escallonia* 'Alice' & 'C. F. Ball'

Near yonder copse, where once the garden smiled,
And still where many a garden flower grows wild;
There, where a few torn shrubs the place disclose,
The village preacher's modest mansion rose.

Oliver Goldsmith: 'The deserted village'

More than a century ago William Robinson complained that shrubs were neglected as garden plants, and that too much time and money was wasted on carpet-bedding and 'other fleeting and costly rubbish'. He chastised gardeners for continuing the endless work of digging shrubberies each winter, for leaving bare earth between the bushes and for damaging the roots. Robinson urged that shrubs should be planted in informal groups and allowed to attain their natural habit without pruning. Then, he argued, the host of lovely shrubs would provide colour and variety.

All the trees, herbs and shrubs grown in gardens have been subjected to selection at some time. Even the process of collecting seeds in the wild is selective, for the most fruitful or most shapely or most floriferous plants will tend to be harvested. Selection proceeds further in gardens and nurseries. Some cultivars are chance freaks or sports (a variegated branch, or maybe a shoot bearing flowers of a different colour) that have been perpetuated with our assistance. Gardeners and nurserymen are ever watchful for such happenings, hoping to obtain a first-class new variety from the sport.

Another way in which new garden forms can arise is by cross-pollination of related species, and the production of a hybrid. Hybrids may appear by chance in gardens where exotic species are growing in close proximity, species which do not occur together in the wild. Again, gardeners who spot an unusual seedling often propagate it, and, with luck, introduce a new cultivar.

These processes are illustrated in the histories of the cultivars that form my Irish shrubbery.

MISS ADAIR'S *FORSYTHIA*

There is one species of the spring-flowering shrub *Forsythia* native in Europe, while about five grow in the Far East. In 1833, *Forsythia suspensa* was introduced from China, and a decade later, Robert Fortune sent another Chinese species, *Forsythia viridissima*, to England. These were more showy than the European plant and soon were widely grown. In Gottingen Botanic Garden in the north of Germany, these Chinese species cross-pollinated. The hybrid seedling, *Forsythia* x *intermedia*, was even more spectacular in flower than the parents and it gradually became popular. In the early 1900s a deliberate breeding programme was conducted by the German nursery run by the Späth family who introduced a particularly good variety 'Spectabilis'. It is still grown and is one of the better spring-flowering shrubs.

Forsythia x *intermedia* 'Spectabilis' was cultivated in Glasnevin about 1911 and was probably distributed by Irish nurseries about the same time. In Miss Nora Adair's garden, called Lynwood, at Cookstown, County Tyrone, a branch on a plant of 'Spectabilis' produced larger and more shapely flowers than the rest of the bush. Miss Adair showed the shrub with the branch that 'had gone wrong', as she put it, to Leslie Slinger of the Slieve Donard Nursery, and he gave her some daffodil bulbs in exchange for cuttings. That was in 1933. As the plants raised from this sport retained the finer blossoms, Slinger decided to introduce it as a new cultivar; the sport was named *Forsythia* x *intermedia* **'Lynwood Variety'**[1] and was made available in 1946. In 1956 'Lynwood Variety' received the coveted award of merit of the Royal Horticultural Society. Leslie Slinger was proud of 'Lynwood Variety', admitting that while he can take no credit for raising it, 'I was in the right place at the right time', and he held the view, supported by many 'good judges of shrubs', that this was 'the finest' *Forsythia*.

'Lynwood Variety' is a particularly attractive *Forsythia*, better than 'Spectabilis'. The bright yellow flowers open in late spring, although in a mild season the flowers will open earlier, and budded branches cut and taken indoors rapidly bloom. The individual flowers are about four centimetres across and usually have four petals, but five or six petals are occasionally present. The petals have broad bases; their margins do not curl underneath as in 'Spectabilis' nor do the tips become twisted.

Forsythia flowers last for about four weeks, and when the blossom has faded the green leaves unfurl, so, for the rest of the year it is a rather dull plant. It is a good hedge shrub and makes a wonderful splash of colour in the spring. However, like many spring-blooming shrubs, *Forsythia* 'Lynwood Variety' does benefit from selective pruning. Leslie Slinger recommended that 'each spring after flowering ... remove entirely the flowering branches', by which I assume he means that the shrubs should be virtually coppiced. This is quite drastic, but well-established young shrubs will respond by producing very vigorous, straight, new shoots from which flowers will burst abundantly during the following spring.

VALENTIA ISLAND

A similar story, but with a different beginning, can be told about a variegated myrtle that has quickly gained popularity in our gardens.

The South American myrtle, *Luma apiculata*,[2] is a handsome evergreen. It is hardier than most gardeners realise and once established will survive even severe frost. It thrives in the mild climate of the south-west and has become naturalized in several places. I know a number of gardens in Cork and Kerry that contain forests of the myrtle.

Luma apiculata trees have splendid cinnamon and white bark. The leaves are dark green, oval in shape and with a pointed tip. In summer the shrubs are covered with deliciously fragrant, creamy-white flowers, but the individual plants bloom erratically. With abundant blossom, there is always an abundance of seeds, and in the ramshackle and wild gardens of Kerry and Cork, seedlings pop up everywhere.

At Glanleam, on Valentia Island, the garden was full of myrtle, and seedlings came up like mustard and cress. Colonel R. J. Uniacke, who owned the estate in the early 1960s, noticed that one of the young myrtles had variegated leaves. He tended it carefully and allowed it to develop into a shrub, which still survives in the garden and is now about five metres tall. About 1965, Colonel Uniacke gave cuttings of this freak to two nurseries, one in Ireland and the other in Cornwall. Treseder's Nursery in Truro put the myrtle on the market in the early 1970s using the name 'Glanleam Gold'. About the same time it was sold by the Glen O'Downs Nursery of County Wicklow using the same name - at one time it was listed as *Myrtus* 'Glen O'Downs'. Nowadays it is readily available in Ireland and is propagated in substantial quantities.

Luma apiculata **'Glanleam Gold'**[3] appears to be as hardy as the plain variety. It tolerates soil containing lime, but flourishes best in rich peaty loam. During the first few years after planting it may require some shelter as the young shoots are easily damaged by cold winds. 'Glanleam Gold' produces fragrant white flowers, like those of the species, each one composed of four concave petals with a curly mass of stamens in the centre. The fruit is a dark purple berry. The centre of each leaf is glossy dark green, and around this is an irregular patch of lighter greyish-green. The leaf margin is lined with cream. When young the leaves and shoots are tinted with red and bronze.

The garden at Glanleam was started in the 1850s by Peter Fitzgerald, nineteenth Knight of Kerry. He planted many tender trees and shrubs including the Chilean fire-bush - trees of this at Glanleam have trunks at least half a metre in diameter. There are countless fine tree ferns and tall specimens of *Pittosporum*. *Griselinia littoralis* is also abundant and naturalized. It is a venerable garden that has recently been revitalized under the careful ownership of Mrs Meta Kreissig. There is a wild beauty about Glanleam with many tender plants growing as they would in their faraway native haunts.

ON BANTRY BAY

Australasian plants including tree ferns and myrtles have become the hall-marks of the gardens of Cork and Kerry, and many of these attain dimensions in Irish gardens that excel those reached by the same species in their natural habitats. Most Australasian and New Zealand plants survive here only because they are provided with an artificial environment; the gardens they grow in could not exist without the envelope of sheltering trees that keeps at bay the worst excesses of the Atlantic winds. Yet those winds are important - they may wreak occasional havoc but they also blow away frost.

One of the most magnificent gardens in the world is on Ilnacullin (Garinish Island) at the head of Bantry Bay, near Glengarriff. The island was a rocky mount covered with furze and heather before 1910, when Annan Bryce, a native of Belfast and a member of the United Kingdom parliament, purchased it. He commissioned the English landscape architect, Harold Peto, to design a house and garden. Only the garden was completed, and while the bricks and mortar of the walls and pavilion survived the gales, many of the plants soon succumbed. In October 1928, Murdo Mackenzie, a Scottish gardener trained in the superb tradition of horticulture that is characteristic of our northern neighbour, arrived on the island. He was unconsciously treading a path blazed by James Mackay and following in the footsteps of Ninian Niven, David Bishop and David Moore.

Murdo's first task was to establish shelter. Once this was achieved, the rare and tender plants throve. The garden, visited today by thousands of people, is largely the work of that cheerful Scot. Mackenzie loved showing young people about, pointing out the triumphs and warning of the pitfalls, extolling the necessity of shelter, and explaining how soil was carted from the mainland to create this paradise. I remember him, sprite-like, weeding out rogue plants and expounding on 'this and that' in his lilting Scottish voice.

About 1950, Murdo Mackenzie noticed that a branch on a shrub of the New Zealand plant *Griselinia littoralis* had variegated leaves. He removed the plant to a safe place near his house, and cut away all the green shoots, leaving the variegated shoot. Slowly the sport asserted itself although the plant had a tendency to revert - the green shoots were always removed. This original plant is now a tree.

13. *Griselinia littoralis* 'Bantry Bay'

During a holiday trip to County Cork in June 1967, Neil Treseder visited several well-known gardens including Fota and Ilnacullin. From Fota he obtained cuttings of a semi-prostrate rosemary which was christened 'Fota Blue'. Murdo Mackenzie gave Mr Treseder propagation material of several plants, including a crimson bottle-brush (later named *Callistemon salignus* 'Murdo Mackenzie'), a tea-tree with two-coloured petals (*Leptospermum scoparium* 'Rowland Bryce'), a pale-flowered seedling of *Escallonia macrantha* ('Bantry Bay') and the variegated *Griselinia littoralis*. Treseder's Nursery of Truro, Cornwall, introduced all these plants in the early 1970s, but only *Griselinia littoralis* 'Bantry Bay' seems to have become well-known.

Griselinia littoralis **'Bantry Bay'** (Figure 13)[4] is a good plant with much more character than the greasy, green hedge shrub so common around Dublin. Alas, it has a delicate constitution and needs a sheltered, sunny corner. The leathery leaves are oval and about six centimetres long. The underside is cream, although the pattern of the variegation on the upper surface shows through. The extent of the variegation varies, but as much as three-quarters of the leaf may be cream. Usually the leaves have green patches around the margins with a cream centre, but the green can extend into the middle too.

Griselinia littoralis is grown only for its evergreen foliage - the spikes of flowers are small and insignificant. In coastal areas it withstands salt-laden winds and may be used in seaside shelter-belts. 'Bantry Bay', however, is a plant to cherish as a specimen, not planted and mutilated as a hedge.

SILVER QUEEN

Variegated shrubs and herbs are not admired by every gardener - some people would not give a variegated plant room, but others collect them like postage stamps. A variegated evergreen has its uses; it can bring light into a dull corner in winter, and in summer the brighter, softer colour provides interest when flowers are few.

One of the best and most widely grown variegated shrub is **Pittosporum tenuifolium 'Silver Queen'**.[5] The species normally has glossy green leaves with a silvery sheen. Like *Griselinia* it is a native of New Zealand and has been cultivated here for about a century, originally under the name *Pittosporum mayi*. In the early 1900s, a variegated branch was spotted on a shrub of this *Pittosporum* - when I wrote this book originally, I said that the sport, bearing leaves margined with pale cream around a greyish-green centre, occurred in the Slieve Donard Nursery, and that James Coey noticed it, but evidently that is not correct. The sport must have occurred before Coey purchased the nursery early in 1912 because this variegated shrub was exhibited by him two years later, during 1914, at the Royal Horticultural Society in London. I suspect that the plant came from Castlewellan and was already being propagated when Coey took over the nursery.

Pittosporum tenuifolium 'Silver Queen' forms an attractive compact shrub. It grows vigorously and there are old plants well over ten metres tall in several gardens. Although it is cultivated for its silvery foliage, the shrub has handsome flowers which many gardeners do not even noticc. The blossoms are hidden by the leaves, but each flower has five recurved petals of rich chocolate-brown alternating with five yellow stamens. They have a fragrance reminiscent of vanilla, and this gentle scent adds to the virtues of a handsome shrub.

James Coey was a significant figure in Irish horticulture during the first two decades of this century. A native of Larne, he was a well-to-do businessman and a breeder of shorthorn cattle; he was a keen amateur horticulturist and an important member of that fraternity of sufferers from 'yellow fever' - a mania for daffodils! He raised a number of fine bulbs, and grew and introduced daffodils produced by other breeders; for example, he bought some of Guy Wilson's earliest daffodils and thereby greatly encouraged Wilson.

For the present subject - shrubs - his importance lies in the purchase on 8 January 1912 of the Donard Nursery at Newcastle in County Down. He acquired Thomas Ryan's lease on the nursery, and began to build it into one of the finest nurseries in Ireland, on a par with Daisy Hill Nursery in Newry. James Coey found a manager for the business, William Slinger, who had come from Yorkshire around 1903 to grow roses for Alex Dickson at Newtownards. Slinger moved to Newcastle to manage the Donard Nursery for James Coey, and gradually gained more and more responsibility in the nursery. When James Coey died in 1921, William Slinger was able to acquire the business and began to establish his name in the horticultural world.

TANGERINE AND SOPHIE'S BLUSH

Under William Slinger and his eldest son, Leslie, the Slieve Donard Nursery prospered and was the birthplace of some outstanding plants. It gained an international reputation for its cultivars of *Escallonia* and African wandflowers (*Dierama*) in particular. Another notable success was garden varieties of the shrubby cinquefoils.

In the late 1920s, Leslie Slinger noticed a plant of *Potentilla fruticosa* with golden flowers - instead of the usual bright yellow this plant displayed a distinct tint of orange in its blossom. It had been raised from a packet of seed sent from the Far East by the plant-collector Reginald Farrer, and the packet had been labelled "Potentilla Red Flowered". Several further generations of seedlings were raised from this orange-tinted shrub, until one was found with a distinct orange tint to the petals; it was introduced as 'Donard Gold'.[6]

A batch of seedlings was raised from 'Donard Gold' and planted out in the nursery. One day the young daughter of Harry Bryce, who was propagator in the nursery, noticed that one seedling had bright orange flowers. Harry took cuttings and slowly built up stock of this plant. In 1958 *Potentilla fruticosa* **'Tangerine'**[7] was launched, and it is still widely cultivated. The flower buds are red, and open to display rich orange petals; this vivid colour is best developed when the plants are grown in partial shade or when the weather is overcast. Like all shrubby cinquefoils, 'Tangerine' is a compact shrub, rarely more than 30 centimetres tall, with plain green, divided leaves.

'Tangerine' was a break-through. It has sported twice, producing two quite different new cultivars. On one occasion a shoot developed that had deeper orange flowers - this was propagated and introduced as 'Sunset'. The other sport had pale cream blossoms flushed with pink. It happened in Mrs Turnbull's garden near Preston in Lancashire, and she gave the new plant to the Slieve Donard Nursery. The pale cream sport is called 'Daydawn'.

'Daydawn' was introduced in 1968 by the Slieve Donard Nursery, and is now sold by many garden-centres. At Baronscourt, County Tyrone, it was planted alongside a white-flowered *Potentilla* called 'Manchu'. Some years later a seedling was spotted near 'Daydawn' by the Duchess of Abercorn who realized that it was unusual; she had it removed to a safe place in the garden. The chance seedling was propagated by Philip Wood, and when a sufficient number of plants was available, it was introduced by Baronscourt Nurseries, in the autumn of 1982. The daughter of 'Manchu' and 'Daydawn' is named 'Sophie's Blush' after the grand-daughter of the late duchess.

Like its relatives, 'Sophie's Blush' is a low, compact plant, ideally suited to a small garden. The red flower buds expand into a full blossom composed of five rounded, overlapping petals that are pale rose shading to cream; they fade to shell-pink. The outer surface of the petals is uniformly pink. The hint of cream in the centre of each bloom is accentuated by the yellow stamens.

Potentilla fruticosa **'Sophie's Blush'**[8] does not blush in the hot sun so, for example, the summer of 1983 was not kind to it. Like 'Tangerine', its lovely pastel colours are best when the plant is grown in dappled shade or when the summer days are cloudy.

ONE OF THE THREE GRACES

The Slieve Donard Nursery is no longer in existence; it was closed in 1975 after the death of Leslie Slinger, because there was no-one left to take over the skilled business of raising fine garden plants. The ground was sold and is now a housing estate, but a single tree of the nursery's golden cypress (*Cupressus macrocarpa* 'Donard Gold') survives to mark the spot where 'Tangerine, 'Windhover', 'Charity' and 'Diana' were born. Yet, just as plant explorers will not be forgotten because their names are enshrined in plant names, so the Slingers and James Coey will be remembered by the many good plants that bear the distinctive names of the Donard tribes.

I could have filled my dream-garden exclusively with the Slieve Donard's cultivars, but other fascinating plants would have been overlooked. And, I am delighted that under the National Collections Scheme of the National Council for the Conservation of Plants and

Gardens (NCCPG) two conservation collections of the nursery's plants have been established in Northern Ireland, so that the cultivars will be preserved for the enjoyment of future gardeners.

The task is in the hands of the National Trust and Belfast City Parks Department, and is being brought to fruition with the help and advice of concerned people. Most of the cultivars have been traced, but some, especially herbaceous perennials, are proving elusive.

In my opinion, one of the finest of the Slieve Donard Nursery's shrubs is *Viburnum carlesii* **'Donard Variety'** (otherwise 'Charis').[9] It was not raised as the result of a deliberate breeding programme, nor was it a sport; it was simply a cultivar selected from a series of seedlings - the very best of the group.

About 1936, the nursery obtained seeds of this Korean *Viburnum* from the Sakata Nursery in Japan. The seedlings were planted out in the nursery in 1939, before they flowered; a few were sold before the war interrupted business. During the next few years a number of the young plants were marked when they flowered - they had good form and fine flowers. Three were chosen for propagation.

The Roman goddesses of the moon and of the dawn were chosen as guardians of two of the cultivars.[10] 'Diana' is a compact shrub with red flower buds and pale pink petals. 'Aurora' is similar but not so tall and the pink flowers are deliciously scented. 'Donard Variety', the best, was renamed 'Charis', after one of the Three Graces who impart grace to the earth. It forms a modest, rounded bush that is ideally suited to cultivation as a specimen shrub. Its leaves are pale green with a rumpled texture. As they open in succession the clusters of waxy red buds become sweetly scented flowers of pure white; a few flower-heads will perfume a room, and a single shrub will fill a small garden with a delightful eastern fragrance.

GOLDEN TREE

An important asset of the Slieve Donard Nursery was its close association with local gardens. I think it is not a coincidence that County Down contained outstanding nurseries and a group of excellent gardens - the one could not have prospered without the other. The Slieve Donard Nursery provided many of the plants that stocked the gardens and in return received new varieties from the gardens. The place most closely associated with the Donard, and the garden most productive of new plants, was Rowallane, which is now owned by the National Trust.

Rowallane is renowned for its great banks of rhododendrons that blossom in the spring and early summer, and for its natural rock-garden. The garden was created by the Reverend John Moore, who began planting in the 1870s, and by his nephew, Hugh Armytage Moore, who took over in 1903 and planted many of the novel plants that were introduced from the Far East after 1900.

Hugh Armytage Moore deliberately cross-pollinated rhododendrons and he raised a number of hybrids, but Rowallane's most famous children are chance seedlings of unknown parentage. Some of the original plants survive in the garden today - in a few cases the first plant has died yet its descendants live.

Over 30 years ago a seedling of the lily-of-the-valley tree (*Pieris formosa*) was found in the Wilderness, a rocky area planted mainly with rhododendrons. This is one of the most spectacular early summer plants, due to its intense scarlet juvenile leaves. In May and June, at Fota, Rowallane and other gardens, the shrubs are pillars of red, sprinkled with trusses of pearly-white flowers.

The Rowallane seedling, now about four metres tall, has creamy-yellow leaves instead of bright red ones. At first the young leaves are pink, but this colour fades as the leaves expand until they are translucent cream. The effect from a distance is remarkable - the plant looks as if it is covered in a mass of butter-yellow flowers.

Pieris formosa **'Rowallane'**[11] has not yet been widely propagated but it is represented in the national collection at the Savill Gardens. It was named by Graham Thomas and is illustrated in his book on the gardens of the National Trust. Like its scarlet cousins, 'Rowallane' is susceptible to cold winds and frost which turn the leaves to a mushy brown. It needs a very sheltered spot and a rich peaty soil.

MRS MACKIE'S ELDER

Another attractive foliage plant is the purple-leaved elder, which has links with a County Down garden. Guincho, overlooking Belfast Lough, is one of the finest private gardens in Ireland and contains a large collection of unusual plants which is of such importance that in 1982 Guincho was designated as a garden of outstanding historical importance.

Mrs Vera Mackie planted Guincho, beginning after the Second World War, using the sloping site and the little wooded valley to great effect. You can look from the stream over a green lawn towards shrubberies with numerous rare plants, while under the oak trees, pink dog's tooth violets and golden daffodils dance in spring. The garden contains numerous Australasian species - some of the specimen plants are unique - and many rare herbaceous perennials. After Mrs Mackie's death the garden had a series of owners, all of whom were benevolent. It is still carefully tended.

Vera Mackie had a keen eye for good plants. When on holiday in Scotland about 1957, she spotted a shrub of the common hedgerow elder with purple foliage. Mrs Mackie collected cuttings and succeeded in raising young plants, one of which still blooms at Guincho. In October 1969, Harold Hillier visited the garden and Vera Mackie gave him some scions of the elder. Hillier Nurseries of Winchester exhibited Mrs Mackie's elder at the Royal Horticultural Society in London under the name *Sambucus nigra* 'Purpurea' and it received an award of merit.

It is remarkable that purple-leaved elders were found by three other gardeners in three different places during the last three decades, yet there are no reports of such a variety in earlier garden books. In 1954 Robert Howat found a plant in Yorkshire and this clone is in cultivation in Kew. Chris Brickell, one-time Director of the Royal Horticultural Society's garden at Wisley, has informed me that another plant was found elsewhere in England and it is in cultivation there. In August 1986, Mrs E. S. Hewson reported that a purple-leaved elder grew wild near Tintwistle in Cheshire. It is impossible to distinguish these three clones, but it was the Guincho one that was exhibited and granted an award of merit!

The purple-leaved variety of elder did not have a valid botanical name when this book was first published. In 1986 I decided to give it a name and chose to use a word that is a translation into classical Greek of the descriptive phrase "with purple leaves"; thus every purple-leaved elder can now be labelled *Sambucus nigra* f. *porphyrophylla,*[12] and Mrs Mackie's award winning one is 'Guincho Purple.'

Sambucus nigra **'Guincho Purple'**[13] is a vigorous plant, and can reach five metres in height. The leaves are green when very young, but they soon turn dusky-purple although a few retain streaks of green 'as if someone has drawn a paintbrush across' them. The flower buds are pink, and while the backs of the petals keep their red tint, the petals are creamy-white inside.

The purple-leaved elder is rather dark, so it is a useful background plant for pale-flowered herbs. In blossom it is most attractive, as the dark leaves set off the fluffy heads of creamy-pink flowers. Of course, like the hedgerow elder, it fruits abundantly, and what a useful shrub this is - Dr Caleb Threlkeld instructs us that

> Vinegar in which the flowers are steeped, is grateful to the Stomach ... the Leaves are good against St Anthony's Fire. The Flowers ... expel Wind, and help the Cholick: the Berries are useful in Hysterick Disorders, and are Diuretick.[14]

ANNE'S PEONY

Another distinguished lady gardener is eponymized in a shrubby peony, with large, ruffled flowers of yellow streaked with red. **Paeonia 'Anne Rosse'**[15], named after the Countess of Rosse, was a hybrid deliberately created by her husband, the sixth Earl of Rosse, in their garden at Birr Castle, County Offaly. The yellow tree peony from western China (*Paeonia delavayi* var. *ludlowii*) was crossed with the variety of the same species (*Paeonia delavayi*) which has flowers of blackest red. One seedling produced fine flowers of yellow and crimson with deep red stamens, similar in size and character to the handsome blooms of Frank Ludlow's form of *Paeonia delavayi*. The original plant at Birr Castle is over four metres tall, and has erect, woody stems crowned with tufts of large, divided, pale green leaves. The flowers open in May, a few days before those of Ludlow's variety.

Michael Rosse named the peony after his wife, and exhibited it at the Royal Horticultural Society in 1961. He received the Reginald Cory Memorial Cup as the raiser of a hardy hybrid that was the result of an intentional cross, and the peony was recommended for an award of merit.

Paeonia 'Anne Rosse' must be propagated from cuttings, rooted under mist in a heated propagation unit. Because this is not easy, the peony is not available in commerce, and is grown in too few gardens. If only we could perfect an easier method of propagating plants with woody, yet herbaceous stems, lovely cultivars like this could be more widely available. It is pointless sowing seeds from 'Anne Rosse', as the seedlings have flowers of quite different sizes and shades.

Lady Rosse shared her husband's love of gardens and worked with him to create the fine arboretum and river garden of Birr Castle. Unlike Lady Ardilaun, Anne Rosse was taught how to weed and dig and plant, and willingly wielded spades and secateurs. Her family, the Messels, formed a garden at Nymans in Sussex, whence came the hybrid *Eucryphia* x *nymansensis* and numerous other plants. Nymans is now managed by the National Trust, and Lady Rosse maintained a deep personal interest in the garden, until her death. The formal garden at Birr Castle, which evokes the knot gardens of the seventeenth century, was designed and laid out by Anne and Michael Rosse after their marriage, and the numerous trees of *Magnolia* that thrive in the River Gardens were planted by them, many having been raised from seeds garnered at Nymans.

LADY MOORE'S PEONY

I must remark about a similar peony that was given an award of merit when shown during 1988 in London by Valerie Finnis (Lady Scott). The scented flowers are smaller than those of 'Anne Rosse', just eight centimetres in diameter, but their colour is similar. The petals are yellow tinged with green, with slightly ragged, red margins. In the centre of each bloom is a magnificent cluster of orange stamens. This peony is also a variant of *Paeonia delavayi* - and the cultivar is named **'Phylis Moore'**[16] after Lady Moore who raised it at Willbrook about 1945.

These two peonies have similar origins - they are postulated to be hybrids between the dark red and the yellow tree peonies which, until recently, were usually classified as distinct species named, respectively, *Paeonia delavayi* and *Paeonia lutea*. For very good reasons these are now considered to be extreme forms of a single, variable species which, even in the wild, can produce yellow flowers streaked with red. The plant explorer, George Forrest, commenting on his observations in western China, remarked that in one locality he had visited more than half of the yellow-flowered *Paeonia lutea* 'bore blooms either blotched with deep crimson at the base or flushed throughout with a most unsightly shade of dull brownish-orange.' Roy Lancaster reported that he saw similar red-blotched flowers on tree peonies near Dali in northwestern Yunnan while participating in an Sino-British Expedition to the Cangshan - virtually in the footsteps of George Forrest.

At Glasnevin, in the 1910s, there were many peonies in cultivation including seedlings raised from seed gathered in China by George Forrest. At least one of these, a seedling numbered Forrest 12561, had yellow flowers with red blotches which perplexed Dr Otto Stapf of the Royal Botanic Gardens, Kew, who commented that 'it might be a cross of *Paeonia delavayi* and *Paeonia lutea*, but that is a speculation.' Several other seedlings from Forrest's expedition were sent to Stapf, whose interesting memorandum continued that they 'seem to be distinct from *Paeonia lutea*. Whether they should be treated as distinct species or as varieties, is at present a matter of taste and expediency.' One such plant, the yellow petals having most pronounced brownish-red blotches at the base, was described by R. E. Arnold and named *Paeonia forrestii*, and another quite similar one with petals marked with a central flash of red-brown, raised by Derek Hill in his County Donegal garden, has been informally named after him.[17]

Given Sir Frederick and Lady Moore's connections with Glasnevin, *Paeonia* 'Phylis Moore' may be a seedling from one of Forrest's original introductions - a few peonies with George Forrest's collecting numbers still survive in the Chinese Shrubbery at the National Botanic Gardens.

LORD HEADFORT'S *HEBE*

Sir Frederick Moore, the doyen of Irish horticulturists for half a century, influenced, assisted and advised numerous gardeners. Among Moore's distinguished protégés was the Marquis of Headfort, who became one of the most remarkable gardeners in Ireland in the early part of this century. In due course, Lord Headfort encouraged the young Michael Parsons, later Earl of Rosse, in his gardening. The correspondence between Moore and Headfort survives to show the extent of their co-operation as an arboretum was planned at Headfort House near Kells in County Meath. Long lists of trees, compiled by Lord Headfort, were annotated by Sir Frederick Moore with comments on hardiness, vigour and ultimate dimensions. Using these remarks, Lord Headfort designed and planted one of the most comprehensive collections of conifers in these islands. Even today, in its decrepit state, the Headfort arboretum contains some of the finest pines, firs and spruces in cultivation. A few of the trees are unique examples of their species in Ireland and Britain.

Headfort contained much more than lofty trees. The Marquis had a passion for rhododendrons and raised many from seeds sent from the Far East by collectors including George Forrest who became a good friend. Lord Headfort's notebooks record the beginnings of his collection, when he received seeds from all over the world, including North America and New Zealand.

A shrubby speedwell, formerly called *Veronica* but now named *Hebe*, was raised at Headfort from seeds collected in New Zealand. The shrub forms a shapely hummock up to a metre tall, and bears bright blue-purple flowers, each with a sparkling white eye. By 1930 this was being distributed by Lord Headfort to his friends and to nurserymen under the old name *Veronica headfortii*.

Hebe '**Headfortii**' (Figure 14)[18] is probably a hybrid resulting from cross-pollination of its seed parent in New Zealand. Its relationships are obscure although it has been placed by some botanists in *Hebe macrocarpa*. The Headfort shrub is a fine garden plant, but it is not hardy and is killed by severe frost - my plant perished in January 1982. The dark green, oval leaves are arranged in opposite pairs along the blackish shoots. The flowers are borne in short spikes, towards the tips of the branches, and they appear in late winter and early spring - in mild areas *Hebe* 'Headfortii' will flower in February.

This is the only Headfort plant still in general circulation in our gardens. Lord Headfort produced several rhododendron hybrids, which exist in a few gardens. Many oriental plants flowered at Headfort for the first time, and Lord Headfort sent numerous specimens to the Royal Botanic Gardens, Kew, where William Trevithick, son of his head gardener, was working as a botanical illustrator. Trevithick occasionally drew these plants and his illustrations appeared in *Curtis's botanical magazine*.[19]

CHARLES AND ALICE BALL

While Headfort, Rowallane, Birr and other gardens have achieved international reputations for their own cultivars, the most significant Irish garden, the one that was the real pioneer, was the Botanic Gardens at Glasnevin. It reached the zenith of its prestige under Sir Frederick Moore, but despite its outstanding position, Glasnevin has never been an international centre for plant breeding. New species have been introduced into cultivation, and new cultivars have been distributed from Glasnevin, but relatively few novel garden varieties were deliberately bred within its walls.

Under David Moore hybrids of *Sarracenia*, the American pitcher plants, were raised in the 1870s; *Sarracenia* x *moorei* was the first. During the keepership of Frederick Moore, breeding programmes were instigated for *Lachenalia, Nerine, Calceolaria* and several shrubby genera - all the *Nerine* cultivars were killed on a frosty night in 1930! I have mentioned the fame of the Slieve Donard Nursery for *Escallonia* cultivars; these are well-known and need no

14. *Hebe* 'Headfortii'

11. Escallonia rubra 'C. F. Ball'

further explanation. However, the first garden in Ireland to breed *Escallonia* hybrids was Glasnevin, and the person who carried out the work was Charles Frederick Ball.

Ball was from Leicestershire. He was brought to Dublin by Frederick Moore in 1907 and eventually became Assistant Keeper. Ball was a skilled horticulturist, having trained at Kew, and worked as assistant manager in Arthur Bulley's famous nursery, Bees of Chester. At Glasnevin he bred a yellow-flowered hybrid slipperwort that was named *Calceolaria* x *ballii* - it has been lost to cultivation. He also raised hybrids of *Mahonia* and *Berberis* but none survives.

C. F. Ball was married in December 1914 shortly after he had enlisted in the Royal Dublin Fusiliers. I have been told that Ball was intimidated into enlisting and that before he did so white feathers, a symbol of cowardice, were sent to him. His regiment was despatched to Gallipoli in 1915, and Ball was fatally wounded by shrapnel on 13 September 1915 as he rested following a period of heavy fighting. His death shocked his gardening friends, one of whom tellingly wrote:

> ... it was a particularly fine thing for a man of his peaceful habits to join and only those who knew him well will ever thoroughly appreciate how much he gave up and what a wrench it was to him to throw up the work he loved so much.[20]

In Glasnevin, Charles Frederick Ball's quiet good humour had been much appreciated; he was generous and helpful, yet shy and studious.

Before he went to battle, Ball had named one of his seedling *Escallonia* hybrids after his bride. My attention was drawn to this shrub by the late Miss Elsie Miller, who trained as a lady gardener under Sir Frederick Moore in 1912; she had a plant of **Escallonia 'Alice'**[21] in her garden and one grows in Glasnevin. It had disappeared from nursery catalogues by the early 1980s but in recent years it has reappeared. 'Alice' grows to two metres in height, and its branches tend to droop; it is hardy but needs to be pruned to keep a shapely form. It has oval, glossy, green leaves and deep rose-red flowers, composed of five petals that become recurved as the flower matures and fades to a rosy pink.

There is another Glasnevin *Escallonia* that was not named until after the Great War. Its branches tend to weep and are clothed with dark green leaves. The flowers have blood-red petals and bright golden anthers which glow in the summer sun. The flowers do not fade, and the red petals drop to the ground like tears. It was named for the gentle man who raised it, **Escallonia rubra 'C. F. Ball'** (Plate 11).[22] Like too many other young soldiers who have been forced to fight in pointless wars and who needlessly died, Charles Frederick Ball 'went to rest covered with glory and honour', but he alone is remembered in a graceful flower.

What passing-bells for these who die as cattle?
Only the monstrous anger of the guns.
Only the stuttering rifles' rapid rattle
Can patter out their hasty orisons. ...
The pallor of girls' brows shall be their pall;
Their flowers the tenderness of silent minds,
And each slow dusk a drawing-down of blinds.[23]

X

A Rock-garden

Gentiana verna 'Clare' - *Juniperus communis* 'Hornibrookii'
Saxifraga rosacea subsp. *hartii* & *Saxifraga* 'Ballawley Guardsman'
Anemone nemorosa 'Robinsoniana' & 'Lucy's Wood'
Anemone obtusiloba f. *patula* - *Hutchinsia alpina*
Campanula garganica 'W. H. Paine' - *Primula* 'Guinevere'
Geranium x *lindavicum* 'Lissadell' - *Omphalodes cappadocicum* 'Starry Eyes'
Penstemon fruticosus var. *scouleri* - *Pseudophegopteris levingei*
Dierama cultivars

**By the craggy hill-side
Through the mosses bare
They have planted thorn-trees
For pleasure here and there ...**

William Allingham: 'The fairies'

The modern rockery evolved from the piles of stones laboriously constructed by eighteenth-century gardeners who dignified the rock-work with romantic names like hermit's cave and sylvan grotto. In the Botanic Gardens at Glasnevin during its first decade, a mound was fashioned of stones, carted at great expense from Howth. There was a spiral walkway to the summit and pockets of soil were planted with what were classed as 'saxatile' plants. Some of these prototype rockeries were made from stones of every possible type; at Chelsea Physic Garden there was a rock-garden made from geological specimens brought from Iceland in the 1760s by Joseph Banks.

Little improvement was effected in the nineteenth century. William Robinson attacked the style of rock-gardens persisting in the latter quarter of the 1800s, complaining that there was too much rock and too little soil. A revolution in this type of garden was brought about at the beginning of this century by Reginald Farrer who wrote several classic books on rockery gardening; his delightful, rambling volumes are idiosyncratic but a joy to read.

Farrer categorized rock-gardens. His Almond Pudding rockery was a mound of soil into which the 'spikiest pinnacles of limestone' were inserted thickly so that their points were in the air. He likened the general effect to a vast, petrified porcupine. Another form he called the Dog's Grave; it started with the same mound of earth, but the stones were laid flat. Farrer thought a Dog's Grave rockery too stodgy. A third form he labelled the Devil's Lapful; I quote Reginald Farrer -

> The finest specimens ... are to be seen in such gardens as Glasnevin ... The plan is simplicity itself. You take a hundred or a thousand cartloads of bare square-faced boulders. You next drop them all about absolutely anyhow; and you then plant things amongst them. The chaotic hideousness of the result is something to be remembered with shudders ever after.[1]

Fortunately rockeries have improved. Farrer and his disciples, including Robert Lloyd Praeger and Lewis Meredith in Ireland, have instructed us how to construct rock-gardens that look like real outcrops of rocks, and how to grow plants in these gardens, so that they appear to spring naturally from the earth.

Rock-gardening provides endless interest. Plants may be selected so that there are flowers all year round, and a small area can support a multitude of varieties. Dr Praeger reckoned that one small portion of his rockery, measuring five metres by four, contained 250 species, 'and these are not scraps, but some of the plants cover a couple of square feet apiece, and in other cases the clump includes a dozen individuals'.

In Ireland we are fortunate in having several fine rock-gardens, some of which are constructed around natural outcrops. The one at Kilruddery, near Bray, is no longer maintained, but at Rowallane, the rockery is again blooming with many interesting plants and improvements go on all the time. We also have one of the greatest primaeval rock-gardens in the world - The Burren in County Clare, a land of which gardeners dream, filled with the finest plants, untended by human hand. However, none of us possesses clints and scailps in our back gardens, so the best we can do is to imitate the wild rockeries.

CLARE'S GEM

The floral symbol of The Burren is the Spring gentian, which blossoms for a few short weeks in the middle of May. It is a great treat to see the short turf studded with its white-eyed, sapphire flowers. This delightful plant was first reported from The Burren by the Rector of Birr, the Reverend Richard Heaton, a Yorkshire man, who came to Ireland in the early 1630s as a chaplain to the army of King Charles I. Since Heaton's time, countless people have travelled to this stony outcrop just to see the spring gentian.

The gentian is so familiar that it needs no description, and suffice it to say, no-one should go to The Burren to dig up plants for their garden - such action is indefensible. As the Spring gentian resents disturbance, the plants removed from the wild will certainly die in a distant garden. This gentian can be grown very easily from seeds, which will germinate like cress when fresh. The seedlings should be kept well fed and then pricked out in little clumps when big enough to handle. They will grow rapidly into a tight mound of leaves, and in the following spring will be covered with flowers.

When in The Burren during the spring of 1983 with Graham Stuart Thomas, guided by Catherine O'Donoghue, I happened upon a gentian with the palest of pale blue flowers - they were almost white. I took photographs, but left the plant alone, to bloom for others, and 'to waste its sweetness on the desert air'. It was not the pure albino mentioned by Reginald Farrer, but it was like a little white periwinkle, glittering on the green turf. In subsequent years, at the same place, other white gentians have appeared, blossomed, and withered back into obscurity, and I have seen slopes where gentians with sky-blue flowers, paler that the predominant azure ones, abound. And, most extraordinary, in 1995 a clump with distinctly mauve petals, more grey than blue. The Spring gentian is not a uniform blue.

The white gentian of 1983 set me searching through past accounts of the Belfast shows of the Alpine Garden Socicty, which are excellent showcases for alpine enthusiasts in this island. In 1967 Mr L. Williamson exhibited a Spring gentian with ice-blue flowers that were larger than usual. He received a medal for his pan of this variety of *Gentiana verna*. The same variety was shown in 1975 and was acclaimed as a 'show stopper'. This ice-blue gentian came from The Burren, having been raised from seed collected there. Will Ingwersen, that eminent authority on alpine plants, grew it under the name ***Gentiana verna* 'Clare'**[2] - he received it from John Main when he was working at Harlow Carr Gardens. It is described as having pale blue - Cambridge blue - flowers with a slight hint of turquoise in the petals. It comes more or less true from seed, as long as it is not pollinated with pollen from a dark blue variety.

No matter how many unusual forms there may be, the true blue is still the best. I cannot resist quoting Reginald Farrer again. For him this species was 'the Gentian of gentians', and he delighted most in the robust Burren plants that throve 'among the rank herbage of Ladies' Tresses, Ladies' Bedstraw, Ladies' Fingers and the whole botanical department of a lady's plenishing'.

A CREEPING JUNIPER

Richard Heaton noticed two other plants during his visit to 'the Mountain twixt Gort and Galloway', the mountain avens and the juniper. The latter is a more enduring rockery plant than either the ephemeral gentian or the carpet-forming mountain avens. Juniper is common in western Ireland. There are shrubs of it clothing the limestone pavement west of Gort, but it is not particular about soil type, and I have seen juniper on peaty moorlands as well as on The Burren. On the River Shannon at Lough Derg, there are woodlands of tall juniper trees, although in most places it forms low shrubs or creeps over rocks.

In 1923, Murray Hornibrook published a manual on dwarf conifers that went to a second edition and was, until recently, the bible of dwarf conifer enthusiasts. In the first edition he noted that he had collected a variety of wild juniper in Connemara that was utterly prostrate. In a letter to Herman Grootendorst written in November 1933, Murray Hornibrook recalled the discovery of the juniper.

The original plant was found in Connemara - a mild, wild district in the extreme west of Ireland, mostly bogland and heather but also a good deal of rough country covered with blocks of limestone. There is quite a considerable amount of wild [*Juniperus communis*] here and there but, contrary to the trade name of the fastigiate form [*Juniperus communis* 'Hibernica'], no fastigiate form of the juniper has ever been found wild in Ireland and the larger proportion of the plants I have ever seen are all low irregular shrubs - I never saw any other prostrate or semi-prostrate form and only the one plant of the form we now discuss. The original plant, to the best of my recollection, was about 1 metre in diameter and perfectly prostrate - possibly the foliage was about 10-15 centimetres in height but the plant was a near a "prostrate mat" as is possible to imagine - it was falling down a sloping, rocky bank ... that is to say that it followed the contours of the rock covering it like a moss.[3]

This prostrate juniper, *Juniperus communis* **'Hornibrookii'**[4] is quite common in cultivation although some plants sold and grown as 'Hornibrookii' are not correctly named. Its small foliage is characteristic, as is the slow growth and the spreading, prostrate habit. The annual growth is less than eight centimetres, and it usually does not grow more than ten centimetres tall.

Murray Hornibrook had a fine garden at Knapton, near Abbeyleix, where he grew many alpine plants as well as his favourite dwarf conifers. He wrote numerous articles on rock-gardens and their plants. In 1922, when the Irish Free State was formed, Hornibrook left Ireland taking with him some of his plants, but he donated the bulk of his collection to the Botanic Gardens in Glasnevin, including many of the most important specimens of slow-growing and dwarf conifers. The original plant of *Juniperus communis* 'Hornibrookii' was not included in the gift - it remained at Knapton as Hornibrook told Grootendorst in November 1933:

I have not seen the plant since I had to leave my home in Ireland after the Revolution in 1922 - the garden exists no more and I rather think that the mother plant is dead - it grew splendidly in my garden the years I had it. I planted it on a ... ledge and it grew to the edge of it and then fell straight down the face of the rock cliff. It never attempted to revert to upright growth, at which I am not surprised as it was not an "alpine" form but was growing quite low down - say between 100 and 200 metres.[5]

The National Botanic Gardens, Glasnevin, received numerous other rare and unusual varieties that Murray Hornibrook had patiently collected - various saxifrage hybrids, the spiral rush and the auricula 'Old Irish Blue' are but three examples. The parting was a great wrench for Hornibrook, but he told John Besant, the newly appointed Acting Keeper, that 'I am glad to think that these [plants] will make Glasnevin contain the finest collection of dwarf conifers in the world, and that my efforts to collect them during the past years will not have been in vain!'. Many of the small conifers have now outstretched their dwarf state at Glasnevin, because they were only *slow-growing* plants and more than 70 years have passed since Hornibrook donated the collection.

There are two other cultivars of juniper of Irish origin - more correctly allegedly of Irish origin. One is misnamed the Irish juniper, *Juniperus communis* 'Hibernica', but its origin is not known. It was catalogued by Conrad Loddiges of London in 1836, at a time when it was naively believed that any plant with an upright habit came from Ireland - the examples of the Irish yew and the Irish furze were cited as proof. This juniper probably acquired its Irish ancestry by association as it is a very compact shrub that forms a column of blue-green and tightly packed, vertical branchlets. The other juniper did come from Ireland and made its debut on television in January 1987. *Juniperus communis* 'Derrynane' was collected at Derrynane in County Kerry by Derek Richardson during his summer holidays in 1970. The original plant was growing beside the sea and was 'as prostrate as a lawn'. Like 'Hornibrookii', 'Derrynane' tumbles over boulders, hugging the ground.[6]

SAXIFRAGES

One of Murray Hornibrook's interests was saxifrages and he raised at least one hybrid in Knapton garden, which is sometimes available from English nurseries; indeed in the last month I spotted *Saxifraga* 'Knapton Pink' for sale on the stand of 'alpine plants' outside our village greengrocer's shop. The mossy saxifrages are among the easiest plants for a rock-garden, although some species are very demanding and difficult.

In Ireland there are a dozen native species of *Saxifraga* and several interesting wild hybrids. These range from the tiny annual wall-plant, rue-leaved saxifrage, *Saxifraga tridactylites*, to the large spoon-leaved *cabáiste an mhadra rua*, the fox's cabbage, *Saxifraga spathularis*, that has acquired a number of spurious names including Saint Patrick's cabbage. Two mossy saxifrages inhabit The Burren. *Saxifraga rosacea*, known as the Irish saxifrage, grows near the coast and forms hummocks of rosettes that glow with pink and are crowned by white flowers in May. *Saxifraga hypnoides*, the archetypal mossy saxifrage, seems to prefer growing in the shade of the stone walls that crisscross the limestone pavements; it also has white flowers.

The wild saxifrages of Ireland are very variable plants, with local races that present many difficulties for botanists. On Arranmore, off the western coast of County Donegal, there grows an extraordinary mossy one with glandular hairs covering the leaves and flower stems. The rosettes are pale green, sometimes with the same rosy tinge as *Saxifraga rosacea*. The blooms are large, composed of five pure white petals that have green veins.

The Arranmore saxifrage was discovered by Henry Chichester Hart at Polldhu on the island's western side in 1880. Several other people collected it later, but it is rare and appears to have died out in some of its stations on the island. It is now protected by law and cannot be collected from the wild. In 1949 the late Professor David Webb of Trinity College, Dublin, who made a detailed investigation of this group of saxifrages, decided that the Arranmore one, which has never been found on the Irish mainland, represented a distinct species and he named it after H. C. Hart, *Saxifraga hartii*.[7] Like *Sorbus hibernica*, this saxifrage may be considered to be one of the few species restricted to Ireland.

Hart's saxifrage was first brought into cultivation more than 50 years ago - Professor Webb told me the remarkable story of its introduction.[8] The lighthouse keeper on Arranmore, D. J. O'Sullivan, was a very keen amateur naturalist, and he sent specimens, about six shoots, of the local mossy saxifrage to Arthur Stelfox at the Natural History Museum in Dublin. Mr Stelfox put these in a plant press to dry, but when he

took them out of the press they seemed rather lively, so he planted them, and they took. About 1944-5, I removed a couple to the old T.C.D. garden and had it there in cultivation for a number of years. Round about 1950 or 1951, probably, I gave plants to Kew, and they later gave them to Cambridge. It seemed to remain pretty constant in cultivation.[9]

Thus for the past half century, Hart's saxifrage has been grown in a few botanical gardens and David Webb named the saxifrage after keeping plants under observation in the Ballsbridge Botanic Garden, although he had not had a chance to see it growing wild. Indeed no botanist alive in the 1950s, apart from Mr O'Sullivan, had seen Hart's saxifrage growing in its native habitat. In 1956 and 1957, David McClintock visited Arranmore, and succeeded eventually in finding the plant in a small gully. He collected a few rosettes, and gave some to Will Ingwersen for propagation and thus Hart's saxifrage entered the trade.

The end of this story is not quite so simple. In the late 1970s, Professor Webb at last managed to get to Arranmore and study the saxifrage in its native habitats. He found it only in one place, on the north coast, a few hundred metres east of the lighthouse. According to his own account, some of the plants had plenty of glandular hairs - the character that he used to distinguish *Saxifraga hartii* from *Saxifraga rosacea* - but others had none at all and were just like the plants of *Saxifraga rosacea* that grow on Clare Island off the coast of Mayo, and there were intermediates. Professor Webb thus decided that Hart's saxifrage was not a distinct species, and so he made it into a subspecies of the Irish saxifrage, *Saxifraga rosacea* subsp. *hartii*.[10]

Saxifraga rosacea subsp. *hartii* is not difficult to grow; it will thrive in a pan in a cold greenhouse, and is hardy. Like many plants that inhabit rocky places, it needs both adequate moisture and excellent drainage, conditions that are difficult to achieve. The easiest way is to construct a low dry-stone wall, and plant Hart's saxifrage, and similar plants, in the cracks between the stones on the north-facing vertical side. At the National Botanic Gardens, Glasnevin, hummocks of *Saxifraga rosacea* subsp. *hartii* throve on such a miniature cliff.

Henry Hart was a fascinating character. He was the naturalist on the British Polar Expedition of 1875, and also worked in Palestine. For many years he lived in Donegal and wrote the standard flora of that county. He had a passion for mountains, and collected plants on many of Ireland's highest peaks. For a wager, he walked from Dublin to the summit of Lugnaquilla in County Wicklow, and back, in one day, keeping to the hills most of the way - the distance is over 100 kilometres.

Apart from the native species there are several garden varieties of mossy saxifrage with Irish connections. Of the cultivars, the finest certainly is *Saxifraga* **'Ballawley Guardsman'**.[11] It has rosettes of bright green, and proliferates easily. The flowers are deep red, and the petals do not fade, as in so many other varieties, to a streaky pink. This was raised at Ballawley Park, near Dublin, by Desmond Shaw-Smith and was introduced by him in the 1940s. With *Bergenia* 'Ballawley' it is one of the few surviving cultivars from that vanished nursery.

WOOD ANEMONES

Too few of our native plants are grown as ornamentals, yet with a new interest in the cultivation of indigenous plants, we may see increased attention being paid to our wild species. The heathers have provided more garden varieties than other native plants, but most of them require acid, peaty soil. Some of the easiest, least demanding wild plants are the spring flowers, primroses, blue-bells and wood anemones. While not strictly rock-garden plants, they flourish in rockeries and are quite happy in lime-rich, boulder clay.

Under the ash trees in my former garden in County Kildare, wild wood anemones spread slowly but steadily. They were pretty in the spring, under the spiny crown of *Mahonia*. At first I only grew the ordinary white variety but there are many cultivars available, ranging in colour from white to pink and blue, and with single or double flowers.

When I first wrote this book in 1983, I claimed that the loveliest of the blue wood anemones is *Anemone nemorosa* **'Robinsoniana'**.[12] It has large flowers, up to five centimetres across, with about seven petals. The blossom is pale blue with a faint suggestion of lavender, while the outside of the petals is the colour of raw silk, a pale fawn. E. A. Bowles admired this lovely anemone, but could not forgive its habit of closing on dull days. There are several other blues, and they can be distinguished from 'Robinsoniana' by their purple petal backs.

I must now add that a finer blue was shown to me by Miss Evelyn Booth in the mid-1980s when I was visiting her at home in Bunclody, at the foot of Mount Leinster. She had a lovely garden, that stepped up from the house by a series of terraces, each one planted with a fascinating array of shrubs and perennials, to a well maintained vegetable garden that yielded tasty globe artichokes, among other things. A wonderful magnolia, growing against the house, offered up its perfumed white flowers at her bedroom windowsill, and a pineapple-scented Moroccan broom (*Cytisus battandieri*) blossomed by the front door. Little stone troughs

12. Anemone nemorosa 'Lucy's Wood'

13. Anemone obtusiloba f. *patula*

burgeoned with choice crocuses, dwarf daffodils and cyclamens, and a fine white African wandflower seeded itself about everywhere. I learned to eat globe artichokes at Evelyn's - even botanists unfamiliar with these armour-plated buds have to watch while someone else takes the first 'bite' - and soon I enjoyed their cold hearts smothered in home-made, herb-rich mayonnaise. Evelyn was one of the original dedicatees of *An Irish flower garden* because I owed so many stories and plants to her. She was an expert fisherman, a keen field botanist, and an accomplished gardener.

Evelyn Booth's wood anemone came from a small copse not far from her house - the copse was Lucy's Wood, and that was the name chosen by Evelyn for her house, so we chose to name it *Anemone nemorosa* **'Lucy's Wood'** (Plate 12).[13] The original clump was growing in Lucy's Wood, but Evelyn Booth transferred a piece to her garden where it proliferated. Each flower has six or seven broad petals which are bright blue with a slight violet tinge on the inside, and the same colour but a paler shade on the outside. The flowers are large, up to four and a half centimetres across, and are held aloft on quite stout, slightly hairy stems. Like every wood anemone, the flowers face the sun from early morning and track it across the sky before closing, as if to sleep, well before dusk.

The anemone named after William Robinson has obscure origins. He saw it in the University Botanic Garden at Oxford about 1870, and was given some rhizomes by the curator, William Baxter, who told Robinson that the plant was believed to have come from Ireland. Bowles did not believe this story, but even if it is not true - we cannot verify it at this time - the name the anemone bears is that of Ireland's most remarkable and influential horticulturist.

Like Bernard McMahon, William Robinson was born 'somewhere in Ireland'. His father was a land-agent for the St Georges, and eloped with one of the ladies of that family, leaving his own family to fend for themselves. William was trained at Curraghmore in County Waterford, and later worked at Ballykilcavan in County Laois. According to the well-known story, he argued with his employer, and departed from Ballykilcavan leaving the greenhouse windows open on a frosty night. The rest of his long life was spent in Britain and is well documented unlike his mysterious childhood and early manhood.

Reginald Farrer described William Robinson as a Moses. 'Out of the dense darkness arose the immortal Mr Robinson. ... He reminds us of beauties which we have almost forgotten and leads us on to a land flowing with sweetness and light'. But the man himself was certainly not all sweetness and light, for Robinson was an irascible, cantankerous bachelor, an enigma who provoked strangely contradictory opinions. 'Mr Robinson, the great and good', was Farrer's obsequious description, yet he complained that in the search for the wild garden, Robinson was leading gardeners astray and doing 'incalculable harm in a vain, impotent striving for the so-called natural'.

SHADOW'S BUTTERCUP

The genus *Anemone* is a large one, containing about 100 species. The majority occur in the northern hemisphere in habitats ranging from Irish woodlands to the highest Himalayan meadows. Apart from the pale blue of the Lucy's Wood or William Robinson's wood anemones, one of the most delicate blue-flowered rock-plants is a species from the Himalaya, *Anemone obtusiloba*. One form of this, ***Anemone obtusiloba* f. *patula*** (Plate 13),[14] was collected on Mount Victoria in western Burma by Lady Charlotte Wheeler Cuffe, and was nicknamed 'Shadow's buttercup'.

This anemone looks like a weedy European buttercup when it is not in bloom. It has a rosette of stalked leaves, clothed in silvery hairs; each leaf is divided into many narrow segments. In May and June long stems extend from the rosette, each one bearing several five-petalled flowers resembling a blue buttercup. The petals are glossy and look as if they are made from fine blue oriental porcelain. The stems tend to lie horizontally, so that the flowers form a ring around the clump of new leaves.

Lady Cuffe found the anemone during her first visit to Mount Victoria in 1911 when she accompanied Winifred MacNabb. She told her cousin, the Baroness Prochazka, that there was a carpet of the blue buttercups on the last saddle of the peak just below the summit. In the following spring, Charlotte Cuffe and Winifred MacNabb returned to the mountain, and collected some of the wild plants. Lady Cuffe brought three strong plants of the blue buttercup to Europe in 1913; two of them arrived in Glasnevin in August. When the plants flowered at the Botanic Gardens, Sir Frederick Moore sent specimens to Kew for naming. The buttercup was identified as a form of *Anemone obtusiloba*, but the Kew botanists decided that Lady Cuffe's plant belonged to an undescribed form with spreading stems. Her variety was illustrated in the *Botanical magazine* in November 1915.

Why was it called 'Shadow's buttercup'? I have already alluded to the resemblance it bears to our wild buttercups, so part of the name is explained. What about Shadow? This was Charlotte's pet-name. When she was very young, Charlotte was extremely delicate and was frequently ill. On one occasion she faded away almost to a shadow, but recovered and was nursed back to robust health. The metaphor became her nick-name. Although she thought it an absurd name, Charlotte obviously liked it, and usually signed her letters 'Shadow'.

The delicate, shadowy girl recovered thoroughly, for Lady Charlotte Wheeler Cuffe is remembered in Kilkenny, where she resided after returning from Burma, as a formidable and energetic person. She lived into her 100th year!

MISS ELLEN'S ALPINE CRESS

I remarked in an earlier chapter that Ireland has produced relatively few prominent lady gardeners and botanists. There are inevitable exceptions, and at the beginning of the nineteenth century, one lady was active collecting native plants, especially minute mosses and liverworts. Ellen Hutchins was applauded for her work by several of her male contemporaries including James Mackay of Trinity College Botanic Garden, who said she was an amiable and accomplished woman, 'unremitting in her investigation of the botany of the south of Ireland'.

Miss Hutchins was born at Ballylickey near Bantry in 1785. She was sent to school in Dublin, but her schooldays ended when she became seriously ill. Professor Whitley Stokes, a lecturer in Trinity College and a friend of her family, nursed her back to health. He influenced Ellen and persuaded her to take up botany as a pastime. Stokes introduced her to other botanists, including Mackay and the English botanical author, Dawson Turner. Miss Hutchins supplied many specimens from County Cork for Turner's works on seaweeds and mosses.

Ellen returned to Ballylickey when she was fully recovered and there cared for her aged mother and invalid brother. In her few spare moments she collected local plants and paid particular attention to the small non-flowering ones such as lichens, liverworts and seaweeds. She painted many of the seaweeds; the precision and delicacy of her work is quite remarkable. As she took an interest in plants that other collectors tended to ignore, Ellen Hutchins discovered many new species. At first she was reluctant to let Mackay and Turner name plants after her, but she eventually capitulated and a suite of mosses, liverworts and seaweeds bears her name.

Sir James Smith, founder of the Linnean Society of London, remarked that Miss Hutchins could find anything. Her contribution to Irish botany was summed up by Professor William Harvey:

> To her the botany of Ireland is under many obligations, particularly the cryptogamic branch, in which field, until her time, little explored, she was particularly fortunate in detecting new and beautiful objects, several of which remain among the rarest species to the present day.

As a crowning tribute to this unassuming girl, the eminent botanist Robert Brown dedicated a genus of alpine flowers to her, members of the cabbage family, *Hutchinsia*. Sadly, for my Irish garden, *Hutchinsia* has almost vanished from botanical books, and the species formerly placed in it are now consigned to other genera within the cabbage family (Brassicaceae). *Hutchinsia alpina*, the little perennial plant of rock gardens, has had to be renamed *Pritzelago alpina*. To make matters even more perplexing, however, *Hutchinsia* has been retained, kept as an English name for a tiny annual that grows on limestone and sand dunes in England, Wales and the Channel Islands. Whatever its Latin name, the little perennial alpine cress once named after Ellen Hutchins is easy to grow and is a delightful memorial for a diligent amateur botanist.

15. *Hutchinsia alpina*, now *Pritzelago alpina*

Hutchinsia alpina (Figure 15), alias *Pritzelago alpina*,[15] forms a mound of dark green foliage. It crawls over rocks and fills cracks between stones, preferring a cool, moist place and reasonably good loam. The tiny leaves, no more than two centimetres long, are composed of three ovate leaflets on a long stalk. In May, the hummocks sprout clusters of flowers on stems about five centimetres tall. The flowers have four, small, pure white petals and resemble miniature wallflowers.

Reginald Farrer described *Hutchinsia* as an astonishingly refined, bright and charming plant. He noted that it was of great value in rockeries as cover for small daffodils and other dwarf bulbs

Miss Hutchins tended a garden at her home in Ballylickey. She received plants from her friends, and Dawson Turner instructed her how to plant some of them. He was deeply affected by her early death, for he was thus deprived of 'a great part of the pleasure I derived from botany'. His tribute was some lines of verse that concluded

> In every native of the hill and vale
> She found attraction, and, where beauty fail'd,
> Applauded odour or commended use.[16]

AN IRISH HAREBELL

Pritzelago alpina grows wild in the mountains of southern Europe, whence comes a starry-flowered harebell named *Campanula garganica*. Murray Hornibrook, writing in *Irish gardening*, included it in a list of easy rock-plants. It thrives when planted in well-drained, rich loam, and should be allowed to creep over stones. *Campanula garganica* forms a compact cushion of small heart-shaped leaves that have scalloped margins. The harebell blooms in July, producing long sprays of flowers, each bloom being composed of five pointed petals arranged like a star with green sepals poking out between the petals. The flower is about three centimetres across and in the centre is a long erect style which is covered with white pollen when the flower opens, and has an expanded blue stigma.

The best variety of this species is *Campanula garganica* **'W. H. Paine'**,[17] named after the manager of the Tully Nursery near Kildare. The cultivar was discovered in the nursery early this century, and was exhibited at the Royal Horticultural Society in London on 30 June 1914 by Watson's Nursery of Clontarf. 'W. H. Paine' received an award of merit and was illustrated in the Society's journal.

Although it has the appearance of a delicate plant, 'W. H. Paine' has survived in cultivation for seventy years, but it is rare. The tips of the petals are deep purplish-blue, which contrasts well with the pure white centre. It can be grown in a pan in an alpine house, but this is not necessary and it will exist happily out-of-doors. It has to be propagated by division.

W. H. Paine was in charge of the Tully Nursery while the famous Japanese Garden was being constructed nearby. The nursery was well-known for its collection of alpine plants which were propagated in vast numbers. The range of terrestrial orchids was also substantial. In February 1911, Paine delivered a lecture at the annual general meeting of the Irish Gardeners' Association, and it was reported in *Irish gardening*. His paper on alpine plants was

> trolled out in that free and fluent style which carried his audience with him as he scaled the Pyrenees and filled his pockets with such good things as made the stay-at-home hardy plant-lover's mouth water; for Mr Paine's graphic description, ranging from grave to gay, from lively to severe, "all out of his own head", left not a few wondering, till climbing higher and waxing warmer on his subject, "the wonder grew one little head could carry all he knew".[18]

Paine, an Englishman, known, perhaps affectionately, as 'Daddy Paine', collected alpines from Irish habitats too! He advertised native plants 'collected from the coast of Clare' including Spring gentian, mountains avens, thrift and something called 'Saxifraga ibernica'. W. H. Paine suffered badly from gout, and eventually had to give up his job because he could only get about in a wheelchair.

GARRYARD PRIMROSES

County Kildare has produced a goodly assortment of fine garden plants, ranging from the Straffan snowdrop to the lost Saint Brigid's Christmas rose. None of the plants was deliberately bred; they were all chance finds by keen gardeners. Kildare was also the birth-place of a race of primroses with bronze leaves which became popular in the mid-1900s, but which have since almost disappeared and are now anxiously sought by gardeners concerned about the loss of fine garden flowers.

The bronze primroses are the Garryard cultivars. The first one arose in the garden of a house named Garryard, at Johnstown near Naas. The person who discovered it was James Whiteside Dane, one-time deputy lieutenant of the county and president of the Kildare Archaeological Society. He moved to Garryard about 1910 and lived there until 1922 when he moved to Annaghmakerrig in County Monaghan.

The date-of-birth of the first Garryard primrose is not known; some authorities state that it appeared in the 1890s but James Dane did not live in Garryard at that time. In 1920 plants of a primrose described as 'Dane's Primrose' were distributed from Glasnevin to Glenstal in County Limerick; this is the earliest record I can find of the Garryard race. Published accounts of the bronze-leaved forms do not appear before about 1930.

The first Garryard primrose was grown by Cecil Monson, a well-known Dublin theatre-man, the author of one rather unsuccessful play, and a skilful and enthusiastic primrose grower.

He obtained it from his mother, who in turn had received plants from Mr Whiteside Dane. *Primula* 'Appleblossom' had bronze leaves, in shape and texture just like those of the wild primrose. It grew well and increased readily. The flowers were borne in clusters on robust red stems, and the individual blooms were remarkably like apple blossom - pink and white. Although James Whiteside Dane gave plants to other gardeners and Glasnevin also distributed it, 'Appleblossom' seems to be extinct. Cecil Monson lost his stock in the early 1940s and never saw the variety again.

Since 'Appleblossom' arose, other primroses with bronze leaves have been raised and they all bear the patronym Garryard although none came from that garden. The next variety was *Primula* **'Guinevere'** shown in Dublin as early as 1935.[19] It is said to have been raised by Mrs Johnson of Kinlough in County Leitrim, the same lady who produced 'Kinlough Beauty' and 'Lady Greer'. 'Guinevere' is plentiful today. It has fine foliage - my plants, grown in a shaded place, have rich purple-stained leaves in summer. The flower is pink tinted with mauve, and it has a yellow eye. 'Guinevere' increases easily and is the most robust of the older Garryard varieties.

Cecil Monson moved to Dromahair in County Leitrim and there he tried to recreate the original 'Appleblossom' by sowing seed from Garryard primroses. Before his death in 1974, he had produced two plants that approached the extinct 'Appleblossom' in their bronze leaves and stout stems; one had deep cream flowers and the second had pink blossoms flushed with deeper pink on the margins of the petals. The fate of these new varieties is unknown, but Cecil Monson did great service in recording information of the early history of the Garryard race. Another of his primroses, a red tinged with cerise, with distinctive white flecks where the petals are lobed, was still available from nurseries a few years ago, but is now not listed although I am sure it survives in gardens around County Antrim - this was 'Doctor Molly', named after Dr Molly Sanderson of Ballymoney.[20]

The gardens of old Ireland were famous for primroses. Even a century ago, in the 1880s, there were keen gardeners in Britain who hoped to find good old-fashioned varieties of garden flowers surviving on this island. Juliana Ewing founded the first, short-lived society devoted to the conservation of garden and native plants, the Parkinson Society. Writing in February 1884, Mrs Ewing suggested to readers of *Aunt Judy's magazine* that nurseries such as Rodger, McClelland & Co. of Newry (the predecessor of Daisy Hill Nursery), and Hartland of Cork might have old varieties of primroses. Ireland, she suggested,

> between a soft climate and some neglect (very conservative of those plants which resent disturbance), has, in all probability, kept many old flowers in over-grown gardens that have become rare, if not extinct, in other parts of the British Isles.[21]

So perhaps began the legend that old garden flowers, especially primroses, abound in Ireland. A century later, in 1984, I published what I believed was the obituary for those 'legendary old ladies in Ireland who are alleged to have a wonderful collection of primroses'. They are extinct, like the dodo. Be that as it may, like another bird, the mythical phoenix, they rise as veritable phantoms every year, because every year without fail I receive letters asking me for the addresses and telephone numbers of primrose collectors, in other words those 'old ladies in Ireland who ... have a wonderful collection of primroses'.

LISSADELL

One of the gardens famed for its primroses and alpines was Lissadell in County Sligo, the home of the Gore-Booths. Eva and Constance Gore-Booth, 'two girls in silk kimonos', were the sisters of Sir Josslyn Gore-Booth who was the driving force behind the famous nursery and daffodil farm. Constance became the Countess Marckievicz and was condemned to death for her part in the Easter Rising of 1916.

Lissadell is best known as the source of several hybrids of the oriental candelabra primroses. 'Ailin Aroon', 'Red Hugh' and 'Lissadell Hybrid' were among the named cultivars. I grew 'Red Hugh' on a shaded, raised peat bed in my Celbridge garden for several years, and then it withered away, probably due to vine weevils. 'Lissadell Pink', a good perennial with tiers of carmine-eyed, pale pink flowers, survives. Jim Reynolds rescued it from an old garden and now cultivates it in his own splendid garden, Butterstream, near Trim, whence one day it will be returned to Lissadell.[22] Sir Josslyn Gore-Booth also produced new varieties of daffodils and a few unique alpine plants. The catalogues of the bulb farm and general nursery were crammed with fascinating plants and that enthusiast for alpines, Henri Correvon of Geneva, described Lissadell as 'the paradise ... one of the most brilliant gardens ... that I have ever seen'. The walls were also clothed in choice specimens, including *Abutilon vitifolium* and *Solanum crispum*.

Of the few surviving Lissadell cultivars, the finest that I know, is a dwarf cranesbill which blooms in June and July. *Geranium* x *lindavicum* **'Lissadell'**[23] has small, silvery-green leaves, about the size of an old ten-pence piece and circular in outline. They have long stalks and the blade is divided into about seven segments each of which is cut into two or three lobes. The clusters of flowers spring from the middle of the mound of leaves on long stalks. There are five overlapping purple petals, conspicuously veined with deeper purple and very dark towards the base so that the centre of each flower is royal purple. The silver, green and purple is a fine combination and *Geranium* 'Lissadell' is hardy and suitable for rockeries. It can be propagated by division but is not common in gardens - I had only seen it in the collections of a few of my gardening friends before this book first appeared, and while it is still rare, a few nurseries stock it from time to time. 'Lissadell' had a sibling named 'Alanah' with silvery foliage and a profusion of vivid crimson-purple flowers - although I thought it was extinct, one English nursery has recently listed it, although whether the plant is the true 'Alanah' remains to be seen.

The garden at Lissadell is no longer the paradise seen by Henri Correvon, but happily plans are being made to restore it. Sir Josslyn died in the early 1940s, but the family still live there. Like the garden, many of the Lissadell cultivars have gone, although as the garden seems to have some hopes of being restored, I wonder whether *Aubrieta* 'Lissadell Pink', *Campanula pusila* 'Lissadell', *Geranium* x *lindavicum* 'Alanah' and some others might still survive?

BLUE-EYED MARY WITH STARRY EYES

Old cultivars do not often come to light, although the painstaking work during the past fifteen years by members of the National Council for the Conservation of Plants and Gardens and the Irish Garden Plant Society, has demonstrated that garden plants can be resurrected. Meanwhile, new varieties continue to arise by chance, as well as by deliberate breeding, and some of these soon acquire a fashionable status.

I was amused, and pleased, to see a relatively new Irish garden variety displayed, along with exclamations of its beauty, at shows of the Royal Horticultural Society in London last spring. Indeed, considering that this plant had only been named in 1990, its progress through the garden network has been rapid.

In 1987, Eithne Clarke called at the National Botanic Gardens, Glasnevin, to ask if a sport that had appeared on a plant of *Omphalodes*, which is often called blue-eyed Mary, in her garden at Rathfarnham would be worth propagating. She brought along some photographs of the flowers, and I was entranced. I told her that I thought it would be well worth propagating and so Mrs Clarke gave me a few offsets which rooted easily. I planted one in my Celbridge garden, and propagated from it, passing an offset to Dr Molly Sanderson with the injunction that she was not to give it away to anyone else. I knew this would have exactly the opposite effect, which indeed was my intention, and soon the new blue-eyed Mary was cropping up in gardens around Ireland. Eventually it became obvious that a name was needed. As this blue-eyed Mary had flowers that looked like stars I had little difficulty finding a name for it.

Omphalodes cappadocicum **'Starry Eyes'**[24] is a splendid and attractive plant - by the bye, *Omphalodes* comes from Greek and means navel-like, and one unattractive name for this plant is navelwort, although it is not one you will often hear used. The individual flowers are about half a centimetre across. The five petals are fused together, forming a slightly concave flower, and each petal has a rim of pale mauvey blue with a darker blue central flash. The eye is white. Thus, each flower has a lovely starry appearance, and as they are clustered together in an erect branching spike held well above the plain green leaves, the effect is dazzling.

There is another excellent form of *Omphalodes cappadocicum* grown in Irish gardens, especially at Birr Castle - under the tree that was planted just inside the entrance gates by An Taisce as a memorial to Michael Rosse, the sixth earl, there is a carpet of this one. Graham Thomas was most impressed by Birr's exceptionally fine variety, which when planted in his garden in Surrey was far more vigorous and produced larger flowers of a better blue than the forms of blue-eyed Mary then cultivated in England. He enquired about its origins and learned from Lady Rosse that

About [1938], I went for the first time to a beautiful neighbouring Carolean house called Gloster, belonging to a charming old recluse Brigadier Hardcross Lloyd - a very cultivated man who had made an exquisite garden. My first sight was an avenue of old trees, with solid carpets on either side right to the house of this celestial blue.[25]

Was Brigadier Hardcross Lloyd's carpet of celestial blue formed by an old cultivar, 'lost' and 'found' again, and has it, perhaps, entered the nursery trade elsewhere under another name? The only way to answer such unanswerable questions is to grow all the varieties of blue-eyed Mary together in the same place, and to hope that some day some one will find, serendipitously, the answer. Meanwhile, we can grow and admire 'Starry Eyes' and I hope this variety will survive with its history intact.

DR SCOULER'S *PENSTEMON*

The problem with cultivars (garden varieties) is that they cannot be recovered if they become extinct, and their stories cannot be told once they are forgotten. Natural species and varieties can be reintroduced into gardens from their native habitats, and in almost every instance, a story can be told about their discovery because there will be an original pressed and dried specimen preserved in a museum. Thus there is little danger of **Penstemon fruticosus var. scouleri**[26] disappearing from Irish gardens, as it is still abundant in the north-west of the United States of America, and we should not forget how it was discovered.

This variety forms a low shrubby plant which will thrive in rock-gardens or herbaceous borders. It has narrow leaves up to five centimetres long, and these are sometimes toothed along the margins. The flowers can be rich lavender, pink or pure white - both the lavender and white forms are grown in Ireland and they are equally attractive. Each tubular blossom has two distinct lips, and looks a bit like an elongated snap-dragon. The upper lip is divided into two lobes, while the lower one is three-lobed and covered in hairs. When well-grown, the low bushes are smothered with bloom in May and June.

Scouler's penstemon was discovered by the Scottish plant-hunter David Douglas in the spring of 1826 when he was working on the Pacific coast of North America. He was based at the trading post of Kettle Falls at the confluence of the Columbia and Colville Rivers. David had travelled from England on the brig *William and Mary* with Dr John Scouler, who was a surgeon and naturalist. The vessel had been chartered to explore the Pacific Northwest, and Douglas had been sent by the Horticultural Society of London to collect seeds for English gardeners. Scouler and Douglas were good friends and they botanized together during the voyage, in exotic places like Madeira, Juan Fernandez (the island of Robinson Crusoe) and the Galapagos Islands - they were there a decade before Charles Darwin. On the continent, the two men went collecting on several occasions. On Saint Patrick's Day 1825, Scouler and Douglas walked eight kilometres to Tongue Point near Fort George, and Scouler returned to base with his 'vascula and handkerchiefs ... filled with mosses and land shells'. Dr Scouler was not with

David Douglas when the penstemon was discovered, but Douglas requested that it should be named after his friend and companion. John Scouler returned to England in 1826. He was appointed Professor of Natural History in the University of Glasgow in 1829 and five years later came to Dublin as Professor of Mineralogy and Geology to the Royal Dublin Society. He maintained a strong interest in botany and tried to encourage local naturalists, including the Connemara botanist, William McCalla.

Dr Scouler is commemorated in a number of plants from the northwest of America. The common species of willow in the Seattle area is *Salix scouleri*. There is a handsome polypody fern named after Scouler, and a fish, a mineral and at least four fossils also bear his name. He retired from the professorship in Dublin in 1853, and after a period of wandering around Europe, he returned to Scotland where he died, a recluse, in 1871. He was a gentle man with an adventurous spirit, who often got into difficulties in his pursuit of plants. In 1846 he was botanizing in Portugal, whence he wrote to William Harvey. Harvey reported Scouler's adventure to Sir William Hooker:

> He has had great sport in Portugal. I have just had a letter from him. He was twice arrested on suspicion [of spying] and once fell among the Miquelites, but got through very well and enjoyed himself thoroughly![27]

HIMALAYAN FERNS

I have not grown *Polypodium scouleri*, which inhabits coastal regions of the Pacific northwest of America from British Columbia to California, and it is only rarely offered for sale. The fronds are leathery and glossy green, and the fern is said to grow well in hanging baskets.

On the other hand, I have grown the fern that rejoices in the name ***Pseudophegopteris levingei***.[28] It is a hardy little fern, which can become quite rampant when the conditions are congenial. At the National Botanic Gardens, Glasnevin, this species is cultivated in pans in the alpine house, but it is very happy out-of-doors. Like many deciduous ferns which produce new fronds in the late spring, frost or cold wind can damage the unfurling croziers. The mature fronds are softly hairy and pale green, and while they superficially resemble the fronds of our native brittle bladder-fern, *Cystopteris fragilis*, this exotic species has somewhat larger and less brittle fronds.

I saw *Pseudophegopteris levingei* for the first time in Graham Thomas's garden at Horsell near Woking, Surrey; it was only recently introduced into cultivation from China by Dr Alan Leslie who collected spores from the fern in the mountains west of Chengdu in Sichuan during 1981. Graham was proud of the new species, but my interest was aroused more by the name than by the delicate, hairy fronds.

Pseudophegopteris levingei is a native of eastern Asia, including the Himalaya, and its name commemorates the Irish botanist Henry ('Harry') Corbyn Levinge, the ninth and youngest son of Sir Richard Levinge of Knockdrin Castle near Mullingar, County Westmeath. Harry Levinge was recruited into the Indian Civil Service, becoming Secretary to the Government of Bengal. In India during the early 1870s, one of his associates was Charles William Webley Hope who was already keenly interested in ferns. In July 1871, Hope collected a few ferns at Simla, and showed them to Levinge who was then his immediate superior. As a result, that same autumn, Harry Levinge 'took to fern-collecting most enthusiastically; and he continued the pursuit and the study of ferns generally until he left India in 1883'. Levinge collected 'chiefly in Sikkim, but also in Kashmir, Garhwal, and in the mountains of Southern India', and he gathered specimens of his fern in the Jhelum valley, Kashmir, on 25 September 1875. When Harry Levinge retired to Ireland in 1883 he intended to work on his Indian specimens, but the largest and finest part of his Indian collection was destroyed in 'the fire of Whiteley's fire-proof warehouse'. Thus Levinge took up the study of the Irish flora, making particular contributions to records of flowering plants and ferns in his home county, Westmeath, and in The Burren. Levinge, who died at Knockdrin in 1896 aged 67, is commemorated not just in *Pseudophegopteris levingei* but also, like Michael Pakenham Edgeworth, by a maidenhair fern, *Adiantum levingei,* and a balsam, *Impatiens levingei*, both also collected in India, and by a probably extinct wood anemone, *Anemone nemorosa* 'Levingei', which was listed in the extraordinary nursery catalogues issued during the 1890s by Patrick B. O'Kelly of Ballyvaghan, County Clare.

FAIRY FISHING-WANDS

For the final plant in my Irish rock-garden, I return to the topic of the lost flowers. The nursery at Lissadell was not nearly as well known as the Slieve Donard Nursery, and although I have already written much about the Donard's plants, there is one group of flowers that the Donard made its own, and in my opinion, they excel all others. These are the wand-flowers, *Dierama*, fairy fishing-rods, the hair-bells of Africa. They are among the most graceful plants that can be grown out-of-doors in Ireland, with bells of petals suspended on almost invisible stalks from long arching stems. They are colourful and elegant, and remarkably easy to grow as long as you have patience. The one thing that fairy fishing-wands do not like is being transplanted or moved. When *Dierama* plants have to be lifted, this should be done very carefully to avoid disturbance to the delicate root attached to each corm. The plants will seem to die, but they are not dead; slowly, given no further disturbance, new leaves will sprout, and eventually after perhaps two or three years, flowers will once again burst forth.

Dierama[29] species and hybrids can be raised easily from seed, which should be sown in the spot where the plants are to grow, or in a container from which the seedlings can be removed without damaging their roots. Within one year healthy plants will be established and the first blooms will appear about three years after sowing. In my Celbridge garden I raised seedlings that blossomed profusely for the first time in 1983 when they were three years old.

The story of the wand-flowers began in the 1910s when William Slinger acquired a few corms, and soon began to raise large numbers of his own seedlings. His son, Leslie, described progress.

One or two breaks in colour were observed and work commenced in hybridising and selection from generation to generation of seedlings. From those early pink and purple flowered varieties a range of fine plants have been produced. The original species has now been entirely swallowed up and has broken up to such an extent that seed from any particular form behaves as one might expect from a hybrid - all manner of colours and forms appear in the seedlings.[30]

To start with, William Slinger selected and named the best forms of the tall, hardy *Dierama pulcherrimum*. This is too stately for a humble rock-garden, but perfect for an herbaceous border and eminently suitable for the banks of a stream or overhanging a garden pool (but they are not water plants).

In 1921 the Slieve Donard Nursery gained its first award of merit for a *Dierama*. The white flowered variety, *Dierama pulcherrimum* var. *album* led the way with its deep pink bells. At one of the Royal Horticultural Society's 1923 flower shows, the nursery staged an exhibit of wand-flowers which 'caused a great sensation and [the] stand was crowded round from the opening to the closing of the Show.' 'Heron' which produced dark wine-red blossoms gained an award of merit from the Royal Horticultural Society that year, and in 1924 'Kingfisher', with large pale pink flowers, followed suit. The names of these tall, graceful varieties were almost always taken from birds - 'Raven' for a plant with deep purple, open bells, 'Snow Goose' for a white flushed with palest pink. The names are evocative - imagine what 'Blackbird', 'Osprey' and 'Barn Owl' looked like. Alas these have disappeared, swamped by a mass of unnamed, spontaneous seedlings, but the Donard strain remains in the countless children that have appeared in many gardens in the past half-century. These fledglings are just as delightful as their parents and very worthy of cultivation. The pure white variety is one of the nicest and, as I mentioned earlier, grew very well in Evelyn Booth's garden at Bunclody.

In the late 1930s, the Donard nursery received seeds from southern Africa of a dwarf red-flowered species of *Dierama*; it was named *Dierama pumilum* although this is now known to have been incorrect. *Dierama dracomontanum*, signifying the Drakensberg hair-bell, is the correct name and this was introduced to gardens after the Second World War gaining an award of merit in 1965. This dwarf species - now the emblem of the Irish Garden Plant Society - was used to pollinate the tall *Dierama pulcherrimum*, and a new race of hybrids, growing not more than one metre tall, was born (Plate 14). The dwarf hybrids, sturdy and free-flowering plants, were first released in 1949 and about a dozen varieties bear the names of characters from William Shakespeare's *A midsummer night's dream*. 'Titania' had pale flowers, 'soft neyron rose'. The bells of 'Oberon' were peony-purple, and 'Iris' was a vivid violet. I saw 'Iris' growing in Dorothy Jobling-Purser's garden, also in Bunclody, more than ten years ago, along with the dwarf parent. But where have the other fairy fishing-wands gone? Have 'Juliet', 'Ariel', 'Hermia' and impish 'Puck', 'as chimney sweepers, come to dust'?

14. Dierama

POSTSCRIPT

High in the Dragon Mountains, maybe there are dragons - I cannot say that I saw any, but I can vouch for this certainty, that there are many beautiful plants in the Drakensberg, and of all the inhabitants of those Dragon Mountains, the hair-bells are the best known to us in Ireland, leaving aside a few red-hot pokers. When Wendy Walsh and I have visited those mountains in the late summer in the company of Auriol Batten, we have seen countless clumps of *Dierama dracomontanum* in shades of pink.

Mount Kemp, not far from the coastal city of East London, is a pimple compared with the Drakensberg. On a hot afternoon, again in late summer, with Auriol Batten, I waded through scrub near the summit and saw the 'most beautiful' - *pulcherrimum* - hair-bell in full bloom. Pale, papery bracts enfolded the deep purple buds that expanded to form hanging goblets of glistening petals in tones of red, blue and purple. A fortnight afterwards, in the Karkloof Hills beyond Pietermaritzberg in KwaZulu-Natal, Geoff Nicholls and I had our picnic lunch surrounded by stately tufts of another hair-bell in full flower; this one was more erect and its blooms were a pale shade of lavender. Having seen these plants, especially *Dierama dracomontanum*, sprouting from the arid slopes of African mountains on blazing summer days with temperatures close to the Fahrenheit century, and knowing that two weeks later, those slopes were blanketed with unseasonable snow, I can see why the hair-bells of the Dragon Mountains find even Ballycastle so congenial.

So what is all the fuss about, the fuss about the cultivars from the Slieve Donard Nursery? Those named *Dierama* varieties continue to intrigue gardeners. Despite numerous claims to the contrary, evident from the names used by nurseries, most (if not all) of the Donard's cultivars are no longer available; plants sold under the Donard's names are very rarely true to name. To be the authentic cultivar, a wand-flower plant must have been cloned - in other words, propagated vegetatively from the single original plant, by division of its clump as it increased - because seedlings resulting from open pollination will be varied, as Leslie Slinger pointed out many years ago. The wand-flowers are, in general, very slow to increase vegetatively, and are also set back badly by lifting and division, so direct clonal descendants are unlikely to be available from nurseries. On the other hand, seed is abundant and seedlings are easily raised in vast numbers. To be sure, a few of the *Dierama* in cultivation do come true from seed, and thus are easy to perpetuate - the dwarf ones are forms of *Dierama dracomontanum* in a number of different colours. As I have remarked, in the wild these plants do vary in colour, and the full range is not available in Ireland - for example, there are species with pale yellow petals, and although the Slieve Donard Nursery tried to obtain these, they are not in our gardens, yet.

South African gardeners have great difficulties with the native hair-bells, for although they are cultivated, the native pests make short work of the flowers - it was remarkable to see both in the wild and in gardens battalions of beetles avidly devouring the petals so that the finest wands were always tattered. Another beast lays its eggs in the seed capsules, and thus almost all seeds are devoured before they mature. In Ireland we do not have pests and diseases to attack *Dierama*. We just have hardy, healthy, blossom-laden plants - gardeners in Natal gasped when I showed photographs of a fountain of *Dierama pulcherrimum* in a Dublin garden. It is no wonder that Conrad Lighton wrote of the African hair-bells that

> Although there are dieramas in many part of South Africa your chance of seeing a field of them waving in the breeze would be better in Ulster or Eire than here. ... I wager you will find none finer than the ones now rejoicing in the names of birds and Shakespeare's fairies where The Mountains of Mourne sweep down to the sea.[31]

We all hold the wand-flowers from the Slieve Donard Nursery to be beyond compare, wonderful, dancing flowers. The Slinger family did us no greater service than to introduce their hardy lineage of *Dierama*, and to expand the colour range from white to deep claret. Long may these graceful plants flourish in our gardens because 'there is not a more beautiful sight than a group of Dierama when in bloom'. The celebrated nursery is itself extinct, just a sweet memory or a tantalizing dream, yet a host of unequalled plants, originally selected and propagated in the shadow of Saint Domangard's peak, Slieve Donard, continues to enthral plantsman throughout the world and to emblazon gardens season after season. Thomas Ryan, James Coey and the Slingers created this 'Glory of Donard'. We owe them thanks.[32]

XI

An herbaceous border

Anemone coronaria 'Saint Bridgid' - *Papaver* 'Fireball'
Schizostylis coccinea 'Mrs Hegarty' - *Viola* 'Irish Molly' & 'Molly Sanderson'
Tropaeolum majus 'Margaret Long' - *Dactylorhiza elata* 'Glasnevin'
Epilobium canum 'Dublin' - *Meconopsis* x *sheldonii* 'Slieve Donard'
Hypericum 'Rowallane Hybrid' - *Bergenia* 'Ballawley'
Anthemis 'Grallagh Gold'
Narcissus 'Lucifer', 'Foundling', 'Cantatrice', 'Wendy Walsh' & 'Susan Elizabeth'

**... There I see thy pleasant ways,
Thy terraced walks, and above all a blaze
Of light-stemmed double poppies thickly sowed
On which old Mother Nature had bestowed
A very wealth of white and rosy rays.**

Charlotte Grace O'Brien: 'Dromoland'

Garden varieties of herbaceous plants do not survive as long as trees and shrubs, so that it is now almost impossible to collect many of the cultivars of perennial herbs that were raised, for example, by the Daisy Hill Nursery. Where have all its golden globe-flowers (*Trollius*) gone, 'Orange Glow', or 'Prince of Orange', or 'Orangeman'? There is little chance that the numerous Michaelmas daisies, including 'Flossy', 'Beatrice', 'Rosalie' and 'Saint Brigid', still survive even in well cared for gardens. The white Christmas rose, grown a century ago and named after Kildare's patron saint, is also only a memory.

However, in gardening there are few hard-and-fast rules, and consequently numerous antique varieties that provoke memories of long extinct gardens are cherished by present-day gardeners. Not all our herbaceous perennials have vanished and a few of the very best quality, first introduced last century, persist. This is my selection of things ancient and modern.

SAINT BRIDGID

Saint Bridgid's Christmas rose (*Helleborus niger*) was a lovely plant, according to published descriptions. It had dark green leaves, like those of a horse chestnut, and flowers of 'a snowdrift-like whiteness'. Frederick Burbidge christened it, using Bridgid's name, as he first saw the plant in the garden of a lady who used the pseudonym Saint Bridgid when she corresponded with the editors of gardening magazines. She had had a 'quaint old' garden in Kildare, near the site of St Brigid's oratory[1], and had been given this Christmas rose by another lady who lived near the cathedral town. That lady, whose name is not known, found the white hellebore in the garden when she came to live in Kildare about 1850. Before that, its history is unknown.

The lady who chose the nom-de-plume Saint Bridgid was Alice Louisa Lawrenson. By the 1880s Mr and Mrs Edward Lawrenson lived in Sutton House, on the south side of the Hill of Howth, having presumably moved there from Kildare. In the much milder garden at Sutton, Alice Lawrenson fully indulged her passion for plants. A lyrical description of her garden was published in May 1882.

> When Bluebells ring out a thousand welcomes to the mossy woods, and Daisies spread themselves over the lawn like a lace veil, an embroidery of pearls on a carpet of living green, then is this hillside garden fair to see. All is genial and lovely in the first flush of spring. ... Anemones, fine and full of fluctuating colour, dance and sparkle in the breeze, for this, albeit a lady's pleasaunce, a garden of flowers of many kinds, is essentially a garden of Anemones in all their subtle variety and beauty.[2]

Mrs Lawrenson's most noteworthy achievement was the selection of a strain of crown (or poppy) anemones, *Anemone coronaria*, with double and semi-double flowers. She had started selecting crown anemones when she gardened in Kildare, and continued the task at Howth, reaping the rewards of the milder climate. Mrs Lawrenson grew her anemones from seeds, sowing early each spring so that by the autumn the plants were in full bloom, ready to cut. During October 1882 she sent a bunch to the editor of *The garden*, William Robinson, who graciously wrote that the anemones were very beautiful. By careful cultivation, Alice Lawrenson was also able to enjoy flowers in the spring, and she sent Mr Robinson another bouquet in April 1884. She had selected her double-flowered anemones from stock of the single or Caen strain. By sowing only the seeds gathered from her best plants, and repeatedly selecting the best each season, Mrs Lawrenson gradually obtained bigger, brighter and fuller flowers. Eventually her poppy anemones became famous and were christened *Anemone coronaria* **'Saint Bridgid'**.[3] Alice Lawrenson was generous, and gave seeds of the anemone to many people - in May 1885 she supplied the Botanic Gardens at Glasnevin with seeds. Today the name 'Saint Bridgid' is applied to any semi-double or double form of this anemone, although much further selection has been carried out since Mrs Lawrenson's time.

After Mrs Lawrenson had introduced her anemone, nurserymen and other gardeners sought to improve the strain and some succeeded. In the mid-1890s, William Baylor Hartland of Cork, the well-known daffodil nurseryman, advertised his own strain of Saint Bridgid's anemones, raised from seeds originally procured from 'the lady who passed through the literature of gardening in its highest sense under the nom de plume of St Bridgid'. About 1900, William Reamsbottom of Geashill in County Offaly took on the task of improving the anemone, and in 1902 his nursery gained an award of merit from the Royal Horticultural Society of London for the Alderborough strain - Reamsbottom also gained a silver-gilt medal for the excellent staging of the exhibit. The Alderborough strain was highly praised in the gardening press. Saint Bridgid's anemones were still grown in the Geashill area in the mid-1980s, continuing the lineage established by William Reamsbottom.

The poppy anemone blossoms in spring and autumn, depending on the time of sowing or planting. It may be grown from seed, although it is more usual nowadays for gardeners to purchase corms. The leaves are dark green and much divided, similar to the leaves of certain meadow buttercups. The flowers are held singly on straight stalks about 20 centimetres in height. Each bloom has numerous coloured petals, forming a ruff around the central mass of stamens and carpels. The flowers range in colour from white through scarlet, to blue and purple. Saint Bridgid's anemones are still widely cultivated, although rarely in the great drifts that were popular in Mrs Lawrenson's day.

At least five other cultivars came from Alice Lawrenson's garden. Four daffodils are attributed to her, and Frederick Burbidge credited her with an interest in very early Star Narcissi; 'Saint Patrick', 'Sirius' (a white and orange one), 'Coral', and 'Lucifer' which has a flaming little trumpet and slightly floppy cream-white petals and is the only one still in cultivation. I have grown 'Lucifer' for many years, and it is in the national daffodil collection at the Guy L. Wilson Garden on the Coleraine campus of the University of Ulster, and in the Irish Cancer Society's collection within the National Botanic Gardens, Glasnevin.

KILDARE'S POPPY

Saint Brigid's county was also the place of origin of a dainty dwarf poppy that could be mistaken, at a quick glance, for an anemone. It is probably a hybrid between the oriental poppy (*Papaver orientale*) which normally is a robust perennial reaching at least one metre in height, and a dwarf poppy, perhaps the Moroccan species named *Papaver atlanticum*. The Kildare poppy only grows to a third of a metre tall. It has fully double flowers, like fluffy powder-puffs, composed of a multitude of narrow petals. The blossoms are bright pinkish-scarlet, fading slightly as they mature.

I came across this poppy for the first time in Graham Thomas's book on herbaceous perennials. He called it *Papaver orientale nana plena*, for want of a proper name. Graham had managed to trace it back to the garden at Kildangan, near Monasterevin, County Kildare, where it had been cultivated for many years by the More O'Ferralls.

Having read about this dwarf poppy, I had to wait several years before I saw it growing in several Dublin gardens and then in Dr Molly Sanderson's superb, but now vanished garden, Ishlan, at Ballymoney, County Antrim. During a visit to Ballymoney, the late Dr Brian Mulligan told me that the poppy was named 'Fireball', and that its history was recorded. Thanks to him, the story can be recalled.

Papaver **'Fireball'**[4] was named by a Dutch nurseryman, H. den Ouden of Boskoop, who had received plants from Murray Hornibrook about 1923. I have checked a list of plants that Hornibrook donated to the Botanic Gardens at Glasnevin about the same time, and a dwarf double poppy was included. Murray Hornibrook had obtained this dainty plant from Lady Alice Coote of Ballyfin, a house once famous for its garden, near Portlaoise; Ballyfin is not far from Knapton, the dower house of Abbey Leix, where Hornibrook lived. Lady Coote's mother, Mrs Webber, was the person who first noticed the poppy - it arose in her garden at Kellyville near Athy, County Kildare, during the late 1870s. The More O'Ferralls could have obtained it either from Lady Coote or from Murray Hornibrook, for keen gardeners will always be happy to give a plant to a fellow enthusiast, when they know it will be cared for.

'Fireball' is ablaze in late May and early June. The flowers are borne on long, erect stalks, and before they open the blossoms are enclosed in hair-encrusted buds. The outer petals are fully formed, like those of any ordinary poppy, but the stamens are replaced by the numerous, narrow inner petals, thereby producing the 'double' flowers. This dwarf poppy does not set seed - its sterility seems to confirm its hybrid origin - but it creeps about by underground stems. Hornibrook described it as a 'beautiful but ineradicable weed' and complained that it was as invasive as an oriental knotweed. But I am reminded that a weed is nothing less than a plant growing where it is not wanted - could such a spritely poppy ever be out of place?

CLONBUR'S LILY

Another chance discovery in a lady's garden is now quite widely grown throughout these islands, although there is great confusion and mixing of varieties. It is the delicate autumnal river lily with deep rose pink flowers. The river lily (also called the Kaffir lily, *Schizostylis coccinea*) comes from the Drakensberg mountains in southern Africa - it grows along the banks of mountain streams which even in late summer are still flowing. Perfidiously the river lily is not a lily, but a member of the iris family, which nicely illustrated the uselessness of common English names for plants. While the river lily grows about 30 centimetres tall in most gardens, it can be taller in very congenial places, where the soil is rich and moist.

The river lily looks like a miniature gladiolus, having a fan of sword-shaped leaves from which emerges a flower spike. Each spike has about 20 flowers, each with six petals[5] that overlap towards their bases to form a shallow, bowl-shaped star. The anthers are yellow. The blooms open in succession, giving the river lily an extended flowering season, often from August into November. This is not a tender plant, and it will thrive outdoors anywhere in Ireland, for it dislikes dry summers. If needs be, it can be grown in a cold greenhouse.

Visitors to the Royal Horticultural Society's September 1921 show were surprised to see a vase of a rose-pink river lily. Hitherto only scarlet flowered plants had been known - that is the predominant colour of the wild plants I saw in the Drakensberg. The judges gave the new variety an award of merit, and it was named *Schizostylis coccinea* **'Mrs Hegarty'**[6] after the lady in whose garden it had been found. Sir Frederick Moore had persuaded Mrs Blanche Hegarty to exhibit the new plant in London, and it was Sir Frederick who gave the cultivar its name.

Miss Blanche Dockeray, daughter of the Rector of Cong and Moytura, married Dr John Adam ('Jack') Hegarty about 1880. The couple lived at Poleska in Clonbur, County Galway, and there started a fine garden. Jack Hegarty treated many of the local gentry, including Lord Ardilaun who lived nearby at Ashford Castle, and Dr Boyd of Ebor Hall, a house on the shores of Lough Corrib near Cornamona. Lord Ardilaun and Dr Boyd often gave the Hegartys plants for their garden, and soon Poleska was stocked with many fine things. The river lily came from Ebor Hall, and under Mrs Hegarty's very expert attention, it flourished at Poleska, and produced a seedling with rose-pink flowers. Blanche Hegarty noticed the pink *Schizostylis* about 1914, for in January 1919 she brought a plant to the Botanic Gardens, Glasnevin. There it was propagated, and young plants were sent to G.N. Smith at the Daisy Hill Nursery, Newry, in January 1921. Sir John Ross-of-Bladensburg was given plants in December 1921, and during the following year some of Mrs Hegarty's variety was sent to Straffan House in County Kildare.

There are now many other pink cultivars of *Schizostylis coccinea* and even white ones. I must admit that 'Sunrise' is an excellent plant, surpassing the old, original 'Mrs Hegarty'. All the same, it is important to keep the older cultivars, and 'Mrs Hegarty' deserves to continue to be cultivated.

According to Arthur Simmonds, writing in the *Journal of the Royal Horticultural Society* in 1945, Poleska provided the poet Katherine Tynan, whose husband H. A. Hinkson was a resident magistrate in County Mayo, with the inspiration for some charming verses under the title 'The garden at Poleska'.[7] I have been unable to discover the poem, but perhaps it was the one including these lines.

What a thing a garden is
For sweet dreams and quietness!
Roses and lilies
Narcissus, daffodillies,
Irises and phlox and stocks
And Sultan hollyhocks.
Love-lies-bleeding - Love-in-a-mist -
Pansies tawny and amethyst.

MOLLY'S PANSIES

Pansies come in a myriad of shades, white to purple, yellow to blue, and there are bicolours and multicolours and all-sorts. It is difficult to realize sometimes that these all sprang from the simple heart's-ease, *Viola tricolor*, that is a native perennial herb found on coastal sand hills. I can remember as a small boy finding these beautiful, donkey-faced flowers at Rossnowlagh on the coast of County Donegal, growing in profusion on the dunes among the rabbit burrows and the prickly marram. The garden pansy is a multiple hybrid that arose around 1830, and since that time countless different varieties have been produced, some as seed lines, others as perennials.

There is a remarkable Irish pansy, a veritable tawny one that many gardeners cherish. The colour of the flower is impossible to describe, because it is so complicated. The overall effect is a luminous bronze, but you will find a farrago of colours attributed to it. The earliest I have traced is in 'Retrospections and visions in an Irish flower garden' penned in the summer of 1936 by an Irish gardener using only the initials E. A.

A charming though unintentionally arranged grouping of rather new plants was seen recently, that of the Primula x Polyanthus Garriarde surrounded by Viola Irish Molly. Molly when well arrayed in fresh emerald velvet is always a striking object. Marking of bronze somewhat resemble tints in the foliage of Garriarde over which the fine heads of soft pink bloom stand out fragrant and beautiful.[8]

Dr Norman Hickin once summarized the various descriptions that he had traced: 'bronzy-yellow with a copper centre' according to Roy Genders; 'basically black but strangely and metallically suffused with green and copper' were the tones perceived by John Raven in *A botanist's garden*; Hickin's own 'impossible description' was 'perhaps a yellowish bronze green turning to purplish copper'.[9] To these can be added Stephen Lacey's 'neither brown nor yellow nor olive green but a mixture of all three', David Stuart and James Sutherland's 'fascinating greenish bronzy-yellow', and Chris Brickell and Fay Sharman's 'unusual khaki-yellow'.[10]

With a gardener's affection and an artist's eye, having encapsulated the flower in purple, burnt sienna, green, yellow and white paints, Wendy Walsh describes this pansy, 'such an Irish pansy, evocative and haunting', in terms of the Irish landscape:

> You must imagine an Irish bog in the autumn, for the colours are there: the red-brown of the fresh peat, the green-brown of the rushes and sedges, with a hint of deep purple overlaid with a glow of gold; a touch of orange from the fruits of the bog asphodel that cluster on the edge of a turf bank, and white - bog cotton - in the centre.

There is really no need to describe this tawny pansy to Irish gardeners because we all know the flower; it is sufficient merely to utter its name, *Viola* **'Irish Molly'** (Plate 15),[11] to conjure up that vivid picture in the mind's-eye. But, whence came 'Irish Molly'? With such a name we must suppose that it is Irish. When did it arise? No-one knows - probably around the turn of the century for Norman Hickin remembered it as a popular plant around Birmingham in 1915 when he was a lad aged five. Who raised it? No name is recorded, as far as I can find.

Viola 'Irish Molly' must not be confused with 'Molly Sanderson' - Irish gardeners would not commit such an offence. *Viola* **'Molly Sanderson'** (Plate 16)[12] blossoms from March until the coldest days of late autumn, and has the blackest flower of all, a remarkable colour, made the more dramatic by the matt sheen of the petals. The large lower petal has a yellow flash at the base, and the two side petals have violet hairs at their bases, so each flower has a yellow eye rimmed by violet. The individual blossom is as wide as it is high, about three centimetres each way, and each one is held aloft on a stout, erect stem. This cultivar, like 'Irish Molly', is perennial, forming a loose plant, with almost heart-shaped leaves to about four centimetres long. Both pansies need to be propagated by cuttings - these can be taken in autumn when they will root rapidly and then the young plants should be over-wintered in a cold frame.

Dr Molly Sanderson was one of the three original dedicatees of this book, and I owe a great deal of my knowledge of the histories of garden plants to her. She possessed a huge store of anecdotes, and was extraordinarily generous with the plants that she grew. I never visited Ishlan at Ballymoney, her finest garden, without bringing away some treasure, and *Viola* 'Molly Sanderson' was among the gifts she gave me. Molly had obtained the jet-black pansy from an English gardener, a fellow family doctor, Scott Stone, who lived at Whitecliffs in Margate, Kent. During a visit to England in 1975, Molly had visited Dr Stone who thanked her for visiting - 'It was a great joy having someone so knowledgeable come round the garden. I hope your husband wasn't too bored. Thank you for sorting out my celmisias ...'.[13] In return she invited him to Northern Ireland. Eventually in May 1980, Scott Stone came to Ballymoney bringing a load of plants for Ishlan, including a black-flowered pansy labelled *Viola niger*, a name of dubious validity. Molly kept Dr Stone's black pansy going in her garden by regular propagation - indeed it flourished, especially in a raised bed. Just over three years later in November 1983, Ralph

15. 'Irish Molly'

16. 'Molly Sanderson'

Haywood visited Ishlan where, by his own account, 'not only did I see plants that I had only read about but many of them were still giving a good account of themselves' on the verge of winter. He brought some cuttings of *Viola niger* back to England and, intrigued, tried to find out if this name was valid. Drawing a blank - Molly's pansy was apparently nameless - Ralph Haywood named it, with her consent, *Viola* 'Molly Sanderson'. The black pansy then became famous and fashionable. Everyone had to grow 'Molly Sanderson'.

Dr Molly, as she was affectionately known to her friends throughout Ulster, was a gifted plantsman. With the help of her husband, Noel, and that 'most valuable helpmate ... (after Noel, of course) ... my garden apron', Molly built Ishlan into one of the finest plant collections I have ever seen, full of interesting plants. There the Chilean bamboo *Chusquea* was at home under Laburnum trees, while blue Himalayan poppies and African harebells (*Dierama*) flourished beside New Zealand daisies and American wake-robins, all in the congenial company of Irish primroses, tatting ferns and wood anemones in profusion. As far as I know this sumptuous pansy and a white-berried Chinese rowan (*Sorbus* 'Molly Sanderson') are the only plants that bear her name in full, and there is also the primrose named 'Doctor Molly'. 'Her' primrose was bred by Cecil Monson, and she always pointed out that neither the pansy nor the rowan were 'her' plants either; she had not raised them. Molly was instrumental in keeping and distributing many other rarities, including *Primula vulgaris* 'Elizabeth Dickey', a lovely double form of the wild primrose, and also the double blossomed *Hepatica transsilvanica* 'Elison Spence'. We have too few gardeners like Dr Molly.

When asked to write about Ishlan, Molly posed the question, 'How does one summarize something as ephemeral as a garden?', and then concluded with this sentence: 'As Noel says, "How can you summarize something that has no ending?".'[14] Gardens oft-times do have endings, usually sad ones, when their gardeners can no longer manage to keep them in an acceptable state. Ishlan was ephemeral and is no more; its ending came when the Sandersons felt it was too large for them, and they moved to a new house with a smaller garden. Both Noel and Molly have died since this book was first written - may they rest in peace.

NEW, OLD-FASHIONED NASTURTIUM

Dr Molly was an amateur plantsman, in every sense of that phrase, having learned her skills by studying others at work, visiting gardens, reading magazines and journals, and above all by growing every kind of plant she could lay her hands on. Others have acquired their knowledge and skill by taking a different path.

Margaret Long, for example, enrolled as a lady gardener at the National Botanic Gardens, Glasnevin, on 8 January 1934, and stayed the apprentices' course leaving after almost two years on 20 December 1935. Lady gardeners training at Glasnevin did everything that their male counterparts did, except in the early days, around the turn of the century, mowing the lawns which was still done using scythes. Sometimes the lady apprentices were given extra jobs such as cleaning seeds harvested in the Gardens. They were not paid, and had to attend lectures each evening as well as working outdoors in every section of the Botanic Gardens. One of Miss Long's predecessors, May Crosbie, wrote that prospective lady pupils required 'health, strength and a liking for the work ... as the work is hard and hours as a rule long.'

After Glasnevin, Margaret Long worked as a gardener at Glengarriff Castle on Bantry Bay in west County Cork, and then at Lord Dunraven's gardens in Kerry. In later years she was involved with the Country Markets, An Grianan at Termonfeckin in County Louth, and various horticultural societies. As befits a person trained in the National Botanic Gardens, she had a keen interest in unusual plants, and one of her particular favourites was the old double-flowered garden nasturtium

The nasturtium of gardeners is descended from a plant that is native in temperate South America - the name nasturtium comes from two Latin words meaning twisted nose, an allusion to the pungent, nose-wrinkling taste. Seeds were brought to Europe by Spanish travellers perhaps in the latter years of the sixteenth century. Somehow, a double-flowered variety arose and this was grown in Britain as long ago as the early eighteenth century. Philip Miller knew it as *Acriviola maxima odorata flore pleno*, and Jacob van Huysum painted a swathe in watercolour[15] for the *Catalogus plantarum*, an illustrated inventory of the latest introductions into British gardens which was produced by the Society of Gardeners in 1724. Thirty years later, Carl Linnaeus coined the name *Tropaeolum* for the gardeners' nasturtium because to botanists *Nasturtium* was the name applied to the watercresses. In his famous *Gardener's dictionary* first published in 1746, Miller wrote about two different species of *Tropaeolum*, including the garden nasturtium which he called 'Indian Nasturtium with a larger Leaf and Flowers, commonly called Indian cress', noting that there was 'one with double Flowers which is propagated by Cutings, for it does not produce Seeds'

During 1987 in Margaret Long's Dublin garden one plant of that antique double nasturtium began producing apricot coloured blooms, rather than tomato-orange flowers. She propagated the 'sport', and in 1995, prompted by Nichola Kyle, I named the new nasturtium after Miss Long - *Tropaeolum majus* **'Margaret Long'** (Plate 17).[16] Each bloom is like a rose, composed of numerous, narrow but irregularly shaped and randomly arranged petals, rather than the typical garden nasturtium with a widely flared trumpet of five orange-red to yellow petals and a long curving spur behind. The petal colour of Miss Long's variety is soft and the flowers are sweetly scented. Unlike the more usual garden nasturtium which is an annual and readily produces a large crop of seeds, the multi-petalled varieties are perennial and sterile, and as Miller pointed out, they never set seed.

This new variety will rapidly vanish if it is not propagated and dispersed among gardeners. Cuttings should be taken in early October. Set in sandy loam under a cloche in a cool greenhouse, they will root easily. In areas where winters are harsh and frosty, some young plants have to be over-wintered indoors, because although 'Margaret Long' is perennial, frost is likely to kill plants left outdoors. Philip Miller's instructions for the single flowered

17. Tropaeolum majus 'Margaret Long'

nasturtium, now two and a half centuries old, remain in force - 'they may be continued through the Winter if they are kept in Pots, and sheltered in a good Green-house, in like Manner as that with double Flowers is preserved, and they may be propagated by Cutings as that is'.

We are not sure where Margaret Long obtained her original red-blossomed nasturtium but it was perhaps from the National Botanic Gardens. She grew it from about the 1930s, and kept it going, as I have just explained one must, by taking cuttings every year.

GLASNEVIN'S HARDY ORCHID

The National Botanic Gardens has been a clearing-house for plants for more than two centuries. Plants and seeds have been imported and new species and cultivars sent out to other gardens. Glasnevin has always maintained close links with the great gardens and keen plantsmen throughout Ireland, and had been generous in distributing novel plants. The Botanic Gardens itself has not produced many cultivars of herbaceous perennials, for interest has concentrated on trees and shrubs. However, a marsh orchid with Glasnevin associations, is grown in gardens in Dublin and further afield.

The history of **Dactylorhiza elata 'Glasnevin'**[17] is confused, and at this time, I fear, never will be clarified. A few facts are certain. On 25 June 1895, Frederick Moore showed two orchids to the Orchid Committee of the Royal Horticultural Society in London. One was given a botanical certificate, confirming that it was *Orchis latifolia* (an old name for the plant now called *Dactylorhiza incarnata*). The second orchid, the better one, with a flower spike over 20 centimetres long, received an award of merit; it was described as a hardy orchid and at the time was named *Orchis latifolia* 'Glasnevin Variety'. The Glasnevin orchid was distributed widely; by 1918 plants were cultivated in the Royal Botanic Gardens, Kew, where they formed an imposing group with stems up to 80 centimetres tall.

Confusion about the history and correct botanical name of the Glasnevin orchid seems to arise because of a story recorded in the middle of the last century about another orchid. David Moore, director of the Glasnevin Botanic Gardens and father of Frederick Moore, found some orchids growing in a meadow at Sandyford in south County Dublin during 1856. These were described as being almost 70 centimetres tall (26 inches), with inflorescences about 14 centimetres (5½ inches) long, and were identified as *Orchis latifolia* (= *Dactylorhiza incarnata*). However, the plant cultivated as *Orchis latifolia* 'Glasnevin Variety' is not a native Irish species; I sent specimens to the orchid taxonomists, Dr Philip Cribb and Mr Jeffrey Wood, at the Royal Botanic Gardens, Kew, and they agreed it was *Dactylorhiza elata*.

Where did the Glasnevin orchid come from? Lady Moore, writing in 1939, stated that her father-in-law, David Moore, found the orchid growing in a garden in south County Dublin. She was usually accurate, but I wonder if this is correct? To return to what is certain, *Dactylorhiza* 'Glasnevin' was exhibited a second time at the Royal Horticultural Society in London, by Mrs

Sadlier of Celbridge, County Kildare, who obtained an award of merit in 1939 for the orchid. Lady Moore reported that Mrs Sadlier's plants had come from Glasnevin many years earlier, and the plants that I knew best, growing in the late David Shackleton's garden at Clonsilla, came from the same Celbridge garden.

By any measure this orchid is a magnificent plant. The leaves are bright green, without any markings. They form a rosette when young but this elongates as the flowering spike emerges. The stems of well-nourished plants can be about one metre high, and the flower cluster at least 20 centimetres long. The inflorescence is composed of innumerable small flowers, each one looking like a winged angel in a long purple robe with purple wings swept backwards. Their skirts - the broad, lower lips of the flowers - are rich mauve with darker lines or spots.

The Glasnevin orchid is easy to cultivate in a rich, well-drained, friable loam and can be increased by division; it needs to be divided every four or five years.

Dactylorhiza elata 'Glasnevin' is one of the earliest hardy orchids to flower. It is an unforgettable sight in full bloom and a worthy subject for an herbaceous border, being taller than the orchid named *Dactylorhiza maderensis* by gardeners, but not as deeply coloured.

DAVID SHACKLETON'S DAISY

I obtained my plants of the Glasnevin orchid from David Shackleton, who was another wonderful source of stories about Irish gardeners in bygone times, and one of my original dedicatees. He was a very particular person, allowing into his walled garden at Beech Park, Clonsilla, only those who passed unwittingly some inscrutable test. I did not pass the test for several years after I joined the staff of the National Botanic Gardens, but one day I received a summons from David Shackleton - it was not an invitation because to have refused would have been final. I arrived at the appointed time and was paraded around the garden for several hours - I was enthralled - before being invited in for a drink. Evidently I had passed and was invited back on many occasions, and even enjoyed the privilege of making a television programme about David and his garden. I remember well the lovely summer days that we spent filming. David was enjoying himself too, making me work for my living - getting stories or comments from him on to tape was like wringing blood out of a stone, but that was part of his mischievous character.

On one occasion, as we perambulated and chatted, circling the raised beds full of choice plants, he showed me a New Zealand daisy, and asked my opinion. I probably muttered something bland, and then asked where it came from. "Glasnevin!", was the reply - there was mischief in his voice, and his eyes twinkled. I was intrigued because David had a low opinion of the National Botanic Gardens, so I probed for the story.

New Zealand daisies were one of David's passions - I still have a list of the species that he grew at Beech Park, and it reads like a complete inventory of the flora of the Antipodes.

When he saw an unfamiliar one, he acquired it. One day, at Glasnevin, he noticed in the scree bed a rather scruffy plant that was not thriving, and bamboozled the gardener in charge into giving him a portion. Like Cinderella going to the ball, the Glasnevin daisy was transmogrified when it reached Beech Park, because it was pampered and planted in the rich peaty mixture that David made for all his plants. A dull looking daisy with dark green leaves cloaked in tattered silver fluff turned into a shining silver rosette, unlike any other plant cultivated in Ireland.

Celmisia '**David Shackleton**'[18] is probably a hybrid involving *Celmisia semicordata*, and possibly was acquired by the National Botanic Gardens in the 1960s from Jack Drake's Inshriach Alpine Nursery at Aviemore in Scotland. It is a fine perennial, forming clumps of rosettes with pleated leaves up to 25 centimetres long. Each leaf is covered with a dense felt of hairs which makes the leaves silver-white - I usually describe the colour as that of a brand new aluminium pan. While this daisy is grown for its splendid foliage, flower heads are sometimes produced: David used to remove these because they were often malformed, but when perfect each one is like a very large common daisy with white outer rays and a disc of yellow.

David Shackleton's daisy made its debut on television in 1987. He intended showing it at the Alpine Garden Society's Irish shows during the spring of 1988, but his illness and death did not allow him this pleasure. Helen Dillon did enter *Celmisia* 'David Shackleton' in the section for silver foliaged plants at the Ulster show in April 1989 and gained first prize, and repeated the success one month later in Dublin.

A walk around Beech Park on a summer evening chatting with David Shackleton was a wonderful pleasure. He was always full of stories of plants and people, and like his acquaintances - Lady Moore, Lord Talbot de Malahide and many others - he was exceptionally generous with his plants and his hospitality. He often said that many of the plants he grew reminded him of donors who had long since died, but those memories were frequently happy ones. Just as one of his most frequent remarks was "I got it from Lady Moore", "I got it from David Shackleton" will be heard for many years around Ireland.

CALIFORNIAN FUCHSIA

In the early 1980s a plant appeared in nurserymen's catalogues called either *Zauschneria californica* 'Dublin' or *Zauschneria californica* 'Glasnevin'. It is a first-class cultivar of the Californian fuchsia, and is a near relative of true *Fuchsia* and the willowherbs (*Epilobium* species). Since then, American botanists have pointed out that *Zauschneria* species differ little from *Epilobium*, and suggested that it would be sensible to demote *Zauschneria*, making it synonymous with *Epilobium*. As a result, there has been a dramatic change of name for this lovely plant - the correct scientific name is now *Epilobium canum*.

I have seen *Epilobium canum* in the wild in California, and have gathered seeds from plants growing in the coastal ranges south of Monterey. In those native habitats, hummingbirds hover in front of the flowers sipping nectar and being dusted with pollen. In the Americas, red tubular flowers are certain indicators that hummingbirds act as the pollinators - nectar, which provides the birds with energy, is a reward offered by the plants to the birds that move from flower to flower in search of more food and consequently transfer pollen. In simple terms, the plants once named *Zauschneria* are bird-pollinated willowherbs.

Epilobium canum **'Dublin'** (alias *Zauschneria californica* 'Glasnevin') (Plate 18) is a persistent perennial, almost a dwarf shrub but it does die down each winter and resprouts vigorously in the late spring following. The leaves are relatively long and narrow and are dark green - in some other varieties the foliage is densely covered with hairs and appears silver-grey. In 'Dublin' the flowers are large, at least two centimetres long, and bright orange-scarlet. Each one is composed of two whorls attached to a long floral tube. The outer whorl of four pointed sepals is scarlet with a fawn tinge in bud. The inner whorl consists of four scarlet petals which are deeply lobed. Thus each flower resembles a tiered petticoat. The plant blooms from early August until late October, and at the height of its season is a mass of scarlet.

No matter what it is called, the Californian fuchsia has been cultivated in Europe since the 1840s and a number of varieties, differing mainly in their habit and foliage, are available. This particular cultivar was obtained by Valerie Finnis (Lady Scott) in Dublin -

> I was walking along a road near the late Lady Moore's garden, about [1960] and saw this *Zauschneria* in a little front garden! I was given cuttings by the kind old owner - never took his name - so when I got home I called it 'Dublin' ...[19]

David Shackleton, whose versions of history were not to be contradicted and were very rarely inaccurate, assured me, when I relayed this story to him, that the plant was growing in the rockery in front of Willbrook, Lady Moore's garden. He was certainly present when the original cuttings were acquired by Valerie Finnis, as he accompanied her on the occasion. Although there is evidently room for argument, Lady Scott's label "*Zauschneria californica* Dublin" soon became the cultivar name. Someone, unfortunately, misremembered the name and source, and began to use *Zauschneria californica* 'Glasnevin'. Or, perhaps, it was the other way round?[20] There is no evidence that this plant was ever grown in the National Botanic Gardens; certainly it was not in cultivation in 1982 when it was added to the collections.

Epilobium canum 'Dublin' is a fine garden plant and is quite hardy. The species tolerates a wide range of soil condition, although it dislikes heavy clay. William Robinson recommended growing the Californian fuchsia on old stone walls, and in Trinity College, Dublin, it is used as a pot-plant - it makes a most attractive decoration.

18. Epilobium canum 'Dublin'

A BLUE POPPY FROM SCOTLAND

The uncertainties associated with the Glasnevin orchid and the *Epilobium* from Dublin demonstrate that the histories of garden plants can become muddled within a short time and thereafter will remain disputed for even longer. It is important that the backgrounds of new cultivars are recorded accurately at the time of naming, but even today new varieties are introduced without such records being published. Sometimes misty histories can be written after much time-consuming research, but too often the true stories of garden plants are lost. In one happy instance, that of the blue Himalayan poppy sold by the Slieve Donard Nursery, I was able to uncover its past, and its history has been confidently recorded. The true story is a very different tale to that generally given.

For a moment, let us leave history aside, because the Donard poppy is one of the finest of all herbaceous perennials. Its flowers are deep, pure blue. At Rowallane, this poppy grows in great clumps in the walled garden, and at Mount Stewart it thrives in the shade of stately eucalypts. At Castlewellan on a gentle summer afternoon, I watched as the evening sun shone through the petals transforming them into carved shells of the thinnest lapis lazuli. *Meconopsis* x *sheldonii* '**Slieve Donard**'[21] has no peers.

David Shackleton gathered a collection of blue poppies, all allegedly the one from the Slieve Donard Nursery, for a variety of sources. They were arrayed in the long herbaceous border that he developed inside the walled garden at Beech Park. Each could flaunt its true character in identical growing conditions, and soon the imposters stood out. The real one was always the best. 'Slieve Donard' is not as tall as other varieties, although it can reach a metre and a half in height. The elliptical leaves have parallel sides, perfectly straight with a few minute nicks at regular intervals - the margins are not toothed. The plant is sterile and has to be propagated by division, either in September or immediately after flowering. Like other *Meconopsis*, this one thrives in a cool, moist situation, and likes a light loam well enriched with leaf mould - it seems to tolerate some lime in the soil.

'Slieve Donard' was originally described as the 'superb introduction of Prain's' when first marketed by the Donard Nursery in the autumn of 1959, and subsequently was labelled *Meconopsis grandis* Prain's Variety. However, that combination of names is invalid and in any case this particular blue poppy has nothing to do with anyone named Prain (generally assumed to be Sir David Prain, Regius Keeper of the Royal Botanic Garden, Edinburgh). Later it was realized that the strictly perennial variety was a hybrid and needed a name of its own especially as it had become a regular feature of the Donard Nursery displays at horticultural shows. The name was amended to *Meconopsis* x *sheldonii* 'Slieve Donard'.

The poppy was acquired from the Slieve Donard Nursery from Mrs Marjorie Dickie of Omagh in County Tyrone. Mrs Dickie had obtained it from a Scottish gardener, Hugo Patten of Edinburgh. Mr Patten had received the blue poppy from Dr Alexander Curle, one-time director of the Royal Scottish Museum, who had raised it by cross-pollinating two Himalayan species, *Meconopsis grandis* and *Meconopsis betonicifolia*; all progeny of this cross must bear the name *Meconopsis* x *sheldonii*.

Dr Curle seems to have produced a batch of hybrid seedlings, and 'Slieve Donard' was just one of the seedlings selected by him for subsequent propagation. Another hybrid blue poppy, raised by him, is also still grown. *Meconopsis* x *sheldonii* 'Ormswell', a name used at Dr Curle's request, was introduced into commerce by Edrom Nursery. 'Ormswell' is listed in *The RHS plant finder*, alongside 'Slieve Donard', suggesting that there are differences between these siblings. Be that as it may, *Meconopsis* 'Slieve Donard' has flowers of the richest gentian blue; they are sumptuous and ineluctable.

SAINT JOHN'S WORT

I have noted the strong links that existed between the garden of Hugh Armytage Moore at Rowallane and the Slieve Donard Nursery. The Donard marketed several Rowallane cultivars, including the very lovely Saint John's wort, **Hypericum 'Rowallane Hybrid'** (Figure 16).[22] Although this is a shrubby plant, it is lush when grown well, and is not out of place in an herbaceous border. Besides, in many gardens its woody stems are killed by frost during occasional hard winters, and its regrowth is so soft that it may be treated almost as an herbaceous perennial.

Hypericum 'Rowallane Hybrid' grows as much as three metres tall and the shoots arch gracefully, the tips weighed down by the large flowers. The leaves are arranged in opposite pairs along the stems; they are ovate, dark green above with paler grey-green undersides. The flowers appear in groups of three at the ends of the main shoots and side branches. Each bloom is about eight centimetres across, a bowl of brilliant yellow like a giant buttercup. The petals have a silky sheen inside. The numerous orange stamens are grouped in five, fluffy clusters and the prominent ovary and style are green.

This handsome plant was a self-sown seedling that is believed to have resulted from the cross-pollination of two Himalayan Saint John's worts. Leslie Slinger noticed the hybrid seedling in the garden at Rowallane and it was first sold by The Slieve Donard Nursery in 1940. One parent was probably *Hypericum hookerianum* 'Rodgersii' and the other was probably *Hypericum leschenaultii*. The former plant has an Irish connection, but it is now very rare in cultivation, having been superseded by its offspring, 'Rowallane Hybrid'. 'Rodgersii' was a selected form of *Hypericum hookerianum*[23] that was raised at Rostrevor, County Down, in the garden of Sir John Ross-of-Bladensburg. The seed had been sent from Burma (as *Hypericum grandiflorum*) by Charles Rogers, the Chief Conservator of Forests, who was, incidentally, a friend of Lady Charlotte Wheeler Cuffe. Indeed Rogers persuaded Lady Cuffe to undertake the formation of the botanic garden at Maymyo in Burma. Charles Rogers also sent seeds to Glasnevin from Burma and, in later years, from Kenya where he lived in retirement.

16. *Hypericum* 'Rowallane Hybrid'

Hypericum 'Rowallane Hybrid' received an award of merit in 1943. It is a useful late flowering plant, coming into blossom in the mildest areas about June and continuing in flower well into the autumn. If it is pruned in spring (or is cut back by frost), the plant will sprout vigorously and flowers will open in the late summer.

BALLAWLEY PARK

The Slieve Donard and Daisy Hill nurseries gained for Irish nurseries an international reputation in the production of unusual and excellent garden plants. A number of other small nurseries sprang up in the wake of their success. Alas, like the Slieve Donard and the Daisy Hill companies, most of these have now passed into history or no longer produce exciting plants.

One of the extinct nurseries was started by Desmond Shaw-Smith at Ballawley Park, in the foothills of the Dublin Mountains. His mother had created a marvellous rock-garden and she encouraged her son to propagate the plants for sale. For about 25 years Ballawley Alpine Nursery supplied Dublin gardeners with excellent rock-plants and small herbaceous perennials. It specialized in alpines and introduced several fine varieties of *Aubrieta* and *Dianthus* but these are now lost to cultivation. One of the most enduring of Shaw-Smith's cultivars is the deep red blossomed mossy saxifrage, 'Ballawley Guardsman', that I have already described.

The outstanding large perennial to come from Ballawley is a hybrid *Bergenia* that bears the nursery's name. *Bergenia* used to be named *Megascea* and even *Saxifraga* - it does belong to the saxifrage family but it is altogether larger than the delicate species of Saxifraga. Tom Smith of Daisy Hill Nursery was one of the first to raise *Bergenia* cultivars and he introduced about a dozen of which a few survive in gardens. One hybrid, *Bergenia* x *smithii*, was named after him.

Bergenia **'Ballawley'**[24] was originally called 'Delbees' because it was thought to have resulted from the cross-pollination of *Bergenia delavayi* and *Bergenia beesiana*; these are both synonyms of *Bergenia purpurascens*, so the parentage is doubtful. Be that as it may, this is a remarkably handsome plant, capable of covering large areas of ground with huge, glossy, bright green leaves, not unlike those of a well-fed cabbage. The almost circular leaves are at least 25 centimetres across and are toothed on the margins. In winter the foliage turns a purplish-brown colour that is most attractive. The flowers are borne well above the mass of leaves on upright red stalks that can be half a metre tall, in slightly drooping clusters. The petals are magenta or purple, and there is a prominent green stigma at the centre of each flower. 'Ballawley' blooms in April and May, but blossom is sparse. It does not tolerate cold wind, and should be given a shady, sheltered spot in the garden, and a rich. loamy soil. Where it has a congenial home, *Bergenia* 'Ballawley' will romp around like a giant leathery lettuce, adorned with magenta flowers.

Desmond Shaw-Smith's *Bergenia* gained an award of merit from the Royal Horticultural Society of London in 1955 when exhibited by Ballawley Alpine Nursery. During 1965, the Slieve Donard Nursery provided plants for trial in the Society's garden at Wisley in Surrey, and after the trial *Bergenia* 'Ballawley' was given a second award of merit.

GRALLAGH'S GLORY

The Royal Horticultural Society of Ireland also granted awards for excellent garden plants, but ceased this practise many years ago. The scheme was modelled on the certificates and awards granted by the sister society in London. Few records of the Irish awards survive, but I have seen the First Class Certificate given to Miss Blanche Poë of Nenagh for a summer-flowering yellow daisy. ***Anthemis* 'Grallagh Gold'**[25] gained this award in July 1948 and a few years later received another award of merit from the Royal Dutch Horticultural Society.

Anthemis 'Grallagh Gold' forms a compact, semi-woody bush about half a metre tall, with greyish-green, aromatic foliage. The finely divided leaves are fern-like. From July until early autumn, 'Grallagh Gold'; bears long-stemmed flowers which resemble the wild ox-eye daisy but are entirely yellow. The ray florets - the outer 'petals' of the compound flower-head - are bright lemon and the inner florets that form the 'eye' are slightly deeper in colour. The blooms are about seven centimetres in diameter and make excellent cut-flowers, lasting for many days in water.

'Grallagh Gold' was introduced in 1946, having been noticed by Miss Poë as a chance seedling in her garden. It has a sibling, *Anthemis* 'Grallagh Glory' that was introduced in 1951, and is sometimes listed as 'Beauty of Grallagh.' It is not as tall, has deeper yellow flowers and smaller leaves and is not as sturdy as 'Grallagh Gold'. Neither of the varieties is long lived; they must be renewed every five years or so, although well-established, carefully trimmed plants may last longer.

Blanche Poë was the daughter of James Hill Poë of Riverston near Nenagh. She was born in County Tipperary but lived most of her childhood in Switzerland. Miss Poë was a skilled horse rider and a competent artist, and probably learned her love of gardening from her father, and her uncle, John Bennett-Poë. On her father's death, Riverston was sold, and Blanche moved to Grallagh where the two *Anthemis* cultivars arose. Apart from these elegant yellow daisies. Blanche Poë preserved, and later distributed, the double snowdrop that is named after her father.

DAFFODOWNDIILLY

There is one other plant, or rather group of plants, that must be included in my Irish flower garden - cultivars of the genus *Narcissus*, the daffodils, jonquils, narcissi, call them what you will. The only problem is choosing one daffodil, for the choice is bewildering; countless fine bulbs are available and many of these have Irish birthplaces.

Ireland has been a most important centre for daffodil breeding for more than a century. Frederick Burbidge stimulated the industry after his arrival in 1879 as curator of the Trinity College Botanic Garden. He was an expert on daffodils and had written and illustrated a monograph on *Narcissus* species and varieties before coming to Dublin. Burbidge encouraged William Baylor Hartland of Cork to collect daffodil varieties from derelict gardens. Hartland, described as 'very enthusiastic and impulsive, of poetic tendency and full of ideas', soon began to raise new cultivars, and he took a special interest in white-flowered daffodils that abounded in old Cork gardens. In 1883 Hartland issued his first daffodil catalogue and in 1886 he produced the wonderful, whimsical *Ye original little booke of daffodils*, a catalogue that raised the hackles of some pompous English horticulturists. The Reverend George Engleheart condemned Hartland's enthusiastic catalogue, and memorably lambasted the cover on which, to quote Engleheart,

> ... a damsel entangled in a growth of impossible daffodils, is apparently defending herself with a poker against the attacks of a flight of noxious insects; while on the opposite side a gouty caterpillar - or is it a cornucopia? - is pouring a shower of objects like jointed dolls and cabbages down upon the ancient John Parkinson and a short-sighted gentleman, whose botanical studies are much impeded by a swarm of bees hovering round his bald head.[26]

William Hartland selected several white daffodils including 'Colleen Bawn' and 'Leda'. He frequently used the motto 'Irradiating the present, restoring the past' in his wonderful catalogues, one of which prompted Guy Wilson of Broughshane, County Antrim, to become a daffodil breeder. Like his mentor, Wilson chose white daffodils as his passion, and in turn, he raised the brilliant 'Cantatrice', a marble-white flower that has won many prizes and is still listed in the best catalogues. The names chosen for a few of his other bulbs are evocative - 'Driven Snow', 'Everest', 'Kanchenjunga'. Wilson was also interested in bicolours, and tried to develop a good pink daffodil. In Waterford, Lionel Richardson led the way with pink varieties - one of his best is 'Salmon Trout', a short-trumpeted flower in salmon-pink and pale creamy-pink. Richardson experimented with double-flowered daffodils, and his work was continued by his widow who introduced 'Pink Gin' and 'Pink Champagne' which are doubles with pink petals. On the other hand, one of Lionel Richardson's finest bulbs is 'Kingscourt', a handsome, clear yellow trumpet daffodil.[27]

There were other daffodil maniacs of lesser significance but only because they produced fewer varieties. Sir Josslyn Gore-Booth raised a number of daffodils that have not endured in catalogues. Miss Fanny Currey named one after her home town of Lismore, County Waterford. Mrs Alice Lawrenson of Howth produced 'Lucifer', and several others. James Coey, who purchased the Slieve Donard Nursery, bred daffodils and helped other breeders, including Guy Wilson, by buying and marketing their bulbs.

More recently, W. J. Dunlop of Omagh raised some good red and white daffodils, including 'Enniskillen', and a fine yellow one named 'Ormeau'. Tom Bloomer was interested in whites, and introduced the outstanding cultivar 'White Star'. Bloomer's work has been carried on by Brian Duncan who has managed to obtain seedlings with a new colour - the names, 'Lilac Charm' and 'Lavender Lass' are quite descriptive. Mrs Kate Reade of Broughshane was influenced by Guy Wilson, and her most outstanding success was a waif with a pink trumpet and reflexed petals that is named 'Foundling'. In contrast, Sir Frank Harrison took a liking for green-eyed daffodils and he also had the good fortune to produce the orange and red 'Rio Rouge', after some seeds had been bombarded with gamma rays.

The older cultivars had their champion too. Dr David Willis, who was superintendent of the grounds of the University of Ulster at Coleraine, assembled a collection of about 1,500 cultivars and, using these, formed the Guy L. Wilson Daffodil Garden. The purpose of such an assembly of plants is to preserve the varieties for future gardeners, and to provide a gene-bank for future daffodil breeders. This collection has been designated a national collection by the National Council for the Conservation of Plants and Gardens. Today, although perhaps the zenith of Ireland's daffodil industry has passed, new varieties are still being created, especially on the Omagh bulb-farm of Brian Duncan, and at Kate Reade's in Broughshane.

Daffodils can be bought in almost every garden centre and even in supermarkets. Those outlets tend to stock good but ubiquitous cultivars, plants like 'King Alfred'. I think it is more worthwhile to resist the temptation of cheap bulbs and to favour a few well-chosen daffodils perhaps costing a little bit more. Many of the good cultivars raised by Ireland's outstanding daffodil breeders are available from specialist bulb nurseries.

My choice is personal and arbitrary. 'Lucifer' is first as it is an old daffodil, with a charm and ragged grace that is absent from modern, almost too perfect flowers. I found it increased easily, but did not bloom well when crowded - clumps of **'Lucifer'** need to be lifted and replanted every few years. As I have noted before, the narrow, translucent petals tend to be a bit floppy, probably because they are flimsy, and the slightly crumpled, short trumpet is a rich orange around the rim only fading into yellow towards the base. **'Foundling'**[28] is ineluctable - there is no other daffodil with such a charming habit and flower. This is a dainty yet sturdy variety. The flower has broad, creamy-white swept back petals and a slightly rippled trumpet the colour of freshly steamed salmon. Guy Wilson's **'Cantatrice'**[29] is another selection, because it is such a beautiful white. For friendship's sake, I must also have **'Wendy Walsh'**[30] which Kate Reade and I selected to name after Wendy, and which Wendy then painted so beautifully for *A prospect of Irish flowers*. I have a freshly-picked flower beside me as I write. The three outermost petals are broader than the oval, inner three; they overlap and form a flat, starry, cream background for the trumpet which has a green 'eye' and lemon-yellow base shading through pale orange into that same fresh salmon colour of 'Foundling' around the fluted and wrinkled rim.

Daffodils are not native plants in Ireland, but they thrive here. They can be seen growing in the most unlikely places. By the edge of a mountain lough at the Pass of Salruck, I have found daffodils flourishing as if wild. Every cottage in Connemara and Mayo has its pathway lined with the old double-flowered daffodil, almost the only flower grown in these damp, rushy gardens. And they brighten the landscape every spring even in The Burren, where, just before the spring gentians blossom in the middle of May, the pheasant's eye or poet's daffodil (*Narcissus poeticus*), the last of this tribe to flower, come into bloom beside cottages and on road banks. So I also have to include one last, very special daffodil in my imaginary garden, albeit a cultivar that was raised in the eastern USA by Mrs Margaret ('Meg') Yerger, another lady smitten by daffodils. Meg loves the poet's daffodil and she has allowed me to have the entire stock of one of her seedlings (from 'Lights Out' crossed with one called 'Praecox Grandiflorus')[31] and, as a wedding present, I have named it **'Susan Elizabeth'**[32] after my wife. 'Susan Elizabeth' has a lovely bright red rim around its yellow cup and a green eye. I have shared this new daffodil with Kate Reade, and with the National Botanic Gardens, Glasnevin, and a clump also grows, sheltered by a wonderful Sicilian clump of *Euphorbia characias*, under Tom Smith's October cherry (*Prunus subhirtella* 'Autumnalis') in our Norfolk garden.

The poet Padraic Colum urged us to plant flower gardens, for although Ireland might not appear to be a wealthy country it has a surfeit of resources. Colum reminded us that beauty is an essential part of our lives, and he suggested that we should spend our spare resources on flowers, on the white flowers of the narcissus. He quoted the prophet Mohammed:

> If thou of fortune be bereft
> And of thy store there be but left
> Two loaves - sell one, and with the dole
> Buy daffodils to feed thy soul. [33]

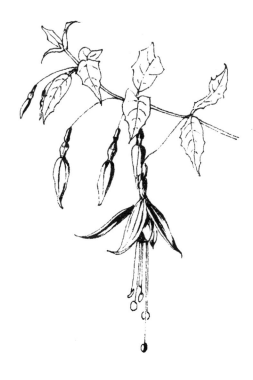

XII

Climbing on the garden wall

Hedera hibernica 'Hibernica' & 'Digitata' - *Parthenocissus henryana*
Lonicera tragophylla - *Aristolochia chrysops* - *Solanum crispum* 'Glasnevin'
Azara microphylla 'Variegata' - *Billardiera scandens* - *Actinidia chinensis*

> Darkly grows the quiet ivy
> Pale the broken arches glimmer through;
> Dark upon the cloister-garden
> Dreams the shadow of the ancient yew.
>
> Through the leafless aisles the verdure
> Flows, the meadow-sweet and fox-glove bloom.
> Earth, the mother and consoler,
> Winds soft arms about the lonely tomb.

T. W. H. Rolleston: 'The grave of Rury'

Gardens have been enclosed by walls from time immemorial. Today, only a lucky few possess gardens with those great stone or red-brick walls that were the mark of eighteenth and nineteenth century kitchen gardens. Yet, even in modern housing estates, with 'open plans', there are walls intruding into gardens - the sides of the house and garage, or the party wall.

A bare wall is an unsightly curse; you have to endure the unchanging boredom of stone, brick or plaster. A wall smothered in greenery is much more rewarding for at least it will change with the seasons. There is a well-known photograph of the now-vanished College Botanic Gardens in Ballsbridge, Dublin, taken by Greenwood Pim in the 1890s, showing an open gate in an old wall and the wall is completely obscured by climbing and clambering plants including an ancient *Wisteria*. The Reverend F. C. Hayes, rector of Raheny, published the original picture in his *A handy book of horticulture*, while William Robinson had the photograph engraved for *The English flower garden*. Robinson praised the 'handsome masses' of climbing plants, liberally and well planted, in the College Botanic Garden.

One of the best collections of wall plants in Ireland today is grown against the walls that enclose the National Botanic Gardens in Glasnevin. Many of these are uncommon species, rarely seen in other gardens, yet most are elegant and useful plants. Among them are shrubs which are capable of growing without support, but which can be trained against walls. Rambling or clambering plants are also included, and these are supported by wires, although trellis work can be used instead. Of course other plants can be cultivated on walls - ferns, foxgloves, snapdragons, wallflowers and even the Californian fuchsia. These annuals and small herbaceous perennials may become naturalized, adding to the colour and character of the wall garden. Moreover native herbs may invade the mortar and the cracks - among the many likely are rusty-back ferns and wall pennywort.

IRISH IVY

Of the self-supporting, clinging plants, ivy is the easiest to grow; it is evergreen and requires little attention. Some varieties do benefit from an annual trimming, and plants grown on a house must be kept from invading the eaves or blocking the windows.

Two species of ivy are now recognised as being native in Ireland. They are difficult to tell apart, and can only be distinguished with certainty by counting their chromosomes. This is not a task easily undertaken, so ordinary folk and field botanists have to rely on characters that are not thoroughly reliable. The common species, *Hedera helix*, has only 48 chromosomes; it tends to cling tenaciously to trees and the foliage turns purplish or brown in winter. The Atlantic or Irish ivy, *Hedera hibernica*, is confined to the extreme west of Europe and is not at all common in Ireland; it has 96 chromosomes. Irish ivy does not have the same tendency to climb, often growing along the ground or cascading over rocks and walls, and its leaves remain green throughout the year.

The Irish ivy of gardens, ***Hedera hibernica* 'Hibernica'**,[1] is a selected variety, well-known for its large, dull, dark green leaves with five-pointed lobes. It is valued as a ground-cover plant and also for its ability to clothe walls quickly. This variety is said to have been collected by a Dublin botanist, William Andrews, in the early 1830s on rocks at Ballybunion in County Kerry, but very little ivy grows there today.

***Hedera hibernica* 'Digitata'**[2] is also of Irish origin and has been in cultivation since before 1825 when it was advertised by the London nurseryman, Conrad Loddiges. 'Digitata' was also known as *Hedera helix* var. *hodginsii*, as it was discovered and introduced by Edward Hodgins of Dunganstown who raised the hybrid hollies. He found it growing near his nursery in County Wicklow. James Mackay, of Trinity College Botanic Garden, collected a similar ivy at Merrion in south Dublin.

'Digitata' is a handsome ivy, with dark green leaves that may be as much as ten centimetres long and broad. The leaves are deeply five- or seven-lobed, with a long central lobe - at its best the leaves resemble those of the passion-flower. The sinuses, between the lobes, are narrow and rippled at the base. This cultivar clings to walls and grows rapidly.

There is another interesting Irish variety of ivy, or at least one with an Irish name. *Hedera helix* 'Donerailensis' may have come from Doneraile in County Cork, but its history is not recorded. It is a dwarf ivy. Each leaf has three narrow lobes with wavy margins. In winter the foliage turns purplish-brown. 'Donerailensis' only retains those characters when grown in a pot, and clearly it is a variety of the common ivy.

In the past decade other cultivars of the Irish ivy (*Hedera hibernica*) have been made available through the British Ivy Society. One variety, named 'Strand' was collected by Alison Rutherford near Newcastle West in County Limerick, and another, named 'Glengarriff' came from west Cork. These retain beautiful green leaves throughout the year, and 'Strand' is a good plant for growing in a pot.

DR HENRY'S VINE

Another excellent climbing plant is a vine that belongs to the grape family and is closely related to the Virginia creeper of North America. ***Parthenocissus henryana***[3] is a Chinese species, discovered over a century ago at Yichang by Dr Augustine Henry.

Henry's vine clings by means of tendrils that develop disc-like 'suckers' at the tips of the tentacles. The 'suckers' adhere to any rough surface, and the coiled tendrils act like tension springs, bringing and holding the shoots close against the wall.

Parthenocissus henryana is deciduous. In winter the bare shoots form a tracery of inter-twining twigs. In summer the wall will be completely obscured by the elegant compound leaves. There are usually five leaflets in each leaf; they have toothed margins and are about seven centimetres long. The backs of the leaflets are glossy green tinged with crimson. The outer surface is patterned - the basic colour is dark green but the veins and ribs are picked out in silvery-grey and pink. The whole leaf has a velvety sheen although it is devoid of hairs. In spring the young shoots and leaves are bright crimson, and in autumn the green returns to flaming red as the leaves fall in a scarlet and crimson cascade.

The green flowers of *Parthenocissus* are small, inconspicuous, and arranged in a cone-shaped cluster like those of the grape. The fruits are like miniature grapes.

Augustine Henry collected his vine shortly after he started collecting plants at Yichang in 1885. He did not introduce it. Ernest Wilson sent seeds from China in 1900. While *Parthenocissus henryana* grows well in Ireland and as a wall plant is more attractive than its much-planted American relative, these climbing vines are spoilt when grown against walls; it is not their natural habit. In the autumn in the eastern United States, the Virginia creeper is one of the most colourful plants, festooning the trees through which it rambles with fire-red autumn foliage.

A VINE WITH TRUMPETS

A second climbing plant associated with Augustine Henry is cultivated in too few gardens, although it is the best honeysuckle of all. It is a Chinese species, **Lonicera tragophylla**[4], not unlike the wild honeysuckle of Irish hedgerows, but its individual flowers are many times longer than those of our native species. *Lonicera tragophylla* clambers through shrubs, coiling around branches; in a garden it needs the support of a trellis or pergola. It prefers a cool root-run, so its lower stems and roots should be shaded by other small shrubs. While it will grow in shade, the best situation for this honeysuckle is in the open.

In a lecture on wall plants, delivered in May 1929, Sir Frederick Moore recommended this Chinese honeysuckle for planting against walls up to three metres high. It will quickly attain that height, but it is better to grow it on a pergola.

Henry's honeysuckle has opposite pairs of leaves, that vary from separate, ovate leaves with short stalks to joined pairs that completely encircle the stem. The flowers are clustered at the tips of the shoots, and a group may contain as many as 20 blossoms. Each flower is about ten centimetres long, as long as your index finger, and is shaped like an ancient fanfare trumpet. The mouth is flared with a large four-lobed upper lip and a narrow lower lip; the lips are curled backwards and the five stamens and the long style protrude from the trumpet's mouth. The trumpets are bright yellow, tending to orange, with occasional streaks of red on the back of the upper lip. Alas they are not perfumed, but their colour and graceful shape most amply compensate.

After I had written the last paragraph I was reading E. A. Bowles' delightful books on his garden, and in *My garden in summer*, I found the following passage:

> This season I find *Lonicera tragophylla* [surpassing all its previous efforts], for it has taken the two past seasons to fill its pergola post, and now has turned its attention to flowering with a whole heart, and so here we have a full orchestra of golden trumpets that ought to produce a stupendous fanfare; but those rich yellow flowers only produce a show, and they offer little or nothing for the nose even - rather disgraceful for a Honeysuckle but forgivable in one so daffodilious in hue.[5]

Like some other plant attributed to Augustine Henry, this species was discovered in the Patung district, so it really should be set down to Henry's mischievous, alas anonymous, native collector. It was introduced by Ernest Wilson and flowered in Europe for the first time in 1904. James Veitch, son of Wilson's patron, expressed the opinion that it was 'by far the best honeysuckle' from the gardener's point of view. With such acclaim and unanimity, why is it so uncommon in gardens?

Lonicera henryi, another Chinese honeysuckle, was discovered by Augustine Henry and was named for him. It is not as spectacular as *Lonicera tragophylla*, but it is a useful, vigorous climber that can rapidly clothe the dead skeleton of a tree. The flowers are only about three centimetres long and are either dull red, fading to purplish-red, or creamy-yellow when grown in shade. The flowers have a faint, sweet perfume. It is grown against a wall in Glasnevin, and needs regular, heavy pruning to keep it in check.

A CHINESE DUTCHMAN'S PIPES

It might seem overwhelming to include a third plant connected with Dr Henry, but the fact is that many of our best climbing plants come from central China, Henry's collecting ground, that 'Klondyke of plant gold'. My next choice is *Aristolochia chrysops* (Plate 19, p.220)[6], a plantsman's delight, an elegant, amusing plant. Again it is a twining species that is suitable for cultivation on a pergola, although it is trained against a wall at Glasnevin, where it rewards with profuse blossom.

The individual flower is borne on a long, horizontal stem which has a heart-shaped bract at the base. At the end of this stalk is a ribbed ovary, which hangs vertically down. From the ovary is suspended the flower looking like one of those curled tobacco pipes beloved of Sherlock Holmes. It has a curved and inflated tube which bends upwards opening at an oval mouth frilled by a three-lobed collar. These lobes have yellow margins and are deep red towards the centre. The complicated flower of *Aristolochia* forms a sophisticated device that ensures the pollination of the flower - any insect entering the tube and crawling inside will find it difficult to get out without effecting the transfer of pollen from stamen to stigma.

The leaves of *Aristolochia chrysops* are shaped like the head of an arrow, and are dark green above with a pale green lower side. The contrast between the dark leaves and the numerous dangling yellow and red pipes is most attractive. It is free-flowering and well worth trying in a suitable sunny spot, but the roots should be shaded from the sun.

Dr Henry collected *Aristolochia chrysops* at Wushan in the east of Sichuan Province in 1888, during the long trek when he found the dove tree. He was interested in this genus as the roots of several species were used by the Chinese to make drugs. *Aristolochia chrysops* was also collected by Ernest Wilson, who sent seeds to Veitch's Nursery, where the plant flowered for the first time outside China in 1905.

GLASNEVIN'S POTATO CLIMBER

One of the most valuable wall plants is *Solanum crispum*, a relative of the potato and sometimes called the potato climber. Like the potato, *Solanum tuberosum*, it is a native of South America. *Solanum crispum* was brought to Europe about 1830 and was grown without provoking great interest. William Robinson noted that it was the only hardy ornamental species of *Solanum*. As early as 1882 accounts were published of a plant 'that used to be very fine' at

19. *Aristolochia chrysops*

the Glasnevin Botanic Gardens with bluer, larger flowers than others. At the beginning of the present century, this form of *Solanum crispum*, more vigorous and floriferous than normal, was distributed from Glasnevin and it was named *Solanum crispum* 'Glasnevin', although in later years it was often labelled *Solanum crispum* 'Autumnale'.

Solanum crispum **'Glasnevin'**[7] was exhibited by the Royal Botanic Gardens, Kew, in 1955 and gained an award of merit from the Royal Horticultural Society. This beautiful shrub was one of three plants used on the stamps issued by An Post, the Irish postal authority, in October 1995 to celebrate the bicentenary of the National Botanic Gardens.

The Glasnevin potato climber was certainly well-known to Dublin gardeners by 1910. Lady Ardilaun grew it at Saint Anne's, Clontarf, and she passed cuttings to Lady Talbot de Malahide for the garden at Malahide Castle where it flourished and bloomed profusely - *Solanum crispum* 'Glasnevin' still grows in the garden at Malahide Castle. At Mount Stewart, the potato climber is used in the red, white and blue scheme of the Jubilee Avenue. There it is grown without support, among Chilean fire-bushes, *Embothrium coccineum*, rhododendrons, eucalypts and *Eucryphia*.

Solanum crispum 'Glasnevin' is not completely hardy; it is susceptible to severe frost, but the walls against which it is usually grown provide the extra protection that it requires. Thus, as a wall plant, it survives in our coldest gardens, as at Birr Castle in County Offaly. In the mildest areas it can be grown as a free-standing shrub, but it is so vigorous that it soon becomes untidy; a severe pruning in autumn will keep it within bounds.

The leaves are bright green and elliptical with a pointed tip. The flowers are borne in clusters of about 40 at the tips of the shoots. Each blossom is shaped like a five-pointed star, with the points swept back. The star is blue, tending to violet in the centre. In the middle is a boss of five bright yellow stamens, surrounding the white style.

One of the great delights of this potato climber is its very long flowering period; in mild areas, and after mild winters, plants will begin to bloom in early March, reaching full bloom in May and continuing until the first frost of autumn.

BELGROVIANA

Azara microphylla, another South American shrub, is a useful evergreen with delicate foliage and highly-perfumed flowers. In its wild form, the leaves are dark, glossy green, but there is also a variegated cultivar that is an outstanding wall plant. Like the potato climber, *Azara microphylla* can be grown as a free-standing shrub - there are excellent specimens in Mount Usher and Castlewellan. However, in cold gardens, the extra protection of a wall is important as it is not reliably hardy. The branches form fans of foliage, like *Cotoneaster horizontalis*, but much more delicate. Only a minor amount of pruning is needed to keep the shrub elegant.

The variegated variety, *Azara microphylla* **'Variegata'** (Figure 17),[8] has small toothed leaves, less than one centimetre long, margined with creamy-white. The pairs of fragrant flowers are minute and concealed behind the leaves which are crowded together and arranged in two opposite ranks along the branches.

I have chosen this shrub for my Irish flower garden because it originated in the garden of one of the great characters of Irish horticulture, William Edward Gumbleton, J.P., of Belgrove, near Cobh, in County Cork. He was affectionately known as 'Gumbo'. William Gumbleton was eccentric, the epitomé of a Victorian gentleman. He had very firm opinions about everything, especially plants - plants which he did not like were called 'tush plants' and were flailed to destruction with the umbrella which he always carried in case he encountered such abominations. He treated several plants in this endearing manner on his first visit to Glasnevin after the appointment of Frederick Moore to the post of keeper.

Gumbleton was like the proverbial magpie; he collected plants, pictures and porcelain. His house was crammed full of bits and pieces. His botanical library contained the finest books, illustrated with coloured plates, and he bequeathed it to the Royal Botanic Gardens, Glasnevin.

I think that Gumbleton had a wicked, boyish sense of humour, and his letters are frequently laced with caustic comments. Amos Perry, a Middlesex nurseryman well-known at the beginning of this century, was described as 'the minor prophet Amos'. Another nurseryman was condemned as a 'hum-bugging puffer'. On the other hand, people that Gumbleton respected were addressed politely, if incorrectly. Charles Ball was sometimes labelled 'The Assistant Keeper of the Irish Kew', and Frederick Moore was 'The Regius Keeper of the Irish Kew, Glasnevin'.

William Gumbleton's horticultural interests were varied. He collected grasses, including varieties of the pampas grass, and he liked the tender species of the daisy family from South Africa - one of these, a sumptuous orange-red blossomed species from Namaqualand, was named *Arctotis gumbletonii*[9] after him. He also had passions for tuberous begonias, red-hot pokers (*Kniphofia*) and varieties of the daisy bush (*Olearia*), but he complained that a form of *Olearia virgata* purchased 'from that ignorant most presumptuous Gauntlett ... is utter Tush'.

The only contemporary account that I can trace of *Azara microphylla* 'Variegata' growing in its home garden was written by Samuel Arnott in 1908. He noted that '*Azara microphylla belgroviana* is a beautiful variegated form of this favourite shrub, and the specimen of the type itself at Belgrove is exceedingly large and well developed'. This plant was moved from Belgrove, after Gumbleton's death in 1911, to the garden of Richard Beamish at Ashbourne House, Glounthaune, nearer Cork. Lady Moore saw it growing there. Writing about a plant at Mount Usher, she recorded that it was 'a child of the late Mr W. E. Gumbleton's original plant'.

17. *Azara microphylla* 'Variegata'

William Gumbleton was buried outside the wall of his beloved garden. The garden was dismantled quickly and the choicest plants were sold by William Baylor Hartland. When I visited Belgrove in the mid-1980s only a few trees and some clumps of pampas grass remained; there was a fine walnut, a dove tree, some eucalypts and a huge *Magnolia campbellii* that was a wonderful spectacle in March when covered with rich pink, goblet-shaped flowers.

Azara microphylla 'Variegata' - what a pity it did not keep its original name 'Belgroviana' - is Gumbleton's abundant memorial. Plant it near the house for in early spring the tiny flowers will scent the air with a delightful perfume. Plant it against a dark wall, so that the cream fans of foliage will be set off by the background of darker brick or stone.

THE SURGEON-GENERAL'S DUMPLING

Azara is not a climber but an upright, free-standing shrub - we just chose sometimes to treat it as a wall-plant. True climbing plants have many different ways of reaching lofty heights; some cling by roots that virtually turn into adhesive pads, others twine, many have tendrils that grasp and curl, and not a few merely launch vigorous shoots heavenward to become ensnared in whatever is above. Ivies climb by aerial roots. The potato climber, which I have described, is one that launches shoots into surrounding vegetation. Peas have tendrils. The Surgeon-General's dumpling is an Australian twiner.

Surgeon-General John White, who haled from Drumaran in County Fermanagh, was one of the first Irishmen to set foot in New South Wales. He was the chief medical officer on the infamous convict fleet that sailed from England in March 1787 bound for Botany Bay, where a penal colony was to be established. Instead of Botany Bay, Governor Arthur Phillip chose to establish the settlement on the southern side of Port Jackson at a place he named Sydney Cove. Thus European settlement of the continent of Australia commenced.

White was not a convict but a free man. He had served on various warships before being appointed Surgeon-General of the colony. Like many medical men he had a substantial interest in natural history, especially botany, which is fortunate too, because he and his fellow surgeons had to put their botanical knowledge to good use when both food and medicines became desperately short during the colony's early years. Surgeon-General White and Assistant Surgeon Dennis Considen - who may also have been Irish - discovered that the gum exuded by various native trees could be used as astringents, in the same way as balsam. Considen and White were the pioneers of eucalyptus oil - White was sufficiently impressed to send a quart of the oil to London. They also experimented with the local plants as cures for scurvy; several fruiting shrubs provided a paltry supply of edible berries which apparently alleviated the symptoms of that disease. The plant now called dumpling or common appleberry was probably one of these antiscorbutics - it was certainly eaten by the hungry convicts.[10]

In between his medical duties, White gathered specimens of the hundreds of extraordinary plants that inhabited the hinterland of Port Jackson. These were pressed and dried, and then sent to London, providing botanists with plenty of new species to name. Thus many Australian species were described using his specimens, although it is strange that none was named in his honour. The Fermanagh-born surgeon-general may be credited as the 'messenger' of, among other plants, the state emblem of New South Wales, the sumptuous red-blossomed waratah (*Telopea speciosissimum*),[11] a shrub that, alas, does not tolerate the Irish climate.

Surgeon-General John White lived in Sydney Cove for seven years, and he must have sent hundreds of specimens to London. He also employed various artists, including at least one convict, the Scottish forger Thomas Watling, to paint the plants that grew around the settlement. The paintings and White's specimens still exist in various museums, and together form a remarkable record of the flora of the land around Botany Bay before the burgeoning city of Sydney covered the area.

One of the plants represented by specimens and a painting was the dumpling, the common appleberry; its botanical name, *Billardiera scandens*, celebrates another, contemporary botanical explorer, the Frenchman Jacques Julien Houtou de Labillardière, who visited Tasmania and Western Australia in the summer of 1792 and 1793.

Billardiera scandens, a delicate climber with wiry stems, belongs to the same family as *Pittosporum*, and is a native plant in south-eastern Australia and Tasmania. Its dark green, evergreen leaves have wavy margins and are variable in shape, usually elongated with parallel sides or tapering like an arrow head. The flowers are delicate, waisted bells, about one inch long, that dangle singly on long stems. The five petals curve outwards from the middle and are pale yellow or creamy-green. Common appleberry blooms in the spring and early summer, and the flowers are followed by olive-green berries. Another species, *Billardiera longifolia*, has straight, tubular flowers followed by dark blue, porcelain-like berries and is perhaps a more familiar plant in Irish gardens; indeed given a little protection it thrives outdoors even in the colder gardens of County Offaly. The Surgeon-General's appleberry will also grow outdoors in a well-sheltered, mild site; give it good well-drained soil with plenty of leaf mould worked in, and something to twine its stems around.

John White returned to England in 1794, probably quite a celebrity. His handsome book, *Journal of a voyage to new South Wales*, first published in London in 1790, was translated into Swedish, French and German. The appleberry had been described and handsomely illustrated in the first part of Dr James Edward Smith's work entitled *A specimen of the botany of New Holland* - New Holland was the name given to Australia by the Dutch in the seventeenth century - which was published during the autumn of 1793. Dr Smith used information sent by John White, as well as White's pressed specimens, when describing *Billardiera scandens*, and the published illustration was certainly based on a watercolour sent from Sydney Cove, because appleberry was not cultivated anywhere in Europe in 1793. Smith remarked that the climber produced 'almost the only wild eatable fruit of the country'.[12] I have never tasted an appleberry; they have a downy skin and the pulp has a sweet apple-like flavour. In some ways they look just like miniature, unripe kiwifruits!

OF KIWIFRUITS, A.K.A. CHINESE GOOSEBERRIES

For my final wall plant, I return to Dr Augustine Henry. He was the greatest of Ireland's exploring botanists, and deserves our plentiful attention. He was greatly respected in China, and not only was a volume of an illustrated flora of China dedicated to him but also one wing of the old botanical institute in Beijing was named after him - the institute now occupies a new building and the Henry connection is maintained no longer.

Henry was interested in the useful plants of the Yichang region. He wrote a small book that was intended to encourage European missionaries to collect plants. 'If any one wishes to help', Henry wrote, 'he will confer a great favour on the writer by sending him specimens of dried plants, drugs, woods, dyes, etc'. While living in central China, Dr Henry collected and pressed specimens of the foliage of a rampant vine that bore brown fruits. In 1886, he sent pickled fruits and dried specimens to Kew for identification, and received the reply that the plant was one that had been named *Actinidia chinensis* by Jules Émile Planchon in 1847. Thus Henry had not discovered a new species, but collected for the first time fruits of a vine identified as yangtao as long ago as the mid-eighteenth century by the French Jesuit botanist Pierre Nicolas le Chéron d'Incarville. In a list of Chinese plant names, Henry noted that the fruits of *Actinidia chinensis* were edible, and in that little book for the missionaries, he remarked that

> *Actinidia chinensis* ... has been referred to in Chinese Names of Plants ... as the Yang-t'ao ... It is a very large climbing shrub with white conspicuous flowers and fruits about the size of a plum, which can be made into good jam with a guava-jelly kind of flavour. The fruit might be much improved in cultivation.

Augustine Henry did not know that this suggestion would come true.

By 1903 he was back in England, and delivered a lecture on plant exploration in China at the Horticultural Club in London, during which he suggested that *Actinidia chinensis* would be worth growing in gardens. About the same time, Henry wrote an article for William Robinson's magazine *Flora and sylva* in which he said that the 'fruit would be a great acquisition, I think'. In 1909, *Actinidia chinensis* bloomed for the first time in Europe, an event greeted somewhat flippantly by Edward Knowldin, writing in *Irish gardening* about gluts of strawberries and gooseberries and foreign competition:

> Then, again, to help the foreigner, some scientific pomologist is always dangling some possibility before their eyes which they are not slow to grasp. Now it is *Actinidea* [sic] *chinensis* which has flowered in Europe for the first time this year, a handsome hardy climber which we are told would in all probability be hardy in Ireland. However, we need not bother about that; they can do that for us on the Riviera, where it has flowered but not fruited for simple reason of being as yet in single blessedness for want of the male sex, which, we believe, will shortly be trotted over from China. When happily married the

Actinidea bears fruit, lashins of it, resembling a small plum, but with (saving your presence!) the guts of a gooseberry, and that is it highly relished by the Chinese seems its chief recommendation as yet.[13]

While Dr Henry had sent the yangtao fruit to Europe, the seeds could not be germinated as the specimen was pickled - the only use they could be put to was as templates for Matilda Smith to draw, and her illustration, based on Henry's gatherings, was published in 1887. This shows a small, almost naked round fruit - the absence of a brown furry coat is important and proves that Henry did collect *Actinidia chinensis*, yangtao.

In recent decades in New Zealand, vines of *Actinidia* have been the basis of a major fruit industry. The strange furry fruits are exported throughout the world under the name kiwifruits. They do not look appetizing, but the green, juicy flesh is delicious, tasting like ripe gooseberries, a mixture of strawberry with a hint of lemon. Kiwifruit orchards cover around 11,000 hectares in New Zealand and have also been established in many other countries because the amenable kiwifruit is profitable. It has even been hailed as the fruit of the twenty-first century. But the hairy fruited *Actinidia* is not Dr Henry's one. Recent research by Dr Ross Ferguson and Chou Feng Liang has shown that the hairy kiwifruit is produced by the plant known to the Chinese as mao yangtao - mao means hairy - and its correct Latin name is *Actinidia deliciosa*.

Actinidia deliciosa is a highly ornamental vine with handsome oval or heart-shaped, thin green leaves, borne on hairy stalks. The young growth is delightful - stems, shoots and young leaves glow bright red through a velvety covering of crimson hairs. The young stems are translucent, and the young leaves have a whitish undersurface that changes quickly to green. The flowers are about five centimetres across, with white or greenish-white petals, and in male flowers there can be about 130 stamens. *Actinidia chinensis*[14] differs in many ways. Its leaves are thicker, almost leathery, and the undersurface is covered with greyish white, star-like hairs. The young growth is yellow-green, not red, and the brown bark on the stems is soon smooth not hairy. The flowers are smaller, rarely more than four centimetres across, and the male flowers only have around 50 stamens. The most tangible difference is in the fruit. The hairy, elongated fruits with dark green pulp come from *Actinidia deliciosa*, while *Actinidia chinensis* produced almost spherical, naked fruits with yellow or green flesh.

A single vine of either species usually produces only male or female flowers, so it is necessary to grow plants of both sexes if fruit is required. Very rarely, bisexual flowers are produced. As long as male and female plants grow in close proximity, fruit will be produced. New clones selected in New Zealand have become available here and these make the choice of sexes easier.

I was confident, when I first wrote about kiwifruit, that the species of *Actinidia* long grown in Irish gardens was the one gathered by Augustine Henry, namely *Actinidia chinensis*, but Ferguson and Liang's studies suggest otherwise. I now believe that these vines may have to be renamed *Actinidia deliciosa*, although I have not studied each and every one. The striking red colour of the young shoots is one character that serves to cast doubt, and *Actinidia deliciosa* is hardier than *Actinidia chinensis* which might not survive the Irish climate. There is a fine, antique *Actinidia* at Mount Stewart, almost swamping a tree; I have seen it on several successive years laden with fruits, but I cannot recall whether they were naked or hairy.

Dr Henry's role in the success story of kiwifruit is a very minor one, but he did suggest that the yangtao was worthy of serious consideration, and certainly the Chinese consider that the fruit is superior to those of mao yangtao, the so-called kiwifruit. In China every year thousands of tonnes of *Actinidia chinensis* fruits are gathered from wild vines, and the Chinese are focusing their scientific research on this species, Dr Henry's one.[15] Yet it is only one of the thousands of plants that he collected. Augustine Henry was a truly remarkable botanist and I like to imagine him, not sitting at the customs desk or trudging through thickets in search of plants, but as he left Yichang, walking over the river-flat to the waiting boat. His departure was described by the *North China Herald and Supreme Court and Consular Gazette*, on 15 March 1889.

Ichang, from our own correspondent, dated 1 March

Dr Henry left Ichang today after a nearly seven years' stay, having had nearly all the primroses of San Yew-tung brought down in his honour, and walking down into the river bed between a row of crackers and Roman candles all one after another lighting up and exploding, as he passed along the sands. These fireworks were the tribute from the Chinese part of the Customs staff. The little European community all dined and lunched each other in his honour to the very last. He will be greatly missed, having shown kindness unto every man. [16]

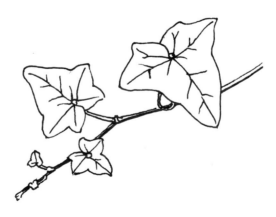

XIII

Behind The House:
An Interlude For Vegetables
And Fruits

Potatoes - Brussels sprouts - Red currants - Apples

> **A row of fragrant apple-trees,**
> **An orchard in its pink-tipped bloom,**
> **Between it and the hill.**
> **A forest tall of real leeks**
> **Of onions and of carrots, stood**
> **Behind the house.**

> *Kuno Meyer: 'The Vision of Mac Conglinne'*[1]

Ireland's gardens are not populated by pretty plants alone; behind the house, out of sight, there is usually a vegetable patch or, when land is plentiful, a walled garden in which vegetables and fruit trees are grown.

The earliest catalogues surviving for any garden in Ireland are contained in the evocative poetry of the Early Christian period. An orchard and a garden of leeks, onions, carrots are mentioned in the twelfth century satirical poem 'The vision of Mac Conglinne'. These fruits and vegetables are alluded to frequently in poetic hymns to an idyllic world. Manchán of Liath prayed

> Grant me sweet Christ the grace to find -
> Son of the living God! -
> A small hut in a lonesome spot
> To make it my abode. ...

A southern aspect for the heat,
A stream along its foot,
A smooth green law with rich top soil
Propitious to all fruit. ...

And all I ask for housekeeping
I get and pay no fees
Leeks from the garden, poultry, game
Salmon and trout and bees. [2]

Centuries later, extensive lists survive detailing the herbs and vegetables cultivated in the kitchen gardens attached to Trinity College, Dublin, soon after its foundation in 1592. Harry Holland leased land from the college, agreeing to take only half of 'all the herbs that grow, lavender, roses, fruit of the trees', and also that in his portion of the garden he was to plant turnips, parsnips, carrots, globe artichokes, onions and leeks, and in the 'low garden outside the wall and great orchard ... cabbages, turnips, and other things as they shall need for 30 persons or 8 messes as the cook hall think good.'[3]

By this period, around 1600, it was well known that Irish gardeners could cultivate a range of plants which, though not generally grown, did better in Ireland than in their countries of origin. Among the plants listed by Dr Peter Lombard were artichokes, squashes, cabbages and hops. The quality of the locally produced vegetables was evidently excellent, and towards the end of the seventeenth century, the Viceroy, Lord Clarendon, was moved to comment that 'the sallet are very good and the roots generally much better than ours in England; asparagus here is very good, large and green'. The earliest Irish printed seed-list, issued by John Johnson, 'gardiner and seedsman, at the Orange-Tree on Corkhill, Dublin', probably in the first five years after 1700, lists a remarkable range of vegetables and herbs, many in variety; Strasbourgh onion and red Spanish onion head his list, and it includes, among others, Arabian lettuce, 'colyflower', 'coli-rapi', short and prickly cucumbers, Indian beans, Sandwich beans, Canterbury beans and 22 different peas.[4]

The seeds of many of these herbs and vegetables were certainly imported in the eighteenth and nineteenth centuries, as advertisements in contemporary journals indicates. Yet, given the long period for which we have reasonable knowledge of a high standard of domestic horticulture and a wide range of vegetable varieties, it is likely that Irish gardeners saved their own seed, and that over many decades distinctive Irish varieties of vegetables were produced. No-one has made an inventory of our indigenous varieties of vegetables, except for potatoes, using old catalogues or periodicals, and even the extensive data-base of the Henry Doubleday Research Association does not contain more than a half-dozen vegetables of Irish origin.

For fruits, likewise, we have patchy information. I know about a handful of Irish strawberries, one an antique and several others that are quite new. The antique strawberry was 'Princess Frederick William', raised by the redoubtable Ninian Niven at the Garden Farm,

Drumcondra, and released in 1860. That 'first rate seedling' bore bright scarlet berries 'of a rich Pine Apple perfume and flavour',[5] but who grows it today? In the present century strawberry breeding was carried out during the 1970s and 1980s at the Soft Fruit Research Centre established by An Foras Taluntais in Clonroche, County Wexford. The aim was not to produce strawberry cultivars for use by ordinary gardeners, but to breed better strawberries for the Irish processing industry, especially ones with better fruit colour, with good red flesh. 'Clonderg', was the first to be named,[6] followed by 'Clonard' and 'Clonree'.[7] Jim MacLachlan, who bred these strawberries, hoped that 'Clonard' and 'Clonree', his favourite, would be dual-purpose strawberries, but none of the varieties was a success. Work is still continuing at Clonroche, evaluating some later selections which arose from native Irish breeding material.[8] Time alone will tell if an Irish strawberry becomes available to commercial growers and ordinary gardens.

The story with apples is different. Although there has never been an Irish pomona, to use the time-honoured name for a book about apples, we have some excellent historical records and the authoritative work on Irish apples is a paper published nearly half a century ago by Dr Keith Lamb in which he described and listed all the indigenous Irish apples that he could trace.[9]

POTATOES

The potato, a native of South America, had reached Ireland by the early seventeenth century. Tradition ascribes the honour of introducing this remarkable vegetable to Ireland to Sir Walter Raleigh, but scholars doubt the ineradicable legend. For a while the potato was a curiosity, but by the mid-1600s it was a plentiful food and its cultivation was well understood. There is a passage in William Coles's book entitled *Adam in Eden*, published in 1657, that seems to be reliable; '... the soyle of Ireland doth so well agree with them [potatoes], that they grow there so plentifully that there be whole fields overrun with them'.

The earliest list of distinct varieties of potato is dated 1730, and appeared in George Rye's *Consideration of agriculture*, published in Dublin. Rye explained that there were 'five sorts ... known to us; the white flat Kidney potatoe, the round White, the Yellow, the round Red, and the Black Potatoe'. The first of these was planted in January and harvested in June, while the Black potato, so-called because the 'skin is very dark ... keeps till Potatoes come again.'[10] William Davidson, who this century chronicled the potato in Ireland, asserted that the black potato must be regarded as the 'first really outstanding variety', but it was exterminated, like several other indigenous varieties, by the devastating attacks of late blight in 1845, 1846 and 1847 which precipitated and exacerbated the Great Hunger, the Irish potato famine. Other varieties were raised between 1730 and the arrival of blight in 1845 - among these were 'Irish Apple', 'Cork Red', 'Cups' and the infamous 'Lumper' often described as a watery potato only fit for cattle.

There were three memorable ridges planted with 'Lumper' in the National Botanic Gardens, Glasnevin, in 1995, during the Gardens' bicentenary and the sesquicentenary of the arrival of late blight. On 20 August moving tributes were paid in dramatic tableaux to the millions of Irish men, women and children who suffered in the subsequent famine, and to David Moore, the Gardens' curator at that time, who was the first to notice the disease on potatoes growing at Glasnevin on 20 August 1845.[11] We have no record of the varieties then being cultivated in the vegetable plots at the Botanic Gardens, but it is not unreasonable to suppose that 'Lumper' was there. This potato is one of the most famous - or infamous - for two reasons. 'Lumper' is a heavy cropping potato and so it was the predominant variety in Ireland during the early 1840s; the people depended almost entirely on its crop. However, because of its susceptibility to late blight, there was virtually a total failure of the Irish potato crop in 1846. Famine ensued.

I had a chance to eat some of the 1995 crop of 'Lumper', and like any new potato freshly dug, boiled and served with butter, they were delicious. They are not available as seed, nor are they sold in greengrocers and supermarkets, and when you see a tuber you can understand why this is not a popular variety any more. 'Lumper' has an extraordinary appearance; it is a knobbly tuber with deeply sunk eyes, which would be a chore to peel.

After the Great Hunger, many new potato cultivars were raised, especially varieties which showed resistance to blight. At first, potato breeding was carried out by individuals, not by institutes - there was no attempt to raise new varieties, resistant to blight, at the Glasnevin Botanic Gardens, for example.

The origin of one potato was a pure chance. James McAlexander, about 1846, planted two potatoes found in a barrel of Dutch flax seed, and thereby raised 'Skerry Blue'. He had purchased the barrel of seed from John Russell of Broughshane in County Antrim, but how the potatoes came to be in the barrel is not recorded. McAlexander (or McAlschinder) lived near the ancient church of Skerry, which is a few miles north of Broughshane, in the diocese of Down and Connor. Thus the potato was named 'Skerry Blue'.[12] This was the third most popular potato in Ireland in 1911, but because of its susceptibility to wart disease it was soon displaced by other varieties.

Remarkably, two Irish potatoes were raised by women. Miss King of Mountmellick, County Laois, is credited with raising 'Flourball', a floury potato that kept well and was resistant to blight. This variety was introduced by Messrs Sutton and Sons in 1895, but I know nothing more about this pioneering lady. A blight-resistant, late potato yielding round, purple-stained tubers, was 'Leinster Wonder', a seedling raised about 1905 by Miss Williams of Killucan in County Westmeath. She had gathered seeds from 'Champion' which Davidson described as 'the most outstanding variety in the history of potato-growing in Ireland'. Again, I have traced no other information about Miss Williams whose potato was introduced by J. F. Williamson of Summerhill, Mallow, County Cork during 1910. Williamson also marketed 'The Colleen', a 'grand second-early' potato which gained an award of merit from the Royal Horticultural Society in 1907. 'Champion II' which was 'the result of a cross between the Champion and another seedling still in the hands of the grower' was produced by James

Robertson of La Mancha, Malahide, and was introduced by Messrs Hogg and Robertson about 1904. Not to be left out, the irrepressible William Baylor Hartland of Ard Cairn Nurseries in Cork, produced 'The Claddagh', which he described as a 'lovely pink-skinned "Main Crop" Russety and beautifully netted Round Potato'. Just as he did with his apples, as we shall see, Hartland sent out free samples of 'The Claddagh'; the editor of *Irish gardening* reported that when eaten 'with milk and butter in the thoroughly Irish manner ... [we have] never tasted a nicer dish of potatoes.'

Other individuals active in the search for better potatoes included Wesley Forbes of Gilnahirk in Belfast who during the early 1900s produced handsome catalogues illustrating his new varieties. He raised 'Lord Dufferin', a main crop potato. One of the last was John Clarke of Moss-side, a small village lying east of Coleraine in the north of County Antrim, who began raising new cultivars during the 1920s. In 1934 his first potato 'Ulster Cromlech' was released, and between that and 'Ulster Brevet' (1972) he produced and named more than two dozen cultivars. Clarke was a quiet unassuming man, who read widely and, having left school at eleven years of age, taught himself the skills of cross-pollinating and selecting potatoes.[13] John Clarke's cultivars always had Ulster as part of the name.

Potato breeding is no longer an amateur adventure; breeding programmes at Loughgall in County Armagh and Oak Park in County Carlow have been funded by the respective governments, and have been highly successful. There have been many new varieties released, too many to summarize. Like roses or apples, are these modern potatoes any better than 'Lumper' or 'Skerry Blue'?

BRUSSELS SPROUTS

In seeking to recount the stories of some of the Irish vegetables, I learned that one of our achievements was the production of better Brussels sprouts. The Brussels sprout was first grown in Britain and Ireland early last century, although it is an ancient vegetable, known to Belgian gardeners for over eight centuries. In 1924, G. O. Sherrard held a trial of the vegetable at the Albert Agricultural College in Glasnevin, just a short walk up the hill from the National Botanic Gardens, and 'was so horrified at the unproductive state of the commercial varieties' that he decided to breed some better sprouts. He used self-fertile plants of a French cultivar, produced by Messrs Vilmorin, named 'Précoce de Fontenay' as a starting point. By the late 1940s, Sherrard had produced several series of plants and was able to begin to select and name new cultivars. 'Billiard Ball' was 'a very fine' sprout, and was given that name because the sprouts were so smooth and firm. Another of Sherrard's varieties had a distinctive grey waxy 'bloom' - this became 'Grey Lady'. He also selected a dwarf variety, suitable for the suburban garden, that produced much smaller sprouts.[14] 'Irish Glacier' and 'Irish Elegance' were his most important Brussels sprouts - they were the leading varieties for commercial production in Ireland and elsewhere for a number of years, and were foundation varieties for subsequent breeding programmes. Another of his sprouts was named 'Glasnevin Supreme' - we managed to obtain some seeds of it from the Henry Doubleday Research Association in 1995, but none of these Brussels sprouts is available in garden centres or from seedsmen today. Like the potatoes, they are antiques, hoarded and safeguarded in conservation collections.

G. O. Sherrard - he was familiarly known as 'G. O.', short for Gerald Ormsby - was the first Professor of Horticulture at the Albert College, part of University College, Dublin, from 1940, and during the late 1950s he was the President of the Royal Horticultural Society of Ireland. In 1903 he was taken on as a 'gentleman gardener' - an unpaid student gardener - at the Royal Botanic Gardens, Glasnevin, so he received some of his training under Frederick Moore at a time when Moore was actively involved in promoting the development of commercial horticulture in Ireland. Trials of various fruit crops were initiated and fruit growing by farmers was actively encouraged.

In the recent past, vegetable breeding in Ireland was confined to some work on onions carried out at the Kinsealy Research Centre - the aim was to produce an early maturing, thin-necked onion with good skin and capable of being stored. As for fruit breeding, the main emphasis was on strawberries; at Clonroche in County Wexford, thousands of strawberry seedlings were raised in the hope of producing a new strawberry suitable for commercial production.[15] Vegetable and fruit breeding programmes are now very costly and have largely been abandoned in Ireland. There is certainly no room left for the amateur, although someone might by chance produce a magnificent new vegetable variety and succeed in persuading a multi-national seed company to acquire it.

RED CURRANTS

An odd-one-out, not the result of a breeding programme, is an Irish red currant named 'Pearson's Seedling', which is still in cultivation. Little is recorded about its origins, but the name suggests it was a seedling rather than a sport, and presumably it was a chance discovery. In Drummond's catalogue for 1964, the red currant was declared to be 'the largest berried and longest bunched' variety in cultivation, having beaten all others at the Royal Horticultural Society of Ireland's show in Ballsbridge.

Andrew Pearson, the gardener who raised *Ribes rubrum* 'Pearson's Seedling',[16] was a gardener in the Chief Secretary's Lodge in The Phoenix Park, Dublin, until 1902. He moved to Cork as head gardener and steward at Lota Lodge in Glanmire, the home of A. F. Sharman Crawford, and remained there for 18 years. In 1920, Mr Pearson returned to The Phoenix Park as Assistant Superintendent, and he supervised the original planting of the Irish National War Memorial at Islandbridge.

You cannot buy Pearson's red currant from nurseries, but fortunately there is at least one plant in the National Botanic Gardens, Glasnevin. Indeed, the only hope that these displaced, old varieties have of surviving is preservation in special collections within gardens like

Glasnevin. Had many apples not been gathered into a national collection at Brogdale in England years ago, many Irish varieties would be extinct.

IRISH APPLES

When I was a boy we lived in a large house with a large, walled-in garden. Against the walls were espalier apple trees. I don't remember what the varieties were because I was too young to take much notice of anything other then the plentiful, tasty apples. There was a very large old pear tree too, which dropped small, sweet pears on to the ground. Later in a smaller house, with only one south-facing party wall, we still had apple trees including one brought from the old garden - it was 'Laxton's Superb'. The other apples we inherited with the garden - four 'Greasy Pippin' trees. That is not a happy name for the apple, but it does describe the fruit very well, because when ripe and in store, the skin becomes waxy and slippery. This particular apple is also known as 'Ballinamallard Pippin' because it is common in that part of County Fermanagh. When almost ripe the flesh is crisp and sweet with a distinctive acid tone; when stored through the winter it become drier and loses its acidity.

Throughout Ireland and Britain during the last decade, there has been a reawakening of interest in the old varieties of apples, just as there has been a revival in the fortunes of some older garden flowers. Old Irish apples have lovely names: 'Irish Peach', 'Kerry Pippin', 'Ard Cairn Russet', 'Ross Nonpareil'. Possibly the oldest named apple connected with Irish orchards is 'Cockagee' or 'Cackagee', prized in the seventeenth century for making cider. By the early nineteenth century many other varieties were available in Ireland, and John Robertson of Kilkenny, who was the first to record them, described seven, including 'Kerry Pippin' and 'Irish Peach' (under the name 'Early Crofton').

The glory of the apple in its many varieties is that, properly cultivated and then carefully picked, a well-planned orchard, even a few trees in a little back garden, can yield a succession of deliciously different flavours and fragrances through the autumn and into the following spring. The apple season, even in Ireland, begins in August and can be made to last into May. An apple plucked fresh from a tree in your own garden, a tree nurtured and cared for with your own hands, or one taken from your own apple store, always tastes nicer than the apples bought from a greengrocer or supermarket. Nowadays a couple of apple trees can be planted in a small garden, thanks to the development of dwarf stocks that enable growers to have small, compact trees. Of course you can still employ the age-old technique of training apples as fans or espalier against a garden wall or a strong wooden frame.

'Irish Peach' was an old variety when John Robertson compiled his pioneering account of Irish apples, yet it is available commercially. This apple may have originated in Sligo, but its history is unknown. It is an early dessert apple, ready to pick and eat at the beginning of August. The flesh is firm, very fine, white and juicy, with a pleasing flavour. For a late apple, 'Ross Nonpareil', another ancient variety reported from County Meath in 1802, would be worth trying. The fruit can be stored for eating between November and January, and has a rich, aromatic flesh. The skin is pale yellow flushed orange with red streaks and russet all over. As for an Irish cooking apple, one that bakes nicely, there is 'Echlinville', raised by Mr Logan who was a gardener at a house with that name near Portaferry on the Ards Peninsula in County Down.[17] It was recorded as early as 1800 and is still available. The large flat apples have a yellow-green skin, dotted with russet, and the crisp, white flesh is firm, juicy and very acidic. It blossoms early - one day after 'Bramley's Seedling'![18]

Perusing one of the old nursery catalogues, published almost a century ago by the extrovert Cork nurseryman, William Baylor Hartland, entitled *Concise list of fruit trees ... that are profitable for Irish growers from peer to peasant* - they do not write nursery catalogues like that any more! - brings back memories of my Fermanagh childhood. Not one to hide his light under a bushel, Hartland advertised Irish apples under the slogan 'Old lamps for new lamps'. He had a high regard for himself, yet provided an excellent service for peers and peasants. By sending just three penny stamps anyone could get a sample of fruit of 'Ard Cairn Russet' in season. Does any nurseryman offer such a service today?

'Ard Cairn Russet', introduced by Hartland in 1890s, is a fine, golden-green apple, flushed with red and entirely covered with russet, that keeps well and while not juicy, the flesh is sweet and slightly aromatic. Hartland sang its praises, noting that it is 'a lovely russety Pearmain-shaped fruit of medium size, most excellent for dessert, sweet, like a banana, colour rich orange shaded vermilion'.

Here is another taste of Hartland's old and new lamps. 'Gibbons' Russet' was an old variety in 1902 and, to quote Hartland, was 'known to the Blackwater cider men years ago as the Ould Devil or Cherry Brandy'. The apple was flat, 'closely netted like a melon, and so perfumed in the fruit house that its odour excludes all other'. So good was this old County Cork apple, and so popular, that Hartland was obliged to note in one copy of his catalogue for 1903 that 'all my dishes were eaten and stolen at the last show here [in Cork]. All the old men said it was the favourite in the Room and they were Right.' So popular, yes, that it is no longer available from nurseries although fortunately the apple is represented in the National Apple Collection which is in the care of the Brogdale Horticultural Trust in Kent. I hope that thence 'Gibbons' Russet' will be repatriated to Cork one day.

I do not have any particular grudge against 'Granny Smith' or 'Cox's Orange Pippin', yet when there are excellent Irish apple varieties why do we not grow them? They were widely cultivated in orchards last century. Now they have all but vanished. Indeed so desperate is the state of affairs that the Northern Ireland Heritage Gardens Committee has been working for ten years on a project to bring back to this island some of the 'lost' varieties from the Brogdale Horticultural Trust. This work is hampered by well-intentioned plant import regulations, designed to keep serious pests and diseases out of Ireland, and there is, as I write, a ban on the importation of apple scions due to the presence in Brogdale of the bacterial disease fireblight which attacks members of the rose family especially apples. The committee hopes, eventually, to repatriate all the surviving Irish apples and to establish reference collections in several places. While, in one sense, these orchards will serve a 'museums' of the Irish apple, they will be active, living orchards, able to provide bud-wood for any enterprising gardener who might care to propagate and later enjoy one of the indigenous fruits. Before too long, gardeners should be able to order, for delivery in three or four years, healthy, disease-free saplings of some of our wonderful old apples.[19]

PROSPECT

The prospects for the older vegetable cultivars is not rosy. Stringent regulations, albeit well-intentioned, stipulate that vegetable seeds can only be sold when the named variety is listed as approved. Similarly only seed potatoes of listed varieties can be legally sold. As a consequence many old cultivars are no longer available from seedsmen. You will not find a Brussels sprout named 'Glasnevin Supreme', nor a pea called after David Bishop, nor 'Lumper' in your local garden centre.

Some of these vegetables are conserved, as I have mentioned, in reference collections, and the principal collection is held by the Henry Doubleday Research Association. The HDRA has a heritage seeds library from which subscribing members may obtain some of the older vegetable varieties, and the Irish Organic Society and its individual members are assisting in the urgent task of propagating and thereby conserving this part of our garden heritage.

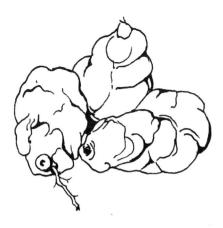

XIV

An Indoor Garden

Dionaea muscipula - Echinocereus pentalophus - Tweedia caerulea
Urceolina peruviana - Littonia modesta - Mackaya bella
Ruttya fruticosa - Coelogyne mooreana - Calceolaria x *burbidgei*
Brownea x *crawfordii - Rhododendron cuffeanum*

Whatever fruits in different climes were found,
That proudly rise, or humbly court the ground;
Whatever blooms in torrid tracts appear,
Whose bright succession decks the varied year ...
These here disporting own the kindred soil,
Nor ask luxuriance from the planter's toil ...

Oliver Goldsmith: 'The traveller'

Master Jon and his fellow gardeners could grow only those hardy trees, shrubs and herbs that would survive the rigours of the northern winter. A few adventurous gardeners were experimenting with plants from southern regions. Many useful medicinal plants and tasty herbs which grew in the Mediterranean countries did not inhabit the fields and woods of Britain and Ireland. Rosemary is one example. It was imported to England about 1340, but was not reliable and may have been lost to cultivation several times before it was firmly established in gardens. It did not set seed, so mediaeval gardeners had to learn to take cuttings and keep the young plants alive through the winter, although the most they had to protect such tender plants were unheated portable tabernacles.

The heated greenhouse was not invented until the sixteenth century. The earliest type was a building with a slate roof, large windows facing south, and a crude stove inside to heat the air. It was partly successful, but was dark inside and fumes from the fire often killed the plants. The invention made the cultivation of citrus trees fashionable, and aristocratic garden-owners competed with one another, trying to produce the best oranges and lemons.

The first recorded Irish greenhouse was constructed at Moira in County Down, by the 'Cock of the North', Sir Arthur Rawdon. It was completed by June 1690, for an officer of King William's army visited Moira before the Battle of the Boyne and saw the new conservatory.

Rawdon's greenhouse would have had a slate roof, but it served its purpose spectacularly, and accommodated the fabulous collection of Jamaican plants that James Harlow brought to Moira in April 1692.

Other garden owners followed Rawdon's lead. At Mitchelstown in County Cork, the Reverend John Keogh, chaplain to Lord Kingston, saw orange and lemon trees flourishing in the early 1730s. The eccentric Lord Trimlestown had bananas, cinnamon trees and pineapples growing at Trim in the middle of the eighteenth century. Mrs Mary Delany wanted to construct a greenhouse for her citrus trees in 1750, but she abandoned the plan in favour of a menagerie!

By this period it was possible to make glass roofs, so more light could be provided for the plants, and the greenhouse received considerably more attention in the latter half of the eighteenth century. In Ireland, the fashion reached a peak in 1785 when, at the cost of £3,000, Peter La Touche constructed a complex of houses 200 metres long, at Bellevue, near Dublin, comprising separate compartments for peaches, vines, pineapples, cherries and oranges and a conservatory. The new botanic garden at Glasnevin contained a range of glasshouses in 1800, and in 1818 work began on an elaborate octagonal house that could be raised higher as its inhabitant, a famous pine from Norfolk Island, grew taller - alas, the tree was killed by frost before its house was completed.

By the mid-1800s, wooden frames had been replaced by iron, and flat, sloping roofs were ousted by elegant, curved roofs. The master glasshouse builder of Victorian Ireland was a Dubliner, Richard Turner, who created the superb ranges of glasshouses in Glasnevin and Belfast botanic gardens. With Decimus Burton, Turner designed the Great Palm House in the

Royal Botanic Gardens, Kew. Its massive iron beams were cast in Dublin and shipped to London. These supremely functional buildings have an enduring beauty. Kew's Great Palm House was a cathedral to the natural sciences, enveloping beneath its bubble of glass the vegetable wonders of the British Empire for the amusement of curious visitors. The sumptuous Curvilinear Range at Glasnevin was filled with plants of great beauty and rarity, often finer than those at Kew.

The changes in glasshouse technology proceeded in step with European exploration of tropical and subtropical regions. Newly-discovered plants often needed special growing conditions, which could only be achieved within a carefully regulated glasshouse. Gardeners gradually learnt how to provide hot, humid habitats as well as cool, arid conditions.

But, the common gardener cannot build a vast dome heated with expensive boilers. Today, the simple, unheated greenhouse is ubiquitous, and allows gardeners to cultivate grapes, cucumbers, tomatoes, cacti, ferns and orchids. Such a cool greenhouse will suffice to house some of the plants that I have selected to conclude this essay. So as not to deprive the more adventurous spirits who have heated conservatories, I have included a few plants that demand a bit more heat and space.

VENUS'S FLY-TRAP

The world's most astonishing plant, called *Miraculum Naturae* by the great Swedish botanist Carl Linnaeus, is a diminutive carnivore with leaves that act like gin-traps. It inhabits damp, sandy places on the east coast of the United States of America, on the border of North and South Carolina, where it was discovered in 1759 by the Irish governor of North Carolina, Arthur Dobbs.

Dobbs was born in Girvan, a little town on the west coast of Scotland, in 1689 because of the conflict between King James and King William. His father had been prudent and sent his young wife away from Ireland while the war raged. Arthur and his mother returned to Ireland after the Battle of the Boyne, and he grew up at Castle Dobbs near Carrickfergus. When his father died, Arthur Dobbs inherited the estate and was an 'improving landlord', taking special interest in planting orchards and woodlands. In 1727, he entered the Irish House of Commons, and in 1732, true to the principles he held, Dobbs was among the fourteen gentlemen who formed a society for improving agriculture, manufacturing industry and the useful arts and sciences which survives today as the Royal Dublin Society.

In the 1730s, Arthur Dobbs was engaged in schemes to settle protestant families from Ireland in the colony of North Carolina. He became a member of a syndicate that purchased four hundred thousand acres in the colony with a view to settling these people. He tried to persuade his fellow countrymen to emigrate, and in 1751 applied to become governor of the colony. Dobbs was eventually appointed and arrived in America on 6 October 1754.

The new governor had a substantial interest in natural history. At home in Ireland, Arthur Dobbs had kept bees, and his careful observations of their foraging behaviour were published by the Royal Society of London in a paper that was of fundamental importance in the study of plant pollination. In North Carolina, he kept a diary, made excursions into the countryside and collected seeds of wild plants. In 1759, following one of his trips, he told an English friend, the Quaker naturalist Peter Collinson, that 'we have a kind of catch fly sensitive which closes upon anything that touches it'. In 1762, Dobbs showed the catch-fly to William Bartram who described it as ludicrous. Bartram sketched it and brought living plants home to Philadelphia. Bartram tried several times to send plants to London, and Dobbs promised to collect seeds for Collinson, but their efforts failed. It was not until 1768 that this miracle of nature reached Europe. Scientists were astonished! The man who brought the sensitive catch-fly to the attention of Linnaeus was John Ellis, another Irishman and London agent for the Linen Board. He wrote a description of it and gave the plant the scientific name it still bears, ***Dionaea muscipula***[1] - Venus's fly-trap. Another name for this carnivorous vegetable is tippitiwitchet, a mysterious moniker which appears to have been coined by John Bartram, and is not, as we have all been led to believe, the plant's name in Cherokee!

This curious little vegetable has a rosette of oval leaves, each one hinged along the mid-vein and armed on the margins with spikes. The leaf-trap is triggered when a fly lands on it; the leaf folds in two and the spikes interlock forming a perfect cage. The unfortunate insect cannot escape. It dies and its body is slowly digested. The flowers of the tippitiwitchet are produced on a short spike about ten centimetres tall; they are pure white and resemble the flowers of a saxifrage.

The Venus fly-trap should be grown in a mixture of damp sand and peat in a cool greenhouse, and, if not teased too much, will thrive and amuse for many years. It may be a ludicrous plant, but *Miraculum Naturae* is a fitting description too.

COULTER'S CACTI

The tippitiwitchet is uniquely American. There are many plants that are found only in the New World, including all members of the cactus family; perhaps a very few species are native in the Old World, but the traditional, barrel-shaped, spine-encrusted plants are found only in the deserts of the two Americas.

Cacti were imported into Europe in the sixteenth century, shortly after Columbus rediscovered America. They were cultivated only in botanic gardens and a few private collections, and did not become fashionable plants in the same way as orchids or ferns. Surprisingly, cacti only became popular in the present century and today many people grow them as house plants. There are many species capable of withstanding frosts that could be cultivated out-of-doors in very dry, well-drained places where the plants are protected, especially from winter rains.

One of the most important collections of cacti to reach Europe in the nineteenth century came from central Mexico and was despatched by Dr Thomas Coulter in 1828. He collected the plants while he was working for the Real del Monte Mining Company, before his trip to California. He sent two lots: one set went to Geneva to his friend, Professor Augustin-Pyramus de Candolle, and the second consignment came to Trinity College Botanic Garden, to James Mackay. There is no surviving account of the Dublin cacti, but those received in Geneva were used by de Candolle as the basis of two papers on cacti in which many new species were named.

Most of Thomas Coulter's cacti came from the Zimapan region, north of Mexico City. In a letter to Augustin-Pyramus de Candolle, Tom wrote that he had 'thirty or thirty-five very distinct species alive in a little garden. As soon as I arrived at Zimapan I started to collect them, remembering your old love of succulents'. In February 1828 the plants were sent to Geneva via Bordeaux, and Coulter kept a numbered set of duplicates in his garden, so that de Candolle could send him the new names.

One of the finest of Coulter's discoveries is a hedgehog cactus *Echinocereus pentalophus*.[2] Professor de Candolle named it in 1828, but he did not see flowers, and was only able to describe the five-angled stems. The cactus was illustrated in *Curtis's botanical magazine* a decade later, after it had flowered for Frederick Mackie of Norwich. This is a sprawling cactus that forms a prickly mat up to a metre in diameter. The stems usually have five longitudinal wings, and each areole is armed with about six spines. The flowers are spectacular - the large open cup is composed of numerous overlapping petals with brilliant rose-red or rosy-violet tips and creamy-yellow bases. The anthers are yellow and the remarkable dark green stigma is divided into about ten filaments.

TWEEDIA

Another collector who sent cacti to Europe, including at least two cases to Glasnevin, was John Tweedie. He arrived in the Argentine a few months after Dr Coulter reached Mexico. Tweedie's success in sending plants to Europe was recognised by Professors William Hooker and George Arnott when they named *Tweedia caerulea*, a blue-flowered trailing shrub, 'in compliment to an intelligent and indefatigable collector of plants'.

Tweedia caerulea is somtimes considered to be a species of *Oxypetalum* - indeed Hooker and Arnott stated that it was similar to *Oxypetalum*.[3] Although sometimes its name is changed to *Oxypetalum caeruleum*, we can still regard it as an appropriate memorial for this Scotsman who greatly enriched Glasnevin and, thereby, all Irish gardens.

Tweedie sent seeds of this plant to Dublin and they were germinated in the Botanic Gardens at Glasnevin while Ninian Niven was the curator. In July 1837 the plant flowered for the first time and Niven immediately sent specimens and a drawing to Professor Hooker. This letter, describing the blue flower, accompanied the samples:

My beloved wife visiting Scotland I send you two drawings and specimens of three plants, new to us good folk on this side of the Channel ... The blue Asclepiadeous plant I received from Tweedie under the name of Asclepias Asedra but as it does not appear to be an Asclepias at all, and the whole appearance of the plant so rare and beautiful ... I send it to you as in a line drawing, as a living specimen.[4]

Tweedia caerulea (Figure 18)[5] is a woody perennial with weak, trailing branches. It is not hardy and should be kept in a cool greenhouse in winter although it can grow out-of-doors in summer. The leaves are arranged in opposite pairs; each one is triangular with a heart-shaped base. The stems and leaves are covered with fine grey velvet. The flowers are grouped at the tips of the shoots. Each blossom has five strap-shaped, sky-blue petals and in the centre is a slightly darker corona, consisting of five raised lobes, surrounding the style and stigma. The backs of the petals are fawn. When the flowers are over, the strange fruits develop looking like dumpy broad-beans with long snouts.

John Tweedie died in Buenos Aires on 1 April 1862. He introduced several outstanding garden plants of which the pampas grass must take pride of place. His sending of annual species of *Verbena*, including *Verbena phlogiflora* (originally named *Verbena tweediana* and *Verbena arraniana*, the latter after his patron and friend the Earl of Arran) provided much material for the carpet-bedding craze of the mid-1800s. He also gave orchids to Glasnevin, various passion-flowers including one that was named after David Moore, and the delightful little blue-flowered bulb *Ipheion uniflora*.

PENTLAND'S LILY

Another pretty South American bulb has Irish associations. It was collected by Joseph Barclay Pentland, and grown in England by the Dean of Manchester, the Very Reverend William Herbert, who named it *Pentlandia miniata* after the Donegal-born diplomat.

Joseph Pentland sent several specimens of bulbs to the dean, who was a keen gardener. How Pentland got to know him is not recorded, but Herbert seems to have received most of Pentland's consignments.

Pentland described his bulb as a red-flowered narcissus. Each bulb produces one or two tapering leaves that are about a third of a metre long and up to three centimetres broad. The foliage dies down in the winter and the flowers emerge in spring before the leaves reappear. The flowering stalk rises to about 40 centimetres and bears six or more orange-red bottle-shaped flowers. The bells hang vertically and are flared at the mouth from which the six stamens and the style emerge. The species proliferates readily and the small bulblets can be removed and potted on when the main bulb is being repotted just as growth starts. I think that this plant could survive out-of-doors in mild, sunny gardens where the soil is well-drained.

18. *Tweedia caerulea*

Pentlandia miniata was discovered in the 1790s but the species was not described until 1827. As the bulb had been named before Pentland's specimens reached the Reverend William Herbert, *Pentlandia miniata* is an invalid name, and Joseph Pentland's red narcissus must be called **Urceolina peruviana**.[6] While he is not commemorated by a generic name, Pentland was the person who introduced the plant into cultivation.

Pentland's narcissus is native in the Andes of Peru and Bolivia, at altitudes above three thousand metres Joseph Pentland obtained his specimens near the ancient Inca city of Cuzco which he visited while touring southern Peru in 1838. During this trip, he went to Lake Titicaca for the second time and established the latitude, longitude and altitude of various sites including Cuzco. At the time he was serving as Her Britannic Majesty's Consul-General in Peru.

I have already mentioned the dwarf subspecies of *Gaultheria* once called *Pernettya pentlandii* that Pentland found in South America. He seems to have had a special interest in bulbs as he collected and introduced a climbing lily, *Bomarea simplex*, which Herbert cultivated in his garden. *Irseme virescens*, a lily with white trumpet-shaped blossoms, was also introduced by Pentland.

Joseph Pentland's reaction to having a plant named after him is not recorded, but John Tweedie thanked the two professors for 'inrolling my name among the imortle list of eminent Botanists'. Tweedie regretted that he

> did not learn more in my youthfull years to enable me to merit much, but following after little more than cabbage planting nor aspiring at more I of course am badly prepared for scientific porsuits.[7]

UNASSUMING LITTON

The commemoration of men and women in the scientific names of animals and plants confers upon these people a form of immortality, for the names should survive as long as the study of natural history or, as in the cases of *Pentlandia* and *Tweedia*, until a scientist decides that the memorial genus is not distinct and must be submerged in another.

Another climbing lily, this one from southern Africa, bears the name of Dr Samuel Litton, one-time librarian and later Professor of Botany to the Royal Dublin Society. As the Professor of Botany he was the head of the Society's botanic garden, now the National Botanic Gardens in Glasnevin.

The first species of this lily was named **Littonia modesta**[8] which may be translated as the 'Unassuming Littonia'. Its fleshy shoots bear leaves whose tips are prolonged into tendrils that can coil around twigs and thus enable the stems to cling and climb. The flowers, which develop at the leaf nodes, consist of six brilliant orange petals with pointed, upward-curling tips and look rather like old-fashioned lamp-shades. The stem rises from a horned tuber, described by Professor Hooker as 'exceedingly curious'. *Littonia* tubers may be treated like *Gladiolus* corms; they should be dug up in the autumn and allowed to rest in winter before replanting in the spring. The lily is not hardy and must be cultivated in a glasshouse.

Littonia modesta was first sent to Europe from Natal in 1853 by Mark McKen, curator of the botanic garden in Durban. His form was not free-flowering. In 1880 another consignment was sent from Durban and these tubers produced plants with as many as 50 flowers on each stem. The new variety was named by Max Leichtlin of Baden-Baden, *Littonia modesta* var. *keitii* after Wilhelm Keit, the former Glasnevin propagator who had succeeded McKen as curator of the Durban garden.

Samuel Litton was born in London, the son of Edward Litton, an amateur theologian who wrote a well-known Latin text-book. Samuel was educated in Liverpool and was so bright that he entered Trinity College, Dublin, at the age of 14. He became a scholar and had a distinguished undergraduate career. He wanted to enter the Church but changed his mind and went to Edinburgh to study medicine. Dr Litton returned to Ireland and in 1815 was elected to the post of librarian in the Royal Dublin Society. Ten years later he succeeded to the chair of botany. He was highly regarded by his contemporaries and received much praise for his lucid botanical lectures. He was, by all accounts, modest. Dr William Hooker remembered this when he chose the name *Littonia modesta* -

> the modest appearance of this plant ... [will] further serve to indicate his unassuming and retiring disposition, which ... prevented him taking that rank in general society to which his acquirements entitled him.[9]

But Dr Litton was also difficult and quarrelled with Ninian Niven and David Moore who served as curators during his professorship. Litton lived in a house in the Botanic Gardens and infuriated Moore by allowing his horse to roam freely in the garden!

JAMES TOWNSEND MACKAY

Samuel Litton's successor as Professor of Botany to the Royal Dublin Society was William Henry Harvey, who had spent several years in Cape Town as a government official and was an acknowledged authority on the flora of South Africa. He was a Quaker, a native of Limerick. When elected to the chair, Harvey was already curator of the herbarium in Trinity College, having succeeded Dr Thomas Coulter, and in 1856 he was appointed Professor of Botany in the College - Harvey was unique in holding these two professorships.

William Harvey's work on the African flora meant that a steady stream of specimens arrived in Dublin from the Cape and Natal. The parcels often contained unnamed species. In 1859, he described a new plant from Natal and named it ***Mackaya bella***[10] in honour of 'my venerable friend, James Townsend Mackay LL.D., author of *Flora Hibernica* and for many years the able superintendent of the Dublin University Botanic Garden'.

Mackaya bella was collected in the valley of the Tongat River north of Durban by John Sanderson who had discovered *Littonia*. It is a shrub with slender branches which are liable to sprawl if left without support - in Glasnevin the shrub is treated as a climbing plant and was trained around a pillar in the Curvilinear Range. *Mackaya* has elegant, dark green, oval leaves with crinkled margins. The flowers are pale lilac, veined with darker purple lines, and resemble those of the wild foxglove. The lower lip is composed of three joined petals, and projects further than the bilobed upper lip. The blossoms are carried in pendant sprays at the tips of last summer's shoots. *Mackaya bella* - the beautiful Mackaya - flowers in early spring, but it is not hardy and has to be grown in a cool greenhouse. It can be kept as a pot plant as it will flower when very young.

James Mackay was one of the Scottish gardeners who injected so much energy and knowledge into Irish horticulture in the nineteenth century. He came to Dublin in 1803 as gardener-assistant to Dr Robert Scott, the Professor of Botany. In 1806, Trinity College leased land for a new botanic garden and James Mackay set about forming the garden at Ballsbridge. The Ballsbridge garden reached its peak very quickly, outclassing Glasnevin in the 1820s and 1830s, and maintaining thereafter a friendly rivalry which was most invigorating for both gardens.

James Mackay's other great achievement was *Flora Hibernica* published in 1836; it was the first comprehensive treatment of our native plants. For his services to the University, James Mackay was given an honorary doctorate in 1850. Described by one of his successors, Frederick Burbidge, as a genial, kindly, studious man and a gifted gardener, James Townsend Mackay is commemorated not only by the beautiful *Mackaya*, but also, as I have related, in the native heather *Erica mackaiana* and several other plants including a tropical orchid named *Zygopetalum mackayi* by Sir William Hooker.[11]

A QUAKER DOCTOR

Another African genus, described by William Harvey, bears the name of one of the great medical characters of eighteenth-century Dublin, Dr John Rutty. Incidently, the suite of African genera commemorating Irish men - *Harveya, Mackaya, Littonia, Ruttya* - is mirrored in Australia by genera named by Robert Brown - *Templetonia* after John Templeton, *Threlkeldia* after the author of the first Irish flora, the Reverend Dr Caleb Threlkeld and *Logania* after James Logan of Lurgan, an amateur scientist and one-time governor of Pennsylvania.

It is not known why Professor Harvey chose to commemorate John Rutty, but the two men came from the same religious tradition; they were both Quakers. Rutty was a native of Wiltshire, and studied medicine at the University of Leiden. He acquired a good knowledge of

20. Ruttya fruticosa

botany, for botany was part of a medical student's course of study in the eighteenth century. Dr Rutty came to Dublin in 1724 and lived in Ireland for the rest of his life. He treated the sick of the city, often without receiving any payment.

Rutty was one of the members of the Physico-Historical Society of Dublin, and actively participated in the society's work on the natural history of Ireland. He directed the field-work of the naturalist and juridical astrologer Isaac Butler, and presented accounts of Butler's work to the society. In 1772, Rutty published his *Essay towards a natural history of the county of Dublin*, which included information on native and cultivated plants as well as many other subjects.

Dr John Rutty was an eccentric bachelor. He was a recluse and lived in a single, rented room. His work on Dublin's natural history began in 1740, and he recorded that he was 'led a long dance on birds, fishes and fossils and in comptations for information, and was greatly hurt in my spirituals by these means'. He tried to persuade other gentlemen to take an interest in botany, but was not successful - perhaps his character and religious zeal put them off. In his *Spiritual diary*, Rutty recorded some of his botanical sorties: 'Yesterday's botanic walk gave peace and delight upon reflection, even as a testimony against idle sons of Aesculapius in this city, immersed in sloth and sensuality'.

In some ways John Rutty is a tragic figure. The last entry in his diary read - 'The voice of God now sounds louder in my great infirmity of being scarcely able to bear the cold'. He died several months later in April 1775, after a long illness, and was buried with 'no other covering than a plain deal coffin' in the old Quaker cemetery in York Street, Dublin, now the site of the Royal College of Surgeons.

When *Ruttya fruticosa* was figured in *Curtis's botanical magazine* during 1958, William Turrill questioned how the name of an Irish doctor could become attached to an African plant. 'No doubt he was a very worthy gentleman', wrote Turrill, 'but he appears to have had nothing whatsoever to do with plants of the genus 'inscribed' to his honour'. This is true, but we should not begrudge this solitary botanist his lovely genus.

Ruttya fruticosa (Plate 20)[12] is relatively easy to cultivate in a heated greenhouse. It is usually propagated from cuttings but it can also be raised from seed. In its native habitats, in southern Arabia and east Africa, it grows as a shrub in rocky scrublands. The leaves are oval and bright green, arranged in opposite pairs on the slender shoots. The flowers are spectacular, like exotic, hovering hummingbirds. Each bloom is brilliant coral-red with a prominent black central boss resembling treacle spilling from its mouth. The petals are swept backwards, and the two upper ones form a hood over the arching stamens and style. The tube of the flower is full of nectar, and the colour, shape and configuration suggests that it is pollinated by nectar-sipping birds.

Ruttya fruticosa has been in cultivation in the National Botanic Gardens, Glasnevin, since

1982 when I obtained cuttings from Glasgow Botanic Gardens. I had hoped this handsome plant would become better known, for it is easy to grow when provided with a little heat.

MOORE'S ORCHID

John Rutty never set eyes upon the plant that now bears his name. Frederick Moore was more fortunate, for the exquisite white and yellow orchid that was christened after him grew in Glasnevin. *Coelogyne mooreana*[13] is a native of Vietnam, and came to Dublin in a batch of unnamed orchids that Moore purchased from the famous orchid nursery of Sander & Sons at St Albans. That company employed professional plant collectors to scour the tropical mountains and forests for new and unusual species as there was a lucrative market for orchids throughout the last half of the nineteenth century and the first half of the present century. The work of those collectors and their successors up to the present day has led to the extermination of some orchid species, and it is now estimated that about 8,000 orchids are either endangered in the wild or already extinct.

Frederick Moore's orchid was collected by Wilhelm Micholitz in forests on the Lang Ban Range in the province of Annam. It grows at altitudes of about 1,500 metres and thus requires warm, humid growing conditions.

Coelogyne mooreana has pear-shaped pseudobulbs, about five centimetres long, from which two leaves emerge, folded like a fan along the seven parallel veins. The cluster of about eight flowers is borne on an erect stalk 25 centimetres tall. The individual bloom is silky white, apart from the lip, in the centre, which is yellow and has yellow papillae on it. The flowers are up to seven centimetres across and, given the right condition, they blossom between August and January. Unlike so many modern hybrid orchids, this species has an enchanting simplicity.

There are many other orchids named after Frederick Moore, including the very rare cinnamon-coloured *Neomoorea wallisii* (formerly *Moorea irrorata*), which reflects his considerable interest in orchids. During his keepership, Glasnevin had one of the finest collections of orchid species in the world. Through the work of his father, David Moore, the National Botanic Garden attained a remarkable position within the world of orchid cultivation, for it was at Glasnevin in the 1840s that orchids were raised from seeds to flowering stage for the first time.

The other great Irish orchid pioneer was John Charles Lyons of Mullingar, who published the first manual on their cultivation. He wrote, printed and bound the original edition in his house on the shores of Lough Ennell. The book was revised and republished twice, once in London and once in Stuttgart. I should also record the contribution of Frederick Burbidge, who published a manual on growing orchids in an unheated greenhouse in 1874, five years before he came to Dublin.

COLLEGE SLIPPER-WORT

Frederick Burbidge was the last of the great curators of the College Botanic Garden, succeeding Frederick Moore and James Mackay. He was from Leicestershire and trained at Kew. James Veitch, the nurseryman, employed him to go to Borneo in 1877, and Burbidge returned home with a fabulous insectivorous pitcher vine, *Nepenthes rajah*, which later grew luxuriantly at Glasnevin. Like so many plant collectors, Frederick Burbidge suffered privation. On one occasion in Borneo, after his feet had been scalded by water from a spilt kettle, he had to walk on wet, slippery paths with his rotting boots tied to his swollen feet. This story and other adventures were reported in his fine book *Gardens of the sun*.

Trinity College Botanic Garden was a less hazardous place to work, and Burbidge contributed much to its prominence during the last two decades of the 1800s. He wrote countless articles for horticultural newspapers on plants and gardens, highlighting Ireland's fine gardening traditions; as already noted, it was Burbidge who brought Alice Lawrenson's white Christmas rose 'Saint Bridgid' to the attention of gardeners.

Shortly after his arrival in Ireland, Frederick Burbidge began to experiment with some of the larger, almost shrubby, species of slipperwort. He cross-pollinated several and raised hybrid seedlings. One of these proved to be a vigorous plant with lovely yellow flowers, shaped like traditional Dutch wooden clogs. The lower lip of the flower is pouched and inflated, while the smaller upper lip covers the stamens. The leaves may be up to 15 centimetres long, and are borne in opposite pairs on the stems; they are covered with minute gland-tipped hairs. When planted in an open bed in a greenhouse, this hybrid grows as much as five metres tall, but it is usually kept in pots and then remains about one metre tall. It could be used as an annual bedding plant. New plants are raised each year from cuttings that have to be kept indoors in winter.

The College hybrid was grown by William Gumbleton in his garden near Cobh, and he named it after Frederick Burbidge. *Calceolaria* **x** *burbidgei*[14] is still cultivated in the Botanic Gardens belonging to Trinity College, now situated in Palmerston Park, not, sadly, in the place that Burbidge tended at Lansdowne Road, Ballsbridge. This lovely flower was featured on the stamp issued by the Irish Post Office in 1987 to mark the tercentenary of the College Botanic Garden.

CRAWFORD AND BROWNE

One of William Gumbleton's contemporaries and fellow gardeners in the Cork area was William Horatio Crawford, whose family owned a local brewery. Crawford was rather like Gumbleton; both were well-off bachelors, who collected pictures and books, and they both enjoyed rare plants. However, in terms of their characters, they were absolute opposites - Crawford was dignified and retiring, whereas Gumbleton was outspoken, pompous and anything but shy. Their taste in plants seems to have reflected this. Gumbleton admired such fussy things as begonias and red-hot pokers. Crawford collected sedate rhododendrons and had a passion for tropical trees belonging to the genus *Brownea*.

There are perhaps six distinct species of *Brownea*, all native in tropical America including some of the Caribbean Islands. In Ireland they must be grown in a heated glasshouse - at Glasnevin these trees are kept in the hottest glasshouse, the stove house. *Brownea* species have large compound leaves made up of numerous elliptical leaflets. The trusses of flowers resemble the flower-heads of rhododendrons, and are composed of numerous blossoms each with five scarlet or red petals. The heads of flowers are about 20 centimetres across and most attractive.

Several hybrids of *Brownea* were raised in Crawford's garden, Lakelands, overlooking Lough Mahon on Cork Harbour. In 1873, William Gumbleton recorded that Crawford's gardener had succeeded in crossing a number of different species. One of these hybrids was named ***Brownea* x *crawfordii*,**[15] after William Crawford, by William Watson of the Royal Botanic Gardens, Kew. It is still in cultivation in Kew. Crawford's fine collection of *Brownea* including his own hybrids was dispersed after his death; some of the plants came to Glasnevin and some went to Kew.

Apart from the connection with William Crawford, I have included *Brownea* in this essay because it was named after a native of County Mayo, Dr Patrick Browne. He was born about 1720 at Woodstock to the east of Claremorris. His family had property in the West Indies, and when Patrick was 17, he was sent to Antigua. The climate did not suit him, and he returned to Europe within a year. Patrick went to Paris and began to study medicine and botany. He graduated from the University of Rheims and then, for a few months, moved to the famous medical faculty in the University of Leiden. Some years later, after practising in Saint Thomas's Hospital, London, Dr Browne returned to the West Indies. In Jamaica and other islands he studied the native plants and animals, collecting information for his monumental book *The civil and natural history of Jamaica* which he published in 1756. Shortly after this, Dr Browne married a native of Antigua and the couple took up residence on the island of St Croix, one of the Danish possessions in the West Indies. Marriage and 'ye cares of life' meant that Patrick Browne could not 'spare time for any researches in Natural History'. He had other interests. Life was comfortable, and he succeeded in earning several thousand pounds each year. However his Caribbean idyll came to an unpleasant end which he described thus to Carl Linnaeus: 'a villain under ye title of judge [and] under ye cloak of friendship gott acquainted with my wife and debauched her, as well as some others of different families'. Patrick Browne was unable to get justice from the Danish authorities, so he left his wife and St Croix, and moved to the neighbouring island of Montserrat.

While in the Caribbean, Patrick Browne maintained a correspondence with European botanists, including Linnaeus. He returned to England at regular intervals, and in 1770 he retired to Ireland and finally settled at Rushbrook, a townland to the southwest of Claremorris in County Mayo. He set about preparing articles on the birds and fish of Ireland and wrote an unpublished flora of western Connaught which I had the privilege of editing and publishing in 1995 in a handsome volume illustrated by Wendy Walsh.[16] Dr Patrick Browne died in 1790 and was buried in the family tomb at Crossboyne. He was, according to his memorialist, a tall, comely man 'of good address and gentle manners, naturally cheerful, very temperate and in general healthy', although he suffered from severe gout in his latter years.

In his Connaught flora, Patrick Browne argued that Ireland needed a public botanic garden, with a greenhouse, so that the general populace could learn more about plants. 'What a source of curiosity have we not in the greenhouse ... [for] time may bring to our knowledge many more plants if there was but proper place to raise them'.

SHADOW'S RHODODENDRON

One of the plants time was to bring to Ireland, to Kilkenny, where Dr Browne thought a botanic garden should be laid out; was a lovely sweetly-scented white rhododendron. It came from Burma, from the slopes of Mount Victoria, and was named in honour of its discoverer, Charlotte Isabel Wheeler Cuffe. I make no apology for returning to her, for she was, in my opinion, one of the most remarkable amateur plant-hunters. She became a botanical explorer by accident, but she learnt her plants quickly and was asked to form a botanic garden in the centre of Burma. To stock this garden she went out into the forests on a pony returning with the panniers loaded with plants. Charlotte Cuffe gave us three exquisite garden flowers - Shadow's blue buttercup, *Anemone obtusiloba* f. *patula* with its enamelled petals, the butter-yellow *Rhododendron burmanicum* and her very own ***Rhododendron cuffeanum.***[17]

This white rhododendron is not fully hardy, and is best grown in a cool greenhouse, although it should survive and flourish outside in mild gardens. The flowers are large and trumpet-shaped, with a lovely perfume. In the wild it grows as an epiphyte, rooted in the moss that covers the bark of the trees in that warm, humid climate.

Lady Cuffe discovered *Rhododendron cuffeanum* in May 1911 on Mount Victoria, when she collected many young plants, some of which she sent to her family in England. She collected more one year later. It has not been collected in the wild since 1912, and thus is her unique contribution to botany and gardening.

This rhododendron reached Glasnevin in August 1913. It bloomed in Dublin in May 1915 and was sent immediately to Kew for naming. The Director, Sir David Prain, informed Sir Frederick Moore that it was a new species and that in due course it would be named *Rhododendron cuffeanum.* In August 1917, an illustration and description were published in *Curtis's botanical magazine*, based on the plant growing in the Glasnevin Botanic Gardens. Today, *Rhododendron cuffeanum* is an extremely rare plant in cultivation. When I wrote this in 1983, there was no plant of it in any Irish garden, and I expressed the hope that one would arrive soon from the only English garden in which we knew it still grew. I still have high hopes that *Rhododendron cuffeanum* will soon bloom again in the National Botanic Gardens, in the restored Curvilinear Range, among a host of other exciting rhododendrons from the high tropical mountains of south-east Asia.

All botanists and plant collectors live in hope of finding something new. Yet Frederick Burbidge was correct when he said that 'no description could possibly convey any idea of the delight which fills one when new and beautiful objects of natural history are discovered for the first time'. In a letter to Sir Frederick Moore, Lady Cuffe described the scenery and the flowers of Mount Victoria. She painted a word picture that does convey some of her excitement.

There is a most exquisite white sweet scented rhododendron which grows epiphytically on other trees like an orchid, never in the ground; a yellow rhododendron; and whole forests of the crimson tree one. Gigantic yews and pines; gnarled old ilex with an undergrowth of moss and pink primulas - on the open saddles are sheets of blue and white ranunculus and sky blue gentians ... and a mauve primula. In the marshy hollows are yellow primulas, and all sorts of ferns: beside a host of familiar plants such as potentillas ... a regular alpine flora in fact - yellow Swiss violets among other things. In places there are masses of wild strawberries, yellow raspberries, and a kind of black one: a sort of arbutus with a pleasantly sweet berry; and lower down orchids of many kinds.[18]

Years later, she recalled that the peak was crowned with a scarlet rhododendron tree 'brandishing defiance to the four winds of heaven'.

Charlotte Cuffe unwittingly fulfilled the role of the plant hunter, as set down by Frank Kingdon Ward, a professional collector who met her in 'her' botanic garden at Maymyo:

The plant collector's job is to uncover the hidden beauties of the world, so that others may share his joy ... It is no unworthy aim, to reveal what God has planted in the lost mountains, since thereby may also be revealed what He has hidden in the hearts of men.[19]

Epilogue

**A paradise beyond was seen
Of shady groves and gardens green,
Fair flowers and fruitful trees,
And flowing fountains cool and clear**

Robert Southey: 'Sir Owen at Saint Patrick's Purgatory'

I have planted again - replanted - my garden with flowers from lost mountains, from gardens long since decayed, and from nurseries that are legends now. And yet I have mentioned only a small fraction of the plants that have associations with Ireland.

All of the plants that I have written about tell tales about the past. What of the future? We are anxious to conserve gardens and plants that are part of our heritage, but we must not fossilize our gardens, or grow only those plants produced long ago. Gardens are living communities and should be maintained as lively, changing entities. New ideas are to be welcomed, new plants must be planted, and improvements should be made so that future generations can enjoy gardens as beautiful as those we delight in today.

The work of preserving gardens and garden plants has to be pursued actively, for neglect is the greatest cause of dilapidation and extinction in gardens. Unlike objects of gold, vellum manuscripts, pieces of porcelain or marble statues, gardens and plants cannot be sealed in glass cases, protected from all contact with the world outside, and thus preserved for our successors. Thankfully, the present concern about Ireland's historic parks and gardens suggests that the futures of most of our fine gardens are assured, and that these living monuments to our forbears' taste and ingenuity will survive intact.

We have learned in the last decade that our gardens are sanctuaries for many 'lost' garden plants, and the propagation and dispersal of these is another important facet of conservation. There is one simple way of preserving the old varieties. It is summed up in the adage which I have repeated several times in the preceding pages - the best way to keep a plant is to give it away. The free exchange of garden plants is one of the pleasures of gardening and one of our duties as gardeners. If we share good plants with one another, then Irish flower gardens will continue to be paradises adorned with great variety.

We should not confine ourselves to growing the old favourites. New varieties will become available to us as plant breeders continue their work - in the daffodil farms and rose grounds of Ireland untried cultivars are being tested and the best will eventually be released for us to grow. Undoubtedly keen-eyed gardeners will notice mutations and sports that may eventually yield novel garden varieties, and the past decade has indeed yielded a goodly number of new plants that owe their perpetuity to enthusiasts. A few have already been mentioned including *Omphalodes cappadocicum* 'Starry Eyes'. But I do not have space to recount all the stories so I must refrain from expatiating about the speckled hellebore, *Helleborus orientalis* 'Graigueconna', found in Rosemary Brown's garden, or *Dryas octopetala* 'Burren Nymph', a double-blossomed mountain avens collected in The Burren by Dr Keith Lamb, not to mention *Pittosporum tenuifolium* 'Nutty's Leprechaun' and *Lobelia* 'Pink Elephant'. And each year, previously unknown species, raised from seeds gathered in distant countries, will be added to our garden flora. Who can foretell the plants that will grace or disgrace Irish gardens in the years to come?

In the foregoing remarks, I do not mean by any means to place my short experience in opposition to those of more science, and more extensive practice. I only beg to offer for adoption to the few, less informed than myself, my observations, and also such information as I have acquired, by bestowing some attention to the remarks of others, more experienced, but not more anxious in the pursuit, than I am. In their present state I offer them, and shall only add -

> *Si quid novisti rectius istis*
> *Candidus imperti; si non, his utere mecum.*

> *John Charles Lyons: On the management of orchidaceous plants*[1]

Acknowlegments

In writing this book I have endeavoured to provide a portrait of each chosen plant and its history. In carrying out my research I have received assistance from many people, to whom again I extend my profound thanks. The plants sometimes presented problems, for although I grow a few myself, and others are to be seen in the collections in the National Botanic Gardens, many were not easily accessible. I wished to see and handle each one, and have been most generously helped by friends who allowed me to wander about their gardens, sometimes at short notice. Their conversations about the plants have taught me much, and I am still learning. My debt to better, more experienced gardeners is immense.

I would like to thank the following people for their greatly appreciated assistance:

Harry Bryce, Philip Wood, Molly Sanderson, David Shackleton, Dorothy Jobling-Purser, Helen Dillon, Keith Lamb, Robert Johnston, Paul and Catherine Hackney, Donal Synnott, Susyn Andrews, Neil Murray, Peter Wyse Jackson, David McClintock, Sam Harrison, Cormac Foley, Mary Forrest, Graham Stuart Thomas, Brian Mulligan, Nigel Marshall, Mike Snowden, Anne James, Rosemary Brown, Evelyn Booth, Will Ingwersen, Raymond Piper, Lady Scott (Valerie Finnis), Ross Ferguson, Alison Rutherford, Philip Shuttleworth, John Harvey, Chris Brickell, Neil Treseder, Robert Walpole, Paddy Woods, Chris O'Mahony, Mary Taylor, Joe Ewan, Rolf Loeber, Robert and Christabel Childers, Daphne Maxwell, Elsie Miller, Les and Ngarita Travers, Paddy Bowe, Dermot Burke, Hilary Richardson, David and Ada McLaughlin, Eileen Porter, Heather Dobbin, Major-General F. Moore, Valerie Ingram, Gina Douglas, Alan Leslie, Peter Barnes, Gren Lucas, Margaret Sweeney, Nichola Kyle.

I am also especially grateful to Sarah Ball, Bernie Shine, and especially Grace Pasley for help, mostly at long distance, in preparing this new edition.

For any omissions, for my forgetfulness, I hope I will be forgiven.

Select Bibliography & Notes

In the list of sources for each chapter that follows, various books and periodicals are cited according to the following abbreviations:

AIF   W. F. Walsh, R. I. Ross and E. C. Nelson, *An Irish florilegium; the wild and gardens flowers of Ireland*. London. 1983.

AIF II   W. F. Walsh and E. C. Nelson, *An Irish florilegium II; the wild and gardens flowers of Ireland*. London. 1988.

APIF   W. F. Walsh and E. C. Nelson, *A prospect of Irish flowers*. Belfast. 1990.

Bean   W. J. Bean, *Trees and shrubs hardy in the British Isles*. London. Vols I-IV. 1970-1980.

DJ   E. C. Nelson and E. M. McCracken, *The brightest jewel: a history of the National Botanic Gardens, Glasnevin, Dublin*. Kilkenny. 1987.

GC   *Gardeners' chronicle*.

GI   *Gardening illustrated*.

IG   *Irish gardening*.

SSH   E. C. Nelson (editor) and D. M. Synnott, *The first Irish flora: Caleb Threlkeld's Synopsis stirpium Hibernicarum*. (1726). Kilkenny. 1988.

TI   E. C. Nelson and W. F. Walsh, *Trees of Ireland, native and naturalized*. Dublin. 1993.

PROLOGUE

1.   A. G. Rigg, *A Glastonbury miscellany of the fifteenth century*. Oxford. 1968. p. 107, lines 157-158.

CHAPTER I

1.   Woad yields indigo, and indigo was used in Celtic manuscripts, for example, in the Book of Kells; see R. Fuchs and D. Oltrogge, 'Colour material and painting technique in the Book of Kells', pp. 133-171, in F. O'Mahony (editor), *The Book of Kells*. Aldershot. 1994.

2.   W. Strabo, *Hortus* (translated by R. Payne). Pittsburgh. 1966.

3.   J. H. Harvey, 'The first English garden book. Mayster Jon Gardener's treatise and its background', *Garden history 13* (1985), 83-101.

4.   E. C. Nelson, 'Sir Arthur Rawdon (1662-1695) of Moira: his life and letters, family and friends and his Jamaican plants', *Proceedings of the Belfast Natural History and Philosophical Society 10* (1983), 30-52.

5.   B.J.

6.   E. C. Nelson and E. Deane, *'Glory of Donard' - a history of the Slieve Donard Nursery, Newcastle, County Down, with a catalogue of cultivars*. Belfast. 1993.

CHAPTER II

1.   AIF plate 14; TI plate 9.

2.   SSH [16].

3.   AIF plate 18; BJ plate 4.

4.   SSH [157].

5.   AIF plate 19; TI plate 29.

6.   AIF plate 19; TI plate 29; E. C. Nelson, 'The nomenclature and history in cultivation of the Irish yew, *Taxus baccata* 'Fastigiata'', *Glasra 5* (1981), 33-44.

7.   AIF plate 1; TI plate 23.

8.   D. M. Synnott, 'Notes on *Salix phylicifolia* L. and related Irish willows', *Glasra 7* (1983), 1-10; E. C. Nelson and D. M. Synnott, 'The Irish willow and the Irish whitebeam', *Yearbook of the International Dendrology Society 1982*, 112-114.

9.   R. D. Meikle, 'Nomenclatural notes on some willow hybrids', *Watsonia 15* (1985), 273-274; D. M. Synnott (1983), 1-10.

10.   E. C. Nelson, 'James and Thomas Drummond: their Scottish origins and curatorships in Irish botanic gardens (ca 1808- ca 1831)', *Archives of natural history 17* (1990), 49-65.

11.   E. C. Nelson, 'Corkscrew rush (*Juncus effusus* L. f. *spiralis* (J. McNab) Hegi) (Juncaceae) in Ireland and Britain', *Watsonia 19* (1993), 275-278; *Cottage gardener 2* (1849), 306-307; GC (10 May 1873), 647; *Transactions of the Botanical Society of Edinburgh 11* (1873), 502-504.

12.   AIF II plate 6.

13.   E. C. Nelson, 'Ferns in Ireland, wild and cultivated, through the ages', pp. 57-86, in J. M. Ide, A. C. Jermy and A. M. Paul (editors). *Fern horticulture: past, present and future perspectives*. Andover. 1992.

CHAPTER III

1.   S. Andrews, 'Hollies in Ireland', *Moorea 1* (1982), 5-14; –, 'Notes on some *Ilex* x *altaclerensis* clones', *The plantsman 5* (1983), 65-81; J. C. Loudon, *Arboretum et fruticetum Britannicum*. London. 1844. p. 116.
2.   AIF II plate 42.
3.   E. C. Nelson and S. Andrews, ' The origin of *Ilex* x *altaclerensis* (Loudon) Dallimore 'Lawsoniana' and a confusion of Hodginses', *Glasra 1* (n.s.) (1992), 111-114; AIF II plate 42.
4.   S. Andrews, '*Ilex* x *altaclerensis* 'Lady Valerie' or 'Ripley Gold' - an enigma', *Moorea 7* (1988), 4.
5.   AIF plate 24; B. O. Mulligan and E. C. Nelson, '*Garrya* x *issaquahensis* E. C. Nelson (*G. elliptica* Lindl. x *G. fremontii* Torr.) in cultivation in the western USA and Ireland', *University of Washington Arboretum bulletin 43* (3) (1980), 10-15.
6.   E. C. Nelson and W. F. Walsh, '*Garrya* x *issaquahensis* E. C. Nelson 'Glasnevin Wine': a new cultivar from the National Botanic Gardens, Glasnevin, Dublin', *Glasra 1* (n.s.) (1992), 96-98.
7.   AIF plate 31.
8.   L. Slinger, quoted p. 82 in E. C. Nelson and E. Deane, *'Glory of Donard' - a history of the Slieve Donard Nursery, Newcastle, County Down, with a catalogue of cultivars*. Belfast. 1993.
9.   E. C. Nelson and E. Deane (1993), 80-82.
10.   AIF plate 44; E. C. Nelson, 'Augustine Henry and the exploration of the Chinese flora', *Arnoldia 43* (1983), 21-38.
11.   E. C. Nelson (1983), 21-38; –, 'The garden history of Augustine Henry's plants', pp. 217-236 in S. Pim, *The wood and the trees, a biography of Augustine Henry*. Kilkenny. 1984 (second edition).
12.   A. Grills, 'A famous Irish nursery: Daisy Hill Nurseries, Newry', *Moorea 10* (1993), 1-10; AIF II plate 47; GC *58* (1915), 244; – *91* (1932), 67; *Bulletin of miscellaneous information (Kew)* (1914), 51; *Bulletin of the Royal Horticultural Society of Ireland 1* (1934), 7; Daisy Hill Nursery catalogues.
13.   GC *29* (1901), 134-135.
14.   see note 13 above.
15.   AIF plate 36; E. A. Bowles, *My garden in spring*. London. 1914. pp. 44-51.
16.   AIF plate 36.
17.   E. C. Nelson, 'The name of the rose ... *Galanthus*'Emerald Isle'', *The Irish garden 4* (1) (1995), 30-32.
18.   E. A. Bowles to Sir Frederick and Lady Moore; Major-General F. D. Moore mss.
19.   G. S. Thomas, *Perennial garden plants or the modern florilegium*. London. 1990. p. 202; M. Allen, *E. A. Bowles and his garden at Myddelton House 1865-1954*. London. 1973.
20.   G. S. Thomas, *Three gardens of pleasant flowers*. Feltham. 1983. p. 20.

CHAPTER IV

1.   A. Henry to E. Gleeson 31 July 1899; National Library of Ireland, Dublin mss, quoted in e.g. E. C. Nelson, 'An Irish mandarin: Augustine Henry (1857-1930)', *Taisce journal 4* (2) (1980), 12-14.
2.   J. Besant, 'The late Professor Henry VMH', GC *87* (1931), 274-275.
3.   *Hooker's icones plantarum* plate 1896.
4.   See E. C. Nelson, 'Augustine Henry and the exploration of the Chinese flora', *Arnoldia 43* (1983), 21-38.
5.   AIF plate 45; E. C. Nelson (1983), 21-38.
6.   APIF plate 2; M. Forrest (compiler) and E. C. Nelson (editor), *Trees and shrubs cultivated in Ireland*. Kilkenny. 1985.
7.   E. C. Nelson, 'The Lady of the rhododendrons - Charlotte Wheeler Cuffe 1867-1967', *Rhododendrons 1981-1982*, 33-41; Bean II, 491.
8.   The cultivar name was first published in E. C. Nelson, *An Irish flower garden*. Kilkenny. 1984. pp. 50-51; S. Harrison, 'Castlewellan National Arboretum', *Moorea 12* (1996), 7-8.
9.   J. C. Loudon, *Arboretum et fruticetum Britannicum*. London. 1844. pp. 2294-2295.
10.   W. P. Moore, 'A letter from Ireland. A review of some of the older gardens with their special plants', *New flora and sylva 1* (1929), 118-123; GC *13* (1893), 709-710.
11.   D. Moore to J. D. Hooker 11 March 1867; Royal Botanic Gardens, Kew mss, English letters vol. 95, no. 321.
12.   *Rhododendron Society notes 3* (1926), 105-107, 179-184; IG *16* (1921), 62; GI *61* (1939), 37-38.
13.   BM (n.s.) plate 534.
14.   E. C. Nelson and E. Deane, *'Glory of Donard'. A history of the Slieve Donard Nursery, Newcastle, County Down. Belfast*. 1993. pp. 65-67.
15.   APIF plate 4; = *Eucryphia* x *nymansensis* 'Grahamii', invalid.
16.   AIF plate 22; E. C. Nelson, '*Eucryphia* x *nymansensis* 'Mount Usher'', *IGPS newsletter 10* (1983), 5.
17.   IG *2* (1907), 172; – *10* (1915), 114-115; – *14* (1919), 128; GC *50* (1911), 351; *Bulletin of miscellaneous information (Kew)* (1906), 219-224; Daisy Hill Nursery catalogues.
18.   T. Hood, 'I remember'
19.   *Proceedings of the Royal Horticultural Society* (1901), xxxviii-xxxix; Bean I, 434.
20.   E. C. Nelson and A. Probert, *A man who can speak of plants: Dr Thomas Coulter (1793-1843) of Dundalk in Ireland, Mexico and Alta California*. Dublin. 1994.

CHAPTER V

1.   J. D. Hooker, *Rhododendrons of the Sikkim Himalayas*. London. 1849. plate 22.
2.   BM plate 4936.

3.　A. J. Richards, *Primula*. London. 1993. pp. 158-160; AIF II plate 17.
4.　AIF plate 41; GC (14 July 1860), 646.
5.　*Journal of the Asiatic Society of Bengal 15* (1846), 79-135.
6.　E. Madden to D. Moore, October 1847; Royal Botanic Gardens, Kew mss.
7.　BM plate 4793.
8.　C. Colvin and E. C. Nelson, "Building castles of flowers': Maria Edgeworth as gardener', *Garden history 16* (1988), 58-70.
9.　*Hooker's journal of botany 6* (1854), 380-383, plate xii; *Plantae Wilsoniae I*, pp. 56-57; *Stream and field 2* (1971), 18-19; R. Gorer, *The growth of gardens*. London. 1978. pp. 119-122.
10.　Herbarium, Royal Botanic Garden, Edinburgh mss.
11.　E. C. Nelson and W. F. Walsh, 'Reginald Farrer, Glasnevin and *Deutzia purpurascens* 'Alpine Magician'. *Kew magazine 10* (1993), 171-178, plate 234.
12.　APIF plate 8.
13.　J. Fryer and E. C. Nelson, 'Two new species of *Cotoneaster* (Rosaceae) from the living collections in the National Botanic Gardens, Glasnevin, Dublin', *Glasra 2* (n.s.) (1995), 127-134; E. C. Nelson, J. Fryer and W. F. Walsh, '*Cotoneaster bradyi* (Rosaceae)', *Curtis's botanical magazine 12* (1995), 198-201, plate 280.
14.　APIF plate 8; J. Fryer and E. C. Nelson (1995), 127-134.
15.　BM plate 9090; GC 34 (12 December 1903), 405; E. C. Nelson, 'The garden history of Augustine Henry's plants', pp. 217-236 in S. Pim, *The wood and the trees, a biography of Augustine Henry*. Kilkenny. 1984 (second edition).
16.　BM plate 8393; GC *48* (8 October 1910), 265.
17.　AIF plate 42.
18.　AIF plate 46; E. C. Nelson in S. Pim (1984), 217-236.
19.　E. C. Nelson, 'Some botanical hoaxes and Chinese puzzles', *Kew magazine 3* (1986), 178-185.
20.　AIF plate 47; E. C. Nelson, 'The Lady of the rhododendrons - Charlotte Wheeler Cuffe 1867-1967', *Rhododendrons 1981-1982*, 33-41; Lady Cuffe's original watercolour of *Rhododendron burmanicum* is reproduced in E. C. Nelson, *The art of flowers*. [Catalogue for] *National Botanic Gardens, Glasnevin, bicentenary exhibition 1995. Botanical illustrations by Wendy Walsh and Charlotte Wheeler Cuffe*. Dublin. 1995. p. 1.
21.　E. C. Nelson, ''That I may earn a living': Henry Hammersley Travers (1849-1928) and the Royal Botanic Gardens, Glasnevin, Dublin', *Royal New Zealand Institute of Horticulture annual journal 16* (1989), 60-66; -, 'An archaic duet: New Zealand's contribution to Ireland's garden heritage', *Royal New Zealand Institute of Horticulture annual journal 16* (1989), 4-11; *An encyclopedia of New Zealand 3* (1966), 445; F. Mueller, *The vegetation of the Chatham Islands*. Melbourne. 1864.
22.　AIF II plate 22; BM plate 8550; see 21 above; E. C. Nelson and E. Deane, *'Glory of Donard'. - A history of the Slieve Donard Nursery, Newcastle, County Down, with a catalogue of cultivars*. Belfast. 1993. pp. 91-92.
23.　APIF plate 5.

CHAPTER VI

1.　Miss F. Geoghegan to F. W. Moore; National Botanic Gardens, Glasnevin, Dublin mss.
2.　IG 8 (1913), 23-24; F. C. Stern, *A study of the genus Paeonia*. London. 1946. p. 62.
3.　G. Nicholson, *The dictionary of gardening*. London. 1884. p. 36; G. Leighton, *The genus Agapanthus L'Heritier*. 1965; JRHS 79 (1954), 28.
4.　E. M. McCracken and E. C. Nelson, 'Julius Wilhelm Keit, a German horticulturist at the Botanic Gardens, Glasnevin', *Moorea 8* (1989), 34-40.
5.　The most recent classification systems for flowering plants, which split the Liliaceae into a number of smaller families, place *Agapanthus* in Alliaceae, the onion family, because *inter alia* the flowers are arranged in umbels.
6.　AIF plate 43; E. C. Nelson, 'The garden history of Augustine Henry's plants', pp. 217-236 in S. Pim, *The wood and the trees, a biography of Augustine Henry*. Kilkenny. 1984 (second edition).
7.　E. Wilson, *The lilies of eastern Asia*. London. p. 80.
8.　G. Staunton, *An historical account of the embassy to the Emperor of China*. London. 1797.
9.　G. Staunton (1797).
10.　BM plate 1905; W. Aiton, *Hortus Kewensis*. London. 1811; JRHS *99* (1974), 339-347.
11.　BM plate 4673; F. W. Moore, 'Some reminiscences', *New flora and sylva 12* (1940), 180-187.
12.　AIF plate 40; E. C. Nelson and A. Probert, *A man who can speak of plants: Dr Thomas Coulter (1793-1843) of Dundalk in Ireland, Mexico and Alta California*. Dublin. 1994.
13.　BM plate 3441; APIF plate 9; E. C. Nelson, 'James and Thomas Drummond: their Scottish origins and curatorships in Irish botanic gardens (ca 1808- ca 1831)', *Archives of natural history 17* (1990), 49-65.
14.　AIF II, plate 26; BM plate 4227.
15.　*Proceedings of the Royal Dublin Society 79* (Appendix I) (1843), vii-viii; E. C. Nelson, 'In honour of David and Frederick Moore', *Moorea 1* (1982), 1-4.
16.　D. Moore to W. J. Hooker: Royal Botanic Gardens, Kew mss; English letters vol. 18, no. 54.
17.　Various sources spell his christian name, consistently, Edmund, but Patricia Boyne, biographer of John O'Donovan, his father, uses the form Edmond, and I have followed her - P. Boyne, *John O'Donovan (1806-1861), a biography*. Kilkenny. 1987.
18.　John and Mary Anne (neé Broughton) O'Donovan were married on 18 January 1840, and their first son, Edmond was born in October 1840, but died aged two; as was the custom, the next born son was named after

his deceased brother.
19.   Quoted in P. Boyne (1987).
20.   R. Dadd, 'The discovery and introduction of *Allium giganteum*', *Kew magazine 4* (1987), 91-96.
21.   AIF II plate 9; E. A. Bowles, *My garden in spring*. London. 1914. pp. 194-195; –, *My garden in summer*. London. pp. 275.
22.   IG *4* (1909), 82-83; M. Joyce, 'Charlotte Grace O'Brien', *Capuchin annual 1974*, 324-340.

CHAPTER VII

1.   E. C. Nelson and P. D. Coker, 'Ecology and status of *Erica vagans* L. in County Fermanagh, Ireland', *Botanical journal of the Linnean Society 69* (1974), 153-195.
2.   E. C. Nelson, *An Irish flower garden*. Kilkenny. 1984. p.98.
3.   E. C. Nelson, 'The origin of *Calluna vulgaris* 'County Wicklow'', *Irish naturalists' journal 20* (1981), 212.
4.   AIF plate 15; E. C. Nelson, 'William McCalla - a second 'panegyric' for an Irish phycologist', *Irish naturalists' journal 20* (1981), 275-283;–, 'William McCalla, discoverer of *Erica mackaiana*', *Yearbook of the Heather Society 3* (1) (1983), 28-32.
5.   E. C. Nelson, '*Erica mackaiana* forma *multiplicata*: a new name for the "multipetalled" form of Mackay's heath, with a history of Crawford's heath', *Yearbook of the Heather Society 1995,* 33-40.
6.   E. C. Nelson, 'Historical records of the Irish Ericaceae, with particular reference to the discovery and naming of *Erica mackaiana* Bab.', *Journal of the Society for the Bibliography of Natural History 9* (1982), 289-299; –, 'Heathers in Ireland', *Botanical journal of the Linnean Society 101* (1990), 269-277.
7.   P. Foss, G. J. Doyle and E. C. Nelson, 'The distribution of *Erica erigena* Ross in Ireland', *Watsonia 16* (1987), 311-327; E. C. Nelson, 'Historical records of the Irish Ericaceae - additional notes on *Arbutus unedo, Daboecia cantabrica, Erica erigena, Erica mackaiana* and *Ledum palustre'*, *Irish naturalists' journal 20* (1982), 364-369.
8.   AIF II plate 11; D. C. McClintock, 'The stories of some Irish heather cultivars', *Moorea 1* (1982), 37-41.
9.   E. C. Nelson, 'James Walker Porter of Carryduff', *Yearbook of the Heather Society 3* (2) (1984), 24-34; –, 'Heathers from Carryduff for limestone pavements', *Home gardening 1* (5) (September 1986), 18-19.
10.   *Proceedings of the Royal Horticultural Society 1967*, 120; E. C. Nelson, 'Two centuries of new plants', *The Irish garden 4* (3) (May-June 1995) supplement, [4-5].
11.   B. O. Mulligan, pers. comm.
12.   G. Yates, '*Erica cinerea* 'Joseph Murphy'', *Yearbook of the Heather Society 1996*, 21-22.
13.   G. Yates (1996).
14.   AIF plate 17; E. C. Nelson and W. F .Walsh, *Flowers of Mayo*. Blackrock. 1995. plate 6.
15.   D. McClintock, 'A double form of *Daboecia cantabrica*', *Yearbook of the Heather Society 2* (11) (1982), 32-33; J. O'Neill and E. C. Nelson, 'The introduction of *Daboecia cantabrica* into England, 1764', *Yearbook of the Heather Society 1995*, 27-32.
16.   E. G. H. Oliver, '*Erica* - update on species numbers', *Yearbook of the Heather Society 1995*, 11-12.
17.   BM plate 4796; *Journal of the Asiatic Society of Bengal 15* (1846), 79-135.
18.   D. Middleton, '*Pernettya* or *Gaultheria*', *The plantsman 12* (1990), 167-177; BM plate 6204; BM (n.s.) plate 127; Bean III, 118-119; *Bulletin of the British Museum (Natural History) historical series 6* (7) (1980).

CHAPTER VIII

1.   This chapter is based on an invited paper read on Friday 19 July 1991 at Rose Emerald 1991 in The Queen's University, Belfast, Northern Ireland; the published version is E. C. Nelson, "The red-rose bordered hem of her' - Ireland and roses', *The rose 86* (1992), 15-18, 83-85, 138-140 (also in *The Canadian rose annual 1991*, 28-39). I have also used material from chapters in the original edition of *An Irish flower garden*, and from E. C. Nelson, 'Old roses for a neophyte', *Moorea 5* (1987), 3-6.
2.   16th century Irish, attributed to Owen Roe MacWard; translated by J. C. Mangan.
3.   T. Moore, 'The last rose of summer'.
4.   Ausonius (c. 310 - c.395), '*De rosis nascentibus*' ('On new blown roses'), translated by H. Waddell, quoted from p. 5, H. Waddell, *The wandering scholars*. London. 1934.
5.   Ausonius, '*De rosis nascentibus*', translated by H. Waddell, quoted from P. Coats, *Flowers. The story of flowers, plants and gardens through the ages*. London. 1970. p. 162.
6.   T. Moore, 'Ode LV (Anacreon)'; see P. Coats (1970), 161.
7.   E. C. Nelson and W. F. Walsh, *The Burren: a companion to the wildflowers of an Irish limestone wilderness*. Aberystwyth & Ennis. 1991. pp. 53-54.
8.   E. C. Nelson, 'This garden to adorne with all varietie: the garden plants of Ireland in the centuries before 1700', *Moorea 9* (1991), 37-54.
9.   Latin lines from W. Strabo, Hortus, translation by R. Payne. Pittsburgh. 1966.
10.   University of Sheffield, Hartlib mss. 70/8/2 (and 70/8/1); quoted in E. C. Nelson (1990).
11.   see note 9 above.
12.   E. C. Nelson, 'Joseph Spence's plans for an Irish garden', *Garden history 15* (1987), 12-18.
13.   AIF II plate 1.
14.   P. Hackney and C. R. Hackney, '*A Rosa pimpinellifolia* L. x *Rosa canina* agg. hybrid in Co Antrim', *Irish naturalists journal 22* (1987), 363-364.
15.   AIF II plate 27.
16.   E. C. Nelson, 'Of *Rosa hugonis* and Father Hugo', *Kew magazine 5* (1988), 38-43.

17. Lady Cuffe's original watercolour is reproduced in E. C. Nelson, *The art of flowers.* [*Catalogue for*] *National Botanic Gardens, Glasnevin, bicentenary exhibition 1995. Botanical illustrations by Wendy Walsh and Charlotte Wheeler Cuffe.* Dublin. 1995. p. 33.

18. Lady Wheeler Cuffe to Sir F. W. Moore, April 1921; National Botanic Gardens, Glasnevin, Dublin mss, quoted in E. C. Nelson, 'The Lady of the rhododendrons - Charlotte Wheeler Cuffe 1867-1967', *Rhododendrons 1981-1982*, 33-41.

19. 'Similar to [*repens alba*, i.e. *Rosa* 'Paulii'], but of more vigorous growth and its flowers, which are much larger, resemble large *Clematis* and of a beautiful rose colour, shading to white in centre' (*Newry roses, catalogue no. 103* (c. 1923), 24). 'New. Like [*repens alba*], but the flowers are larger and of a bright rose colour' (*Wholesale catalogue 1912-13*, 55). G. N. Smith (GC (1929), 154) stated that 'this was raised in our nursery' about 1904, as the result of crossing *Rosa rugosa* with *R. gallica*. Dr Onno Wijnands renamed the cultivar, sometimes also named *Rosa* x *paulii* 'Rosea' (*Dendroflora 23* (1986), 44-45), *Rosa* 'Newry Pink'.

20. For help in ascertaining the history of 'Tipo Ideale', I am grateful to Dr Cammarano Umberto, Borgomanero, Italy. Lady Moore published the name and a description as early as 1921, technically establishing the cultivar name 'Tipo Ideale', which should take precedence over 'Mutabilis'.

21. *Newry roses, catalogue no 59* (1903-1904), 1. There is no justification for including "Macrantha" in the cultivar name - *Rosa* 'Daisy Hill' accords with the current rules of nomenclature and was the rose's original published name. However 'Macrantha Daisy Hill' is widely used, e.g. G. S. Thomas, *The Graham Stuart Thomas rose book.* London. 1994. p.186.

22. O'D. Browne, 'Roses', [and] 'Dr. J. Campbell Hall', IG *3* (1908), 121.

23. see note 22 above.

24. Hall's other roses were 'Lady Rossmore' (1906), 'Annie Crawford', 'Sheila Wilson' (1910), 'Miss Muriel Wilson' (1912/1922; introduced by Prince 1923), 'Julia Countess of Dartrey' (1927), 'James Ferris' (1927), and 'Lord Rossmore' (1930), Lady Anderson' (1920; introduced by A. Dickson). My thanks to Brent Dickerson for his valuable assistance in preparing this list.

25. APIF plate 6.

26. AIF II plate 48

27. Alex. Dickson & Sons, *Rose catalogue for 1906 & 1907*. Newtownards. p. 32.

28. N. P. Harvey, 'Irish roses', *The rose annual 1954*, 29-33.

29. E. Willmott to F. W. Moore, undated; National Botanic Gardens, Glasnevin, Dublin mss.

30. This cultivar name was published as early as 1918 in Lady Ardilaun's own appreciation of her head gardener which was appended to the obituary of Andrew Campbell published in *Irish gardening 13* (1918), 13. Thus, the name was not first coined about 1950 when Hilling's Nursery introduced the rose commercially. There may be truth in the story that Lady Moore suggested that it should be called 'Souvenir de St Anne's', reflecting thereby a garden as great as La Malmaison.

31. Daisy Hill Nursery received the rose from the National Botanic Gardens, Glasnevin, in October 1927, but I have no evidence that the firm marketed it.

32. G. S. Thomas, *The old shrub roses.* London. 1978 (revised edition); –, *Shrub roses of today.* London. 1980 (revised edition); –, *The Graham Stuart Thomas rose book.* London. 1994.

33. G. S. Thomas, 'Fortune's double yellow rose', *The garden 112* (1987), 94-95; E. C. Nelson, 'Some things old, some things new', *IGPS newsletter 44* (1992), 12-13, photograph p. 10.

34. George Moore, quoted from P. Coats (1970), 166.

35. W. B. Yeats, 'The mountain tomb'.

36. F. Ledwidge, 'June'.

37. W. B. Yeats: 'To Ireland in the coming times'.

CHAPTER IX

1. The correct cultivar name is 'Lynwood Variety', not 'Lynwood'; E. C. Nelson and E. Deane, *'Glory of Donard'. A history of the Slieve Donard Nursery, Newcastle, County Down, with a catalogue of cultivars.* Belfast. 1993. pp. 68-69; AIF plate 28. Plants selected during the Long Ashton Research Station clonal selection scheme have been released and are listed in *The plant finder* as 'Lynwood LA '79' - it is more than likely that this is not the original, true 'Lynwood Variety'.

2. There are various synonyms for this, including *Myrtus luma* and *Myrtus apiculata*.

3. AIF plate 21; S. Galvin, 'Glanleam, County Kerry', *Moorea 2* (1983), 7-12.

4. C. Foley, *An illustrated guide to the gardens of Ilnacullin.* Dublin. 1982.

5. E. C. Nelson and E. Deane (1993), 95-96; AIF plate 30.

6. As noted in E. C. Nelson and E. Deane (1993), 97, Harry Bryce gave me an alternative history for 'Donard Gold', that it was a chance seedling found at Rowallane. Bryce did not contradict the rest of the story.

7. E. C. Nelson and E. Deane (1993), 98-99.

8. AIF plate 26.

9. E. C. Nelson and E. Deane (1993), 110-111.

10. The shrubs were released with other names, but the nursery decided to alter the names; the original name for 'Aurora' was 'Donard Pink', and, as noted, for 'Charis' was 'Donard Variety'. Only 'Diana' has not had an alternative name (E. C. Nelson and E. Deane (1993)).

11. G. S. Thomas, *Gardens of the National Trust.* London. 1979. plate 5.

12. E. C. Nelson, 'Purple leaved elders: a nomenclatural note', *The plantsman 8* (1986), 189-190;–, 'Purple-leaved elders - postscriptum', *The plantsman 8* (1986), 192.

13. AIF II plate 38.

14. SSH [142-143].
15. AIF plate 23.
16. R. Lancaster, 'Award plants 1988 part 2', *The garden 114* (1989), 254-255.
17. D. Hill, 'A hybrid tree peony', *The garden 103* (1978), 247 (with colour photograph); S. O Gaoithin pers. comm.; a cultivar name has not yet (July 1996) been published, but the peony has been painted by Wendy Walsh for display in Glenveagh.
18. AIF II plate 35.
19. E. M. Woodgyer, '*Leptospermum lanigerum*', *Curtis's botanical magazine 12* (1995), 186-190, plate 227; E. C. Nelson and E. M. McCracken, *The brightest jewel: a history of the National Botanic Gardens, Glasnevin, Dublin*. Kilkenny. 1987.
20. F. W. Moore, 'Obituary of C. F. Ball', IG *10* (1915), 161-162; E. C. Nelson and E. M. McCracken (1987), 208-211.
21. Miss E. Miller, pers. comm.
22. AIF plate 32; BJ plate 14.
23. W. Owen. 'What passing-bells ...'.

CHAPTER X

1. R. Farrer, *My rock-garden*. London. 1908. p. 8.
2. E. C. Nelson and W. F. Walsh, *The Burren: a companion to the wildflowers of an Irish limestone wilderness*. Aberystwyth & Ennis. 1991. pp. 146-150; *Bulletin of the Alpine Garden Society 35* (1967), 356-357; – *38* (1970), 356; – *43* (1975), 297.
3. M. Hornibrook to H. J. Grootendorst, 22 November 1933; National Botanic Gardens, Glasnevin, Dublin mss (these letters were donated by H. J. Welch).
4. M. Hornibrook, *Dwarf and slow-growing conifers*. London. 1923. p. 68; -, *Dwarf and slow-growing conifers*. London. 1939 (second edition). p. 111.
5. see note 3 above.
6. 'Juniper's tv debut', *Horticulture week* (9 January 1987), 6.
7. *Proceedings of the Royal Irish Academy 51 B* (1948), 249-250;– *53 B* (1950), 219-220.
8. E. C. Nelson, 'Nomenclatural and historical notes on Irish garden plants - two new cultivars of *Pittosporum; Saxifraga hartii; Hepatica* 'Elison Spence'', *Moorea 4* (1985), 42-44.
9. D. A. Webb to ECN, 18 October 1984.
10. *Botanical journal of the Linnean Society 95* (1987), 246; *Journal of life sciences Royal Dublin Society 4* (1983), 143-160; D. A. Webb and R. J. Gornall, *Saxifrages of Europe*. Bromley. 1989. p. 185.
11. Ballawley Alpine Nursery catalogues.
12. W. Robinson, *The English flower garden*. London. 1884; *The plantsman 3* (1981), 167-174; E. A. Bowles, *My garden in spring*. London. 1914. pp. 209-215; R. Farrer (1908), 5.
13. AIF II plate 15; E. C. Nelson and M. R. D. Seaward, 'Evelyn Mary Booth 1897-1988', *Glasra 1* (n.s.) (1990), 87-89.
14. BM plate 8636; E. C. Nelson, 'The Lady of the rhododendrons - Charlotte Wheeler Cuffe 1867-1967', *Rhododendrons 1981-1982*, 33-41; Lady Cuffe's original watercolour of her anemone is reproduced in E. C. Nelson, *The art of flowers. [Catalogue for] National Botanic Gardens, Glasnevin, bicentenary exhibition 1995. Botanical illustrations by Wendy Walsh and Charlotte Wheeler Cuffe*. Dublin. 1995. p. 2.
15. *Flora Europaea I*. Cambridge. 1993 (second edition).
16. D. Turner, *Fuci sive plantarum fucorum gener*i. Yarmouth. 1819. vol. 4, 74, 152.
17. GC *50* (18 November 1911), 351; IG *9* (1914), 113-115; *Proceedings of the Royal Horticultural Society 1914*, cxxxviii; J. G. D. Lamb and P. Bowe, *A history of gardening in Ireland*. Dublin. 1995.
18. IG *6* (February 1911), xvi.
19. E. C. Nelson, 'Primroses', *IGPS newsletter supplements 1 and 2* (1984) (reprinted as a booklet, and as 'Irish primroses'. *National Primrose and Auricula Society yearbook (Southern) 1984*, 56-63); -, 'The primrose from Garryard, Ireland', *Primroses 42* (1) (1984), 12-13.
    Shaw (see note 20 below) misinterpreted my comments about 'Guinevere'. I believe 'Guinevere' and a primrose named 'Garryard' to be one and the same. On the other hand, the first of the so-called Garryard primroses was named 'Appleblossom'. 'Appleblossom', now extinct as far as we know, had red stems, bronze leaves and flowers like a bunch of pink and white appleblossom. 'Garryard', illustrated in black-and-white in *Gardening illustrated* on 6 April 1935, had single mauve-pink flowers with a yellow eye, just like 'Guinevere'.
20. Illustrated in B. Shaw, *The book of primroses*. Newton Abbot. 1991. plate 52.
21. H. K. F. Gatty (editor), *Aunt Judy's annual volume*. London. 1884. p. iv [April], quoted in E. C. Nelson, 'Once upon a time - Juliana Ewing', *The garden 109* (1984), 38-40.
22. J. Reynolds, 'Butterstream', *Moorea 12* (1996), 3-4.
23. Previously named *Geranium argenteum* 'Lissadell'; this cultivar, being a hybrid between *G. argenteum* and *G. cinereum*, should be named *Geranium* x *lindavicum* - see P. F. Yeo, *Hardy geraniums*. London. 1985. p. 172; GC *50* (18 November 1911), 351; Lissadell catalogues.
24. When originally named with was incorrectly identified (*mea culpa*) as *Omphalodes verna*; E. C. Nelson, 'Notes on Irish cultivars with some new names', *Moorea 8* (1990), 46, 48.
25. G. S. Thomas to ECN, 20 June 1983.
26. AIF plate 39.
27. W. H. Harvey to W. J. Hooker, 9 September 1846; Royal Botanic Gardens, Kew mss; English letters vol. 24 no. 251.

28. 'Harry Corbyn Levinge', *The Irish naturalist 5* (1896), 107; C. B. Clarke, 'H. C. Levinge', *Nature 53* (1896), 583-584; D. M. Synnott, E. C. Nelson and W. F. Walsh, '*Pseudophegopteris levingei* (Thelypteridaceae)', *Curtis's botanical magazine 12* (1995), 195-197, plate 279.

29. E. C. Nelson and E. Deane, '*Glory of Donard'. A history of the Slieve Donard Nursery, Newcastle, County Down, with a catalogue of cultivars.* Belfast. 1993. pp. 44-57.

30. see note 29 above.

31. C. Lighton, *Cape floral kingdom. The story of South Africa's wild flowers, and the people who found, named and made them famous the world over.* Cape Town. 1961. p. 129.

32. This postscript is adapted mainly from two sources: E. C. Nelson, 'Dierama - what's all the fuss about?', *IGPS newsletter 44* (1992), 4-5; –, 'The Slieve Donard Nursery Company: a history', pp. 1-24, in E. C. Nelson and E. Deane (1993).

CHAPTER XI

1. E. Knowldin, 'St Brigid's anemones', *The Irish farmer and stockowner* (14 November 1914), 668.

2. W., 'A garden of anemones', *The garden 21* (1882), 357-358.

3. AIF II plate 30; J. G. D. Lamb and P. Bowe, *A history of gardening in Ireland.* Dublin. 1995.

4. AIF II plate 43.

5. 'Mrs Hegarty' has petals 15-18 mm wide, 28-30 mm long; deep rose pink (RHS CC 62c); anthers yellow. 'Viscountess Byng' has petals 10-12 mm wide, 22-28 mm long; pale pink (RHS CC 65B); dark purple-brown anthers. (B. Hesketh, 'Schizostylis 'Mrs Hegarty'', *NCCPG Manx Group newsletter 3* (May 1984), [7-8]).

6. GI *43* (17 December 1921), 803-804; JRHS *70* (1945), 73-78.; A. Pankhurst, *Who does your garden grow?* Colchester. 1992. pp. 58-59.

7. Barrington Quinan to ECN, 14 June 1984; according to Mr Quinan, his mother, Lady Quinan, daughter of Dr and Mrs J. A. Hegarty, provided the information in Simmonds' account of Mrs Hegarty. Despite my best endeavours and those of the staff of Mayo County Library, Castlebar, no poem by Katherine Tynan explicitly titled 'The garden at Poleska' has been traced.

8. E. A. 'Retrospections and visions in an Irish flower garden', GI *58* (15 August 1936), 481-482. E. A. is an intriguing person who, according to these initials, wrote several other articles in *Gardening illustrated*, on primroses ('Treasures in an old garden. Primroses and polyanthus', GI 21 January 1928, 37-38; 'Early primroses', 5 February 1938, 75) and there is also one on 'Coloured primroses and polyanthus' signed E. A. in *New flora and sylva 9* (1936), 233-240. Only once is a full name printed - in 1928 the article was signed Mrs Ethel Adams, and the address merely given as County Tyrone. The frequent, direct references to Ireland, and other common factors, suggest that these articles are all by the same person.
    Finally, 'Garriarde' should be 'Garryard'; see Primula 'Guinevere', chapter 10.

9. *IGPS newsletter 18* (1985), 1, 6.

10. S. Lacey, *The startling jungle.* Harmonsworth. 1986. p. 117; D. Stuart and J. Sutherland, *Plants from the past.* London. 1989. p. 237; C. D. Brickell and F. Sharman, *The vanishing garden. A conservation guide to garden plants.* London. 1986. p. 227.

11. I have traced no history of this plant - it may not even be Irish. Roy E. Coombs (to ECN, 28 February 1983) kindly commented that 'a number of pansies and violas were raised in Ireland, two raisers being Samuel McKee and J. D. Stuart of Belfast. 'Belfast Gem' and 'Irish Molly' are likely to have been raised in Ireland ...'.

12. R. Haywood, 'Viola 'Molly Sanderson'', *The garden 111* (1986), 245; P. Barnes and R. Haywood, 'Viola 'Molly Sanderson'', *The garden 112* (1987), 188; these two accounts are preceded by T. Hobbs ('Ishlan, a garden in Co. Antrim', *The garden 111* (1986), 19-23) who noted 'a very black viola, labelled *Viola niger*, but at Chelsea 1985 it was called 'Molly Sanderson'.'); A. Pankhurst (1992) 157-158.
    I have tried to clarify the history of the pansy, because Haywood gives no account of its origin, and Pankhurst's story is inaccurate. According to letters from Dr T. S. Stone among Dr M. Sanderson's correspondence (now in the National Botanic Gardens, Glasnevin, Dublin), Drs Noel and Molly Sanderson visited Stone's garden in Margate for the first time in 1975, and Dr Stone did not make his visit to Northern Ireland until May 1980. Pankhurst stated that when Haywood wanted to name the *Viola* cultivar after Dr Molly Sanderson, she contacted Dr Stone's widow for her to approve the name 'Molly Sanderson', but as Mrs T. S. Stone died in c. 1975, this is impossible. None of Dr T. S. Stone's letters to Dr M.Sanderson contains references to this black pansy. I am grateful to Peter Barnes for his assistance in trying to unravel the story. Like so much in the history of garden plants, I left the recording of this too late, and by the time I came to write about this wonderful plant. Molly Sanderson was no longer alive.

13. T. S. Stone to M. Sanderson, 8 September 1975: Sanderson Papers, National Botanic Gardens, Glasnevin, Dublin.

14. M. Sanderson, 'Ishlan', pp. 136-141 in S. Connolly and H. Dillon (editors), *In an Irish garden.* London. 1986.

15. The original is in the Royal Society of London; see colour plate 40 in W. Blunt and W. T. Stearn, *The art of botanical illustration.* Woodbridge. 1994 (new edition).

16. E. C. Nelson, 'The name of the rose ... *Tropaeolum* 'Margaret Long', *The Irish garden 4* (1) (January-February 1995), 31.; –, 'They gardened Glasnevin: a register of gardeners, labourers, student-apprentices and lady gardeners in the Botanic Gardens at Glasnevin, Dublin 1795-1945', *Occasional papers, National Botanic Gardens, Glasnevin, 4* (1990).
    A remarkably similar, if not identical, cultivar, described as a 'real cracker', was marketed in the Spring 1997 by Thompson & Morgan Ltd. (see *Radio times 294* (12-18 April 1997, no. 3819), 34), under the name Nasturtium 'Apricot Twist'.

17. R. Piper and E. C. Nelson, *Piper's flowers*. Belfast. 1987. plate 6.
18. E. C. Nelson, 'Notes on Irish cultivars with some new names', *Moorea 8* (1990), 41-49; D. Shackleton, 'Beech Park', pp. 142-147, in S. Connolly and H. Dillon (1987); H. Dillon, 'By Dublin's fair city', *The garden 115* (1990), 430 (colour photograph).
19. Lady Scott to ECN, 25 April 1983; *Zauschneria californica* 'Dublin' was printed in *Bulletin of the Alpine Garden Society 47* (1979), 4 (this is the earliest reference I have traced); see also note 20 below.
20. Another version of this story is related by Roy Lancaster ('*Zauschneria californica* 'Dublin'', *The garden 116* (1991), 27-29), who added 'It was not found in the Botanic Gardens [Glasnevin] as one story has it, nor in the garden of Lady Moore at Willbrook, although she may well have acquired it later.' Yet another version of the 'correct history' is given by Seamus O'Brien (*IGPS newsletter 64* (1997), 22).
    This plant is also claimed as an introduction by Blooms of Bressingham, Norfolk. Alan Bloom has stated (*Alan Bloom's hardy perennials. New plants raised and introduced by a lifelong plantsman*. London. 1991. p. 148) that 'when visiting Glasnevin ... in 1958 I was very taken with a zauschneria in a blaze of fiery orange scarlet. It had no label but was obviously an improvement on the well-known [*Zauschneria*] *mexicana*. ... A swap was of course arranged and I could but give it the name 'Glasnevin'. So it has remained ever since and is still unsurpassed in my estimation, especially as it has proved to be hardier and more vigorous than any others I grow.'
21. AIF plate 29; E. C. Nelson and E. Deane, '*Glory of Donard*' - *a history of the Slieve Donard Nursery, Newcastle, County Down, with a catalogue of cultivars*. Belfast. 1993; D. Shackleton (1987).
22. E. C. Nelson and E. Deane (1993) 74-75; AIF II plate 41.
23. As pointed out in my commentary on this plant in '*Glory of Donard*' (E. C. Nelson & E. Deane (1993)), there is confusion between Charles Rogers, who collected the seeds in Burma, and John Rodgers, head-gardener at Rostrevor. The plant evidently was named after John Rodgers and the cultivar name is valid. *Hypericum hookerianum* 'Charles Rogers', proposed by Dr Norman Robson, should be considered a synonym.
24. AIF II plate 39.
25. AIF II plate 37; *IGPS newsletter 5* (1982), 4-5.
26. G. H. Engleheart, *The garden 30* (1886), 323.
27. AIF plate 38.
28. AIF II plate 44.
29. AIF II plate 37.
30. APIF plate 1.
31. Seedling 75 O-1.
32. Registered 1996.
33. IG 5 (1910), 65-66.

CHAPTER XII

1. J. T. Mackay, *Flora Hibernica*. Dublin. 1836. p. 135; *Yearbook of the International Dendrology Society 1975*, 59-61; *IGPS newsletter 9* (1983), 7-6.
2. see note 1 above.
3. Bean III, 93.
4. AIF II plate 19; BM plate 8064; F. W. Moore, 'Wall plants', JRHS *55* (1930), 53-63.
5. E. A. Bowles, *My garden in summer*. London. 1914. p. 204.
6. BM plate 8957.
7. AIF plate 33; *The garden 21* (29 April 1882), 286.
8. AIF II plate 31.
9. B. D. Morley and E. C. Nelson, 'Irish horticulturists II: William Edward Gumbleton (1840-1911) connoisseur and bibliophile', *Garden history 7* (3) (1979), 53-65; BM plate 7796; A. le Roux and T. Schelpe, *Namaqualand. South African wildflower guide 1*. Claremont. 1988. pp. 192-193.
10. T. Low, 'Foods of the First Fleet', *Australian natural history 22* (1987), 292-297.
11. E. C. Nelson, 'John White A. M., M. D., F. L. S. (c. 1756-1832), Surgeon-General of New South Wales: a new biography of the messenger of the waratah', *Archives of natural history* (in press);–,From the banks of Erne to Botany Bay: John White (c.1756-1832), Surgeon-General of New South Wales', *Familia 2* (3) (1987), 73-82.
12. J. E. Smith, '*Billardiera scandens*', tab 1 in *A specimen of the botany of New Holland*. London. 1793.
13. E. Knowldin, 'Current topics', IG *4* (1909), 138-139.
14. A. R. Ferguson, 'Botanical nomenclature: *Actinidia chinensis, Actinidia deliciosa* and *Actinidia setosa*', pp. 36-57, in O. J. Warrington and G. C. Weston (editors), *Kiwifruit: science and management*. Auckland. 1990.
15. A. R. Ferguson, 'The species with the greatest potential', *New Zealand kiwifruit* (April 1992), 16-17.
16. I am grateful to Dr Ross Ferguson for his continued help with the kiwifruit's history and, as previously expressed, for this quotation from the *North China Herald*.

CHAPTER XIII

1. Mac Conglinne (translated by Kuno Meyer); quoted from K. Hoagland (editor), *1000 years of Irish poetry*. Old Greenwich. 1975.
2. Quoted from *Kings, lords and commons*. Baile Atha Cliath. 1970; also quoted in S. Mac Réamoinn (editor), *The pleasures of Gaelic poetry*. London. 1982.
3. E. C. Nelson, ''Reserved to the Fellows': four centuries of gardens at Trinity College, Dublin, pp. 185-222 in C. Holland (editor), *Trinity College Dublin and the idea of a university*. Dublin. 1991.

4.   J. H. Harvey and V. Kinane, 'The earliest known printed Irish seed catalogue', *Long room 38* (1993), 49-53.
5.   GC (20 August 1859), 693; – (11 February 1860), 118.
6.   J. MacLachlan 'Clonderg: a new strawberry for processing', *Farm and food research 12* (6) (December 1981), 183.
7.   'Clonderg' was the progeny of 'Senga Sengana' pollinated by 'Cambridge Vigour'; 'Clonard' came from Domanil' also pollinated by 'Cambridge Vigour'; 'Clonree' was raised from open-pollinated 'Cambridge Favourite'; J. B. MacLachlan, 'Three new strawberry cultivars being prepared for release', *Farm and food research 14* (1) (February 1983), 24-25.
8.   I am grateful to Jim MacLachlan for his account of this work (in litt. 18 November 1996).
9.   J. G. D. Lamb, 'The apple in Ireland; its history and varieties', *Economic proceedings of the Royal Dublin Society 4* (1951) no. 1.
10.   W. D. Davidson, 'History of potato varieties', *Journal of the Department of Agriculture, Ireland 33* (1935), 57-81; –, 'The history of the potato and its progress in Ireland', *Journal of the Department of Agriculture, Ireland 34* (1937), 286-307.
11.   E. C. Nelson, *The cause of the calamity. Potato blight in Ireland, 1845-1847, and the role of the National Botanic Gardens, Glasnevin.* Dublin. 1995.
12.   Quoted in R. McKay, *An anthology of the potato.* Dublin. 1961.
13.   A. Wilson, *The story of the potato through illustrated varieties.* 1993.
14.   G. O. Sherrard, 'The breeding of Brussels sprouts at the Albert College', *Scientific horticulture 11* (1955), 124-129.
15.   D. W. Robinson, 'Commercial horticulture and research in Ireland', pp. 191-203 in E. C. Nelson and A. Brady (editors), *Irish gardening and horticulture.* Dublin. 1979.
16.   W. Murphy, '*Ribes sativum* 'Pearson's Seedling', *IGPS newsletter 52* (1994), 3.
17.   Sometimes spelled Ecklinville; the eighteenth century house has been replaced by another, and is now named Rubane House; see B. Jupp, *Heritage gardens inventory 1992.* Belfast. 1992.
18.   J. Bultitude, *Apples. A guide to the identification of international varieties.* London. 1983.
19.   E. C. Nelson, 'Any old apples', *Field and countryside 2* (7) (April 1985), 57;–, 'Golden apples', *The Irish garden 3* (5) (September-October 1994), 30-31.

CHAPTER XIV

1.   AIF II plate 21; E. C. Nelson (editor) and D. L. McKinley, *Aphrodite's mousetrap. A biography of Venus's Flytrap with facsimiles of an original pamphlet and the manuscripts of John Ellis, F.R.S.* Aberystwyth. 1990; D. H. Rankin and E. C. Nelson (editors), *Curious in everything. Arthur Dobbs (1689 - 1765) a tercentenary celebration.* Carrickfergus. 1990.
2.   BM plate 3651; E. C. Nelson and A. Probert, *A man who can speak of plants: Dr Thomas Coulter (1793-1843) of Dundalk in Ireland, Mexico and Alta California.* Dublin. 1994.
3.   Names are a quagmire! In some of the latest publications (for example, *The Royal Horticultural Society A-Z encyclopedia of garden plants* (1995)) the name for this plant has reverted to *Tweedia.* I follow suit.
4.   N. Niven to W. J. Hooker, 24 July 1837; Royal Botanic Gardens, Kew mss, English letters vol. 9 no. 284.
5.   AIF II plate 20; BM plate 3930.
6.   BM (n.s.) plate 399; *Botanical register 25* (1839), plate 68.
7.   J. Tweedie to W. J. Hooker, 26 May 1836; Royal Botanic Gardens, Kew mss.
8.   AIF II plate 24; BM plate 4723; E. C. Nelson and E. M. McCracken, *The brightest jewel: a history of the National Botanic Gardens, Glasnevin, Dublin.* Kilkenny. 1987.
9.   BM plate 4723.
10.   AIF II plate 25; BM plate 5797; E. C. Nelson (1991).
11.   Veronica [i.e. F. W. Burbidge], '*Androsace lanuginosa*', *The garden 30* (1886), 311.
12.   BM (n.s.) 329; H. Fassnidge, 'Dr John Rutty of Melksham, Wiltshire', pp. 11-16 in *Quakers in natural history and medicine in Ireland and Britain* (*Occasional papers 8 National Botanic Gardens, Glasnevin, Dublin*).1996.
13.   AIF plate 48.
14.   AIF II plate 35; E. C. Nelson and W. F. Walsh, 'Genesis of a tribute to Trinity College Botanic Garden', *Moorea 6* (1987), 45.; E. C. Nelson (1991).
15.   AIF II plate 46 (reproduced as frontispiece to *Flowers of Mayo* - see note 16 below).
16.   E. C. Nelson and W. F. Walsh, *The flowers of Mayo. Dr Patrick Browne's Fasciculus plantarum Hiberniae (1788).* Dublin. 1995.
17.   BM plate 8721; E. C. Nelson, 'The Lady of the rhododendrons - Charlotte Wheeler Cuffe 1867-1967', *Rhododendrons 1981-1982,* 33-41; Lady Cuffe's original watercolour of *Rhododendron cuffeanum* is reproduced, beside a photograph of the plant she collected, on pp. 24-25 in E. C. Nelson, *The art of flowers.* [*Catalogue for*] *National Botanic Gardens, Glasnevin, bicentenary exhibition 1995. Botanical illustrations by Wendy Walsh and Charlotte Wheeler Cuffe.* Dublin. 1995.
18.   C. I. Wheeler Cuffe to Baroness Prochazka, quoted in E. C. Nelson (1982 - see note 17 above).
19.   F. Kingdon Ward, *From China to Hkamti-Long.* London. 1924; quoted by A. Coats, *The quest for plants.* London. 1969. p. 86.

EPILOGUE

1.   p. 50. A facsimile of Lyons' book (1843) with a modern introduction is published: E. C. Nelson (editor), *John Lyons and his orchid manual.* Kilkenny. 1983.

Irish Garland

1   *Galanthus* 'Straffan'
2   *Hieracium scullyi*
3   *Schizostylis coccinea* 'Mrs Hegarty'
4   *Ilex aquifolium* (leaves)
5   *Erica cinerea*
6   *Sisyrinchium angustifolium*
7   *Garrya* x *issaquahensis* 'Pat Ballard'
8   *Potentilla fruticosa*
9   *Geranium sanguineum*
10   *Cotoneaster frigidus* 'Fructu-luteo' (fruits)
11   *Primula nana* (= *P. edgeworthii*)
12   *Viola* 'Molly Sanderson'
13   *Hedera helix* 'Donerailensis'
14   *Epilobium canum* 'Dublin' (= *Zauschneria californica*)
15   *Crataegus monogyna* (haws)
16   *Prunus spinosa* (sloes)
17   *Hypericum* 'Rowallane Hybrid'
18   *Geranium sanguineum* (autumn leaves)
19   *Luma apiculata* 'Glanleam Gold'
20   *Mimulus* x *bartonianus*
21   *Cytisus scoparius* 'Killiney Red'
22   *Tweedia caerulea*
23   *Ilex* x *altaclerensis* 'Lawsoniana' (leaves)
24   *Rosa* x *hibernica*
25   *Rosa bracteata*
26   *Hamamelis mollis*
27   *Sarcococca humilis*
28   *Ipheion uniflora*
29   *Escallonia* 'C. F. Ball'
30   *Prunus subhirtella* 'Autumnalis'
31   *Primula* 'Guinivere'
32   *Carex buxbaumii*
33   *Geranium traversii*
34   *Sarracenia* x *moorei*
35   *Primula* 'Old Irish Blue'
36   *Rosa* 'Souvenir de St Anne's'
37   *Hypericum androsaemum* 'Mrs Gladis Brabazon'
38   *Dryas octopetala*
39   *Adiantum capillus-veneris*
40   *Solanum crispum* 'Glasnevin'
41   *Dierama dracomontanum*
42   *Daboecia cantabrica* 'Charles Nelson'